Adapt and Thrive
The Sustainable Revolution

Adapt and Thrive
The Sustainable Revolution

Peter J. McManners

Published by Susta Press a division of Susta Limited
www.susta.co.uk

Copyright © Peter J. McManners 2008

Copyediting by Hilary McGlynn
Production management by Stacey Penny
Cover and page design by Stefan Brazzo

Typesetting by
Florence Production Ltd,
Stoodleigh, Devon EX16 9PN

Printed and bound in the UK by
MPG Books Ltd, Bodmin, Cornwall

A CIP catalogue record for this book is available from the British Library

ISBN 978–0–9557369–0–2

The paper used for the text pages of this book is FSC certified.
FSC (the Forest Stewardship Council) is an international network
to promote responsible management of the world's forests.

FSC
Mixed Sources
Product group from well-managed
forests, controlled sources and
recycled wood or fiber
SA-COC-1565
www.fsc.org
© 1996 Forest Stewardship Council

For
Thomas and Rosa

Table of Contents

List of Figures:

List of Boxes:

Preface

I have taken time to reflect on what I see happening to our world, and contemplate some alternatives. Not everyone will agree with my assessment. Some people will oppose the actions I propose. I hope that many more will take advantage of the opportunities I foresee to build a better society as part of a sustainable world.

Whilst writing this book, the debate over the issue of climate change has grabbed the world's attention. Climate change is not a new phenomenon – the Earth's systems slowly cycle between one ice age and the next. But the predicted rapid changes caused by the activities of mankind is of deep concern. Many people will lose their lives as a result of it. We are seeing the early indicators, with record summer temperatures across Europe in 2003 causing more than 20,000 deaths and Hurricane Katrina in 2005 killing more than 1,800 in the United States. In addition to the deaths directly attributable to climate change, there will be many more people who lose their livelihoods, as farms become deserts and coastal communities are submerged. Looking further into the future, the worst refugee crisis the world has ever seen is pending, as rising sea levels threaten to swamp a large proportion of the world's most densely populated country, Bangladesh.

Research I carried out in the early 1990s into global databases opened my eyes to the amazing ability we were then developing to understand the natural systems and processes of planet Earth. Scientists were already troubled by some of the predictions coming out of their models, but incontrovertible proof for mankind's involvement in climate change was hard to find.

We now have the proof for our role in climate change, but this is just a symptom of deeper problems in our relationship with the natural ecosystem on which we rely to survive. The actions that are currently being discussed to counter our worries about climate change appear momentous. It will take effort to curb carbon emissions through measures such as improving energy efficiency and a massive expansion in renewable power. These measures will bring dramatic changes and improvement in our world; but we will find that they are not enough.

When I look at the world, it is through three lenses. As a geographer, I see the compelling need to change the way we treat our planet. As an engineer, I see technical solutions to many of the challenges we face in making the changes. As a management expert, I have a wide range of business theories and models that we can extend to mobilize business as the primary agent of change. In each view, I see examples of excellence, reminding me of the incredible ingenuity of mankind. When I bring my three views together, I find that currently they do not fit one with the other.

As more and more of the world's political and business leaders notice the disconnections – and the world's population is already experiencing the consequences first-hand – a wave of change will be initiated that is far greater than anything anticipated so far. This will be a revolution that disrupts the world system, reconfigures society and shakes up the business environment.

One of the problems facing the world is a narrow focus on conventional economics. Many of us realize that this is not good enough: the environment is suffering and people are not generally any happier or more secure. We want to solve these issues, but we cannot break the deadlock between our economic aspirations and the growing imperative to protect the environment.

We must push past current rhetoric and look beyond established theories. This means leaping outside the current collective mindset, without the comfort of seeing clearly where our feet will land. In this book, I have not felt constrained by what has gone before, and my ideas conflict with perceived wisdom in a number of areas, but this is what we need to break out of the spiral of decline we have initiated.

My intentions match those of the many people who champion change to protect our environment. We all want to see the world run according to a safer set of principles. I am driven by a concern for the environment, but my ideas derive from my engineering background and my understanding of how business schools teach managers to think. My ideas are, therefore, more hard-edged than many environmentalists will feel comfortable with. But a realistic solution to the environmental crisis that faces us needs to reflect the real world in which we live.

Three years ago, as I developed the concept for this book, I was optimistic that policies to conserve our natural environment would be easy to find. As I searched for solutions, pessimism took over. I began to realize that the problems were more deep-rooted, interconnected and complex than I had at first imagined. The whole of society would have to change. My initial thoughts had been to seek to persuade business to be more altruistic and behave in a responsible manner. But it was hard to see how this would fit easily with the prime business metric of increasing shareholder value – except through amorphous indicators such as improved reputation. My optimism returned when I realized that it was unnecessary for business to become quasi-charitable. The potential opportunities for business are massive. It is firmly in the interests of business to drive many of the actions I propose and to shape the world I envisage.

In order to present my ideas, I have had to look into the future, and have gone further than many people will easily accept. I look beyond our immediate responses to climate change to the revolution that our concern over climate will trigger, which I term the Sustainable Revolution. The countries that choose to lead this transformation will prosper, supporting their business communities in establishing seed opportunities that will mature through the first few decades of the 21st century. The potential for governments to build secure, stable societies and for corporations to grow enduring long-term value is enormous.

The facts are there to see, and the future I predict comes from straightforward logical deduction. What prevents my analysis from gaining immediate acceptance is that the changes are so great, and the mind-set shift required so complete, that it may be difficult to believe that it would be possible or feasible.

To have the time and space to develop my theories, I have relocated to Finland, on the northern edge of Europe. Finland is a beacon of both business competitiveness and sound environmental stewardship, just the combination we need to build a vibrant and sustainable world. You will notice the influence of this small and special country on my thoughts as I write. Finland comes up again and again in examples that indicate how we can learn to live in tune with the natural world.

Whilst writing these paragraphs, I am sitting on a rock in the Arctic wilderness of northern Finland. Spring has arrived and most of the snow has melted. The first shoots are starting to show through. I have completed my first five hours of hiking away from the road and there are no more signs of people than the occasional footprint on the path in front of me. I contemplate if I am happier in the city of Helsinki, with its comfort and urban pleasures, or up here in Lapland, as nature starts to awake from a long cold winter. I feel fortunate that I am able to experience both.

My travels have often involved periods of urban living interspersed with being close to nature; sleeping out under the stars one night and staying in a comfortable hotel the next. I remember lying on my back in the Australian bush watching the tremendous display of the southern sky; gazing out over a frozen lake in Lapland watching the northern lights; camping on a dead flat African marsh baked solid by the sun in the dry season; snoozing in a hammock in the jungles of central America to an orchestra of chirping, crawling and slithering creatures. Of all the hotels I have stayed in, there are few lasting memories. They were presumably comfortable, and my sleep less interrupted, but also a pale second best to the zest, variety and raw beauty of our natural world.

The feeling of oneness with nature which, for me, flows from these experiences is an illusion. We are in conflict with the natural world, using it, exploiting it, enjoying it whilst we still can, and ever so slowly strangling it to death. I want a society in tune, and in harmony, with the natural world. I believe that it can be done, must be done and I have no objection to healthy profits for those who make it happen. I do not want my children, grandchildren, or their children to miss out on the wonderful natural world we inhabit. And I want them to prosper. This book seeks to lay a foundation for them.

Overview

In the developed world, the Information Age, and the associated drive towards globalization, is taking us beyond the Industrial Revolution. But worldwide, the result is an increase in the pressure we are applying on the Earth, as industrial processes migrate to other parts of the world and countries in the developing world seek to mimic our evident success. The natural systems on which we rely are under threat – not only from climate change, but also from other threats such as the poisoning of our oceans. There is an increasingly urgent need to take action, but this conflicts with the world's economic aspirations. We need to move quickly to eliminate the problems of our era if human society is to be sustainable into the long future.

In Part 1, the coming of the Sustainable Revolution is explained and analysed. The dawning reality that we must learn to have respect for the environment sits uneasily with our continual drive for greater wealth and more consumption. The Earth's systems can support only so much destructive economic activity. How society responds over the first half of the 21st century will decide the nature of the world that our children inhabit in the future.

If we want our world to be a place where we can be safe, healthy and at peace, then the society that emerges must be based upon the principles of sustainability. The concept is simple: the economy, society and the environment are interdependent, interconnected and indivisible. To implement this concept, many green advocates have outlined what they believe should be done, but rely on individual people to do the 'right thing'. This will not be the basis of our future. Human nature will not change. The foundations will be built on selfish determination to build sustainable societies, with the aim of delivering a better life for oneself and the close community around us.

In Part 2, I expand on the concept of building a truly sustainable world by examining a wide range of issues from energy and agriculture to transportation, manufacturing and urban living. As I focus on the fabric of society, I find that it cannot be separated from natural ecosystems. We must consider the two together as inextricably linked. The most visible threat to our shared world is climate change. But we are being slow to understand and accept the fundamental nature of the changes required in response.

One required response is clear. We need to wean society off its addiction to fossil fuels. This requires much more than simply identifying alternative fuels. Instead of accepting an ever-increasing need for energy as fact, we must solve the imbalance between sustainable energy supplies and demand. Learning to live within the renewable energy available to us locally, supplemented by global sustainable energy flows, will require dramatic and deep-rooted changes to the infrastructure of society.

The transportation sector will have to change. Its uncontrolled expansion is not sustainable. We can expect further success in improving the energy efficiency of our vehicles and aircraft. But this will not be enough to offset our growing demands to move larger quantities of freight and more people ever further distances. If we are willing to consider a wide-ranging portfolio of integrated policies, then an alternative solution becomes economically viable. This alternative reduces the quantity of goods and number of people requiring transportation, and the distance over which they are moved.

The required policies will bring fundamental change and improvement in our lives – particularly in cities, where the majority of the world's people will live. Here the focus should be on building cohesive communities that are economically viable and in symbiosis with the environment.

Manufacturing is another area for fundamental change. Production operations are currently under enormous pressure from global competition. As the world community demands sustainable processes, this sector will go through a renaissance. Production will shift to small, responsive units serving local markets with highly differentiated products. The new economies of scale will come from coordinating innovation and design at a global level, as opposed to the centralization of physical production in massive factories.

Looking beyond the industrial base, at sectors that have a very close relationship with the natural world, I start with water. We have to protect our drinking supplies of course, but we need to conserve the whole world hydrology. In particular, our oceans need to be rescued from slow strangulation by long-life pollutants. The only realistic way will be to eliminate substances that nature cannot break down from our society, and close down the world trade in waste.

Agriculture will become increasingly important. Short, transparent supply chains delivering local produce for local markets will take precedence in building a sustainable market. But the demands we place on agriculture will continue to increase: not only for food for a growing world population but also for feedstock for biofuels and biodegradable materials. The conflict between land use, energy and food will be tough to resolve.

Throughout all these sectors is one issue that we care little about – waste. Often we just want to get rid of it: out of our immediate vicinity and out of mind. This is our natural instinct, which in the natural world is sufficient. But in our industrialized world, such an attitude is very dangerous. Effective waste management within our societies must become automatic.

In Part 3, I show how we can force the pace of change. The actions I propose are contrary to many entrenched policies. Acceptance will not be easy, particularly as those who stand to lose will vigorously defend their positions.

Action is required from us all, but we are reluctant to act alone, when our neighbours do nothing. Our politicians will eventually bring in collective arrangements, but only when the groundswell of public opinion shifts sufficiently to support the measures required. Ambitious younger politicians would be wise to shift their position in advance of public opinion, in order to have the credibility to ride the impending Sustainable Revolution. Business should also move early. Not because it would be right, but because it will be profitable to exploit the opportunities that arise from leading the Sustainable Revolution.

We will find that we need to extend and improve the economic mechanisms of society. Capital markets need to be brought under tighter control to revert to their true role of supporting enterprise and society. Social economics should re-engage with the principle that the raison d'être of our economic system is the well-being of the population. The environment must be brought inside the economic system through the application of environmental taxes and other mechanisms that could lead to a major realignment of world wealth.

Collectively we are destroying our world. If we continue to deny that real change is needed, then we can be sure that the Sustainable Revolution will be a traumatic and unpleasant transition. It could just as easily liberate mankind. It is our choice. The need to act is paramount. This book shows how.

Part One

THE COMING OF THE SUSTAINABLE REVOLUTION

1 Adapt or Die

Man has always lived in a changing world, adapting to survive as circumstances change. Civilizations have grown in stature whilst others decline; one successful empire is replaced by another. The balance of the world order shifts as ideas and fashions ripple through society. Now, in the opening years of the 21st century, we face some difficult problems. Capitalism is not at fault but the current mechanisms of capitalism need to change. A wave of change and disruption is gathering momentum. The next revolution will affect us all, providing enormous opportunities for active participants, but killing off those who read the signs too late.

There are potential catastrophes such as nuclear war or incurable plagues that could wipe out the human species, but, leaving those on one side, we should still have deep concern about the nature and quality of the world we expect to inhabit in the future. We rely on the Earth's natural systems for so many things we take for granted, but we are putting them under stress as never before. Climate change, extinction of species and long-lasting pollutants are some of the results of our haphazard dash for progress.

In the past we made mistakes, and were forced to adapt our methods and processes. Localized mismanagement of the environment was soon brought back into line as global systems reimposed their authority. Londoners used to endure 'pea-soup' smog on a regular basis when open coal fires were the normal method of staying warm. In the search for a solution to this, power stations were placed away from the city and other sources of heating, such as natural gas, were adopted. The immediate problem of choking smog has been solved, but, as I explore later in this book, our changes have not gone far enough. Such experience has led us to assume that the Earth is a stable system with the ability to overcome the environmental problems we create. But, in the 21st century, we are pushing this assumption with all the industrial might and technical know-how we can muster, in a grand but stupidly irresponsible experiment. The Earth has responded with rising global temperatures and significantly more extreme weather events, but hard scientific evidence of where this will lead is patchy and gives support to a wide range of opinions. Without definitive evidence, the debate will continue, but by then it will be too late, and we will have to live with the consequences.

This is a time of great danger for our world. This book argues that nothing short of revolutionary change can save us. The disruption will be severe and will impact all areas of society. Trying to anticipate and understand the outcome is immensely complicated. Each person contributes their fragment to the mosaic of society; each organization brings its own strengths and attributes to the world community. Some organizations and businesses can anticipate, adapt and so evolve successfully. Others die. Those who fail to grasp the new reality will be pushed aside.

There are some major and obvious pressures on the current world order. China is emerging as a major industrialized power and workhouse. India is growing fast as the favoured destination for outsourcing of a whole range of activities. In parts of Europe, the European social model is rubbing uncomfortably against free-market capitalism. There is now also hard evidence from the scientists on the Intergovernmental Panel on Climate Change that our climate is changing and that the Earth is warming up, and that this is due to human activities.[1] These and many other issues threaten to unbalance the world system, which must adjust to some new equilibrium. What has been described as our 'autistic' economics[2] cannot cope with our uneven and belated attempts to reconcile economic growth with the wider issues of social inclusion and protection of the natural environment.

The present world economic system, based on foundations laid after World War II, must change. We need to achieve a dynamic equilibrium between man and his surroundings, which will conserve and strengthen our natural world. The principles we are using, and the institutions that apply them, will have to adapt. Free trade, fiscal policy, the role of the World Trade Organization (WTO) and management of business are some of the areas for reform. Changes in one will interact with modifications to another, until a new stability emerges.

It is in the interests of all mankind that this disruption starts sooner rather than later. It will be the insiders who are active in disrupting the current system who will be in the best position to exploit the huge opportunities that will arise.

Business, in particular, has a prime mercenary role to play. Business people have always found a way to profit from the calamities we face; such as arms dealers surreptitiously building business empires whilst their customers are killing each other. The opportunities to profit from the impending revolution are just as great, but there will be no stigma attached to building a sustainable world – quite the reverse. The businesses that lead the transformation can be proud of their role, not because they have suddenly become altruistic but because they have maximized the long-term value to the corporation. Investors who back them can also sleep easy at night, not because they have become ethical investors (although perhaps that, too) but because they have secured a solid and enduring return on their capital.

Many of the ideas I present in this book push beyond the envelope of accepted wisdom, and may well be disputed. Economists will accuse me of undermining some of their most cherished theories as I develop an alternative direction for globalization. Environmentalists may feel betrayed by the realistic, hard edge I bring to their cause. Some business people will not agree with the argument I make in Chapter 23, that business should act in its own self-interest to help build the future I portray.

Nevertheless, I hope that others will pause, reflect and then build on my ideas, because the quality of our future lives depends on it. We need political leaders who can transform our society and business leaders who can build vibrant and successful corporations capable of surfing the leading edge of the impending tidal wave.

Many people are in denial. They say there is no need to panic: it can still be business as usual. The environmentalists should shut up: crying wolf too often does not help their cause. The problems arising from climate change are not severe. Current environmental regulations are enough: we can comply with them, but we do not want more. Oil will continue to flow for a few more decades, so long as high oil prices support investment in increased capacity. In any case, market forces will resolve all the problems, assisted by new mechanisms such as carbon trading. Some of us see beyond such dangerous complacency, but currently our numbers are few.

To a senior executive or politician with a demanding role deep within the structure of society, it is easy to deny that there are substantive problems. These people do not have time to look outside their fast-moving worlds – business-critical or political issues take up all their attention. A politician or business person might enjoy the natural world as recreation, unwinding as a sailor, climber or walker, but feel they cannot afford to let their leisure pursuits interfere with the job. Even those in positions of power who have realized that the environment is at risk are unable to do much about it; a Chief Executive hoping to keep his or her job cannot allow personal concerns to undermine the company's search for profitability.

We have come to see progress in our changing world in terms of increased affluence, better infrastructure and more efficient agriculture. This is leading us to a world of concrete interspersed with industrial agriculture and patches of nature fenced off as living museums. We must decide if this is what we want for our world. I have begun to understand the futility of our narrow economic focus on such development and thus the need for radical change. It would be pointless if progress were banned and we had to return to the methods and technologies of the past, under the banner of 'returning to nature', and in so doing stifling mankind's fundamental drive and innovation. We need to find ways of applying our technology and methods to building the world we desire, creating sustainable, cohesive societies in tune with the natural world.

This is vital because man's world and nature's world are one: we are part of nature and cannot separate ourselves from its constraints. We rely on nature to process our waste and recycle oxygen into the atmosphere to enable us to breathe. The natural processes of conception, development and birth are central to humanity and our survival. We take all this for granted, trusting that it will always be so. Yet, at the same time, we are shunting off our pollution into the deep ocean, we are burning increasing quantities of fossil fuel and we are building up stores of radioactive waste.

We can no longer afford to be so ambivalent. Many of the activities on which society depends abuse the natural world. This is despite being run by honest managers and implemented by businesses whose shares are held by the pension funds of ordinary people. Nature has only so much resilience, and we have already pushed things too far in some areas for our planet's systems to make a full recovery. Nature will always find a balance, but it is increasingly likely to be an outcome that we wish we had never caused, as we try to live in a wrecked environment of our own making.

The two extreme scenarios described below illustrate the range of outcomes we could face a hundred years from now as we enter the 22nd century.

Earth – as a Prison

An increasing number of accidents in an international and often poorly regulated nuclear power industry have led to significant rises in levels of background radiation. Fish from the sea carry dangerous levels of toxins. Almost all the natural world outside national parks has been bulldozed. Even in the protected areas, the flora and fauna are suffering badly as the Earth's systems are no longer providing the support they need. Easily exploited fossil fuels have been expended. Carbon dioxide (CO_2) levels in the atmosphere have led to fundamental changes in the world's weather patterns.

The world's population is now more than 10 billion. The wealthy live in sealed domes with filtration equipment to ensure clean air and water. Food grown inside the domes and fish raised in tanks are free of toxins and the residents are healthy and beautiful, with very long life spans. Yet these privileged people yearn for the past when their ancestors swam in the sea and walked in the forests without breathing equipment. Outside the domes, a huge underclass of people scratch out a living, with low life expectancy and a high rate of deformities amongst their offspring.

The relationship between these two worlds is one of conflict and despair. The nuclear power plants running the domes continue to pollute the areas outside, but even the domes are under threat as the accessible uranium deposits are running low. The cycle of degradation continues.

Earth – as Utopia

The rapid pace of technical development continues. Collaborative international research finally delivers a workable solution to the challenge of power from nuclear fusion. Clean energy is in abundant supply in the developed world. Raised CO_2 levels have brought about climate change but the situation is stabilizing. The principle of respect for the natural world has been embraced throughout the world. Agriculture is efficient and sustainable. Although reserves of fossil fuels have not been fully depleted, further exploitation has been banned under international treaties. Carbon-based biofuels from organic sources are widely used in the poorer countries. An energy economy has taken root in the richer countries, based on fuel cells powered by a transportable fuel (either hydrogen or a synthetic liquid hydrocarbon), produced using power from the large, clean nuclear fusion plants.

Man has expanded space travel, with a permanent station on the moon and a number of landings to explore Mars. This allows the possibility of making the Earth a protected natural environment, with all remaining activities that might damage the ecosystem exported to the moon or other planets. The population has stabilized and although there are widely different levels of development, countries are free to choose their own methods and make their own choices within a sustainable framework. People are empowered and generally content.

The Reality

Mankind will change its ways either by choice and deliberate design, or through force of circumstance, and the result will probably fall somewhere between the extremes of the two scenarios above. Humans are unique in nature in being able to plan for the future, giving us the capacity to adapt our behaviour in advance of the crushing power of forced adaptation – if we so choose.

Fundamental change only takes place when enough pressure has built up to upset the existing balance, then it tips, often very quickly, to find a new equilibrium. People are naturally resistant to change, so social inertia must also be overcome. Even when politicians can see the 'right' action to take, it is a brave (or foolish) politician who does not wait for public opinion to catch up. As I discuss in Chapter 17, astute politicians do not anticipate, but wait for the tipping point, then hitch a ride on the wave of public feeling.

Business is subject to the same inertia. Bold and unconventional thinking must be backed by the courage and drive to take it forward. It seems much easier to copy the proven successful strategies of others; but reacting only when pushed means being left behind. A company that waits until the tipping point has passed will be unable to react in time. Business leaders who anticipate the future and have the strength to take action will make sustainable profits, setting the standards for others to match.

Business is responsible for much of what goes on in our world. It can, therefore, be blamed for many of the world's problems. If our world is destroyed, big business will be held accountable. However, business and market forces are powerful and effective, and, if imaginatively channelled, can save the world just as easily as destroy it. If this is starting to sound like a sermon, think again. Business is not a religion, nor is it a charity. Businesses are built on a relentless search for profits. This underlying principle is not going to change. But the way that businesses operate will certainly change in line with adaptation within society, with the proactive leaders reaping the greatest rewards.

It is very hard to forge a new direction without having a specific destination in mind to use as a reference point. The reference point I propose is the scenario 'Earth as Utopia'. This might seem impractical and impossible, but is obviously taking us in the right direction. But a politician facing re-election, or a business person pressurized by investment analysts, is engrossed in dealing with the immediate challenges. Utopia might just as well be a distant dream. The ideas in this book intend to provide them with a new sense of direction, which leads very practically and profitably towards the Utopian ideal.

We do not really expect to achieve Utopia, but some place in that general direction – perhaps like Finland, which comes out top of world league tables of both competitiveness and environmental stewardship. This small country is only part-way along the journey to a truly sustainable future, but has gained a significant head start. I have chosen to live in Finland to write this book and I use Finland as a recurring example to show practical ways that we can succeed.

Some of my ideas may appear outlandish, because my examination of our world has been followed through to logical conclusions unencumbered by the requirement to defend any part of the status quo. We seem to have broad agreement on what we want – a comfortable and safe society in tune with the natural world. It is also becoming clear what we need to do – change our ways; the vexing problem is not knowing how. In the next chapter, I look at the efforts we have made so far in striving towards a sustainable world, before moving on to confront the reasons why progress is stalled.

2 Striving for a Sustainable World

Sustainable development is development that meets the needs of the present without compromising the ability of future generations to meet their own needs.

The Bruntland Report[1]

The theory of sustainability, based on the three mutually reinforcing pillars of the economy, society and the environment, is attracting a growing following. It is becoming accepted that the economy cannot be considered separately from social and environmental issues, remembering that the converse is also true. Building a fair society and protecting the environment must be based on sound economics.

The route to a sustainable world will not be easy. The developed world will be reluctant to turn its back on the economic progress that has been made over the last century (and the associated lifestyle). The underdeveloped world will not want to forgo its chance of an industrial revolution to pull its populations out of poverty. It will not be easy to persuade either the rich or the poor to change in our struggle to find pragmatic policies with the potential for sustainability in the real world. Action is required by all peoples and all countries; but the world community has so far failed to find a way.

The foundations of the movement calling for a more sustainable world date back to the declaration[2] that was agreed at the Earth Summit in Rio de Janeiro in 1992. Central to the discussion of poverty, war and the growing gap between industrialized and developing countries was the question of how to relieve the global environmental system through the introduction of the paradigm of sustainable development.

The Rio Declaration states that, 'Human beings are at the centre of concerns for sustainable development. They are entitled to a healthy and productive life in harmony with nature. In order to achieve sustainable development, environmental protection shall constitute an integral part of the development process and cannot be considered in isolation from it. Peace, development and environmental protection are interdependent and indivisible.'

The Rio Declaration is an important statement of intent. It is backed up by the Commission on Sustainable Development and an action plan called Agenda 21. The principles were reaffirmed in 2002 at the World Summit on Sustainable Development (WSSD).[3]

Despite the good intentions and considerable effort by the Commission on Sustainable Development, and others, very little substantive progress has been made. The UN is constrained by the need to incorporate a wide range of opinions: the full 27 principles of the Rio Declaration cover every conceivable concern. Real action will come from governments and other organizations that have more freedom of choice and freedom to act. The UN has articulated some high-sounding objectives. The only way to make progress towards these is to translate them into a message that the people with power in politics and business can embrace.

Like many 'new' concepts, sustainability is not new at all. History contains examples of societies and peoples that have embraced the concept – consciously and subconsciously – ranging from Native Americans to Australia's Aborigines. For example, when discussing important decisions, Native Americans would take into account the effect they would have seven generations into the future. On the other side of the world, Australia's Aborigines lived for tens of thousands of years on the dry continent. They learned to live within the natural system in a society that adjusted to the resources available. It is ironic that these models of sustainability proved to be anything but, when they came up against the socio-economic imperatives of colonizers from the industrializing world. Our ancestors – just a few generations back – did not know the value of what they were destroying. We are poised to relearn some of these lost lessons in building a sustainable modern world.

For a society to be sustainable, economic, environmental and social factors must all be in balance. Over the last century, we have concentrated too heavily on economics; this must change. We need to find ways to deal with environmental issues in a manner that will conserve the Earth for many generations into the future. In doing this, we will have to give our social context a high priority. Other-wise, no matter how well intentioned our plans, they will unravel as populations expand and our instinct to defend our own immediate future takes selfish precedence.

The Historical Perspective

Early man was a nomadic hunter, living off the land and moving with the seasons to follow the animals he killed and ate. Life was about survival. The system in which he lived was inherently sustainable, although his personal survival was not. If nature was kind, the tribe had the resources to raise children and expand. When times were hard, the strongest would lead a move to better hunting grounds, leaving the weakest to fall by the wayside and die.

The farming revolution brought more security to food supplies and stability to society. In Europe, farming originated in Greece around 7,000 BC and migrated through the Balkans to western Europe, reaching Britain in around 4,000 BC and Scandinavia around 3,500 BC. The Neolithic people occupied one fertile alluvial plain after another. As people became more settled, land became a possession to be owned, rather than a shared resource. Unsustainable farming practices did not survive for more than a generation or two. A very close and direct relationship between the land and its population was established, leading to a society that had an instinctive feel for how much land a family needed to survive.

The mercantile societies that developed in Europe through the Middle Ages, provided huge opportunities for advancement. Merchants were the main agents of change, using sailing ships to transport commodities and goods around the world. The imperative of living within the resources available locally had been removed. Towns grew in size and importance as trading hubs.

The Industrial Revolution of the late 18th and 19th centuries brought machinery and automation. It also led to a major migration of people, from living in the countryside and employed in agriculture, to living in cities and working in factories. The Industrial Revolution meant a lot more could be produced, more cheaply, bringing great wealth to many people and places, but also pollution and social deprivation. The connection between people and the land had been severed. Success in the newly industrialized world often came from economies of scale; the bigger the better.

The information revolution that we are currently undergoing is powered by computers and the networks that connect them, enabling the global market to operate in cyberspace. Commercial corporations are now global entities that do not owe allegiance to any one country. This is the context within which we are struggling to implement the principles of sustainability in the real modern world.

Discarding the Old

Each revolution has built on what came before. Farmers found a better market for their produce through trade facilitated by the merchants. The merchants had a mass of products to trade produced in the factories of the industrial barons. Industry is served by the knowledge workers of the information revolution, searching worldwide for the cheapest production and most lucrative markets. We have not thrown away the benefits of the old, but have added in new capabilities. The best is retained, as methods and processes evolve, and the worst discarded.

Looking back on a past age, we can observe what was wrong, and with hindsight see what needed to be discarded. If we could go back in time and rerun history, we would bypass the worst of the old ways, but it is much harder for contemporary players to see their errors. We humans are blind to our faults until they hit us square between the eyes.

There is a common theme behind the inadequacies of each age, including today's information society. This is disconnection leading to a loss of control. This can be a spur to innovation and open up new directions, but it can also be highly destructive.

When farmers took over from hunters, some lost touch with the natural mechanisms of the ecosystem. The first farmers in the US Midwest converted prairie to crops and ran their farms profitably until an extended drought in the 1930s turned much of the land into a dustbowl. Many went bankrupt before they learnt to reconnect farming with nature's constraints.

The mercantile society expanded trade in both quantity and the distances over which goods were traded. Consumption became disconnected from the source of goods. Production took place in some remote location, leading to the exploitation of people and countries. One aspect in particular of this large-scale operation of trade – the slave trade – became so repugnant when the realities were widely known that society was forced to rethink its values. The changes and improvements in society which followed were an early precursor to the modern concept of universal human rights.

As the benefits of mechanization were exploited, the Industrial Revolution disconnected the pursuit of wealth from individual well being and the quality of the local environment, For example, the textile mills in northern England were run in ways that we would today find unacceptable. Workings hours in excess of 65 hours a week were common, and children were employed from as young as 10 years old. The working conditions were dangerous and unhealthy. Looking back, it is tempting to blame the mill owners – who became rich in the process – but it would be wrong to do this. Many of them were compassionate, fair and sought to improve conditions, but to make the sort of changes we would today expect would have bankrupted them within the society of 18th century England. Society as a whole had to agree that these conditions were unacceptable and, over time, bring in national social and environmental legislation to redress the imbalances. There are parallels here with the current problems the world is facing. Whatever blame we decide to attribute to business, it is society that must first choose to make the changes required.

The information society may be different. Rather than disconnecting people and activities, it is reconnecting them, with information from around the world just a few clicks away. However, this free flow of information (and capital) is leading to new disconnections: commerce is being disconnected from government. The big multinational companies have historical geographical roots, and the head office will have a physical location, but it is not clear which, if any, government they answer to.

We need to find ways to reconnect business with government and communities in order to deal with the problems thrown up by the information revolution and the associated drive towards globalization. As we move beyond the information revolution, the negative aspects of today's world will become clearer, and be discarded. History tells us that we can be optimistic: the good aspects of the information economy will remain and the negative ones will be eliminated.

I predict that the next revolution will be the Sustainable Revolution.

The Sustainable Revolution

In the decades ahead, we will be able to describe and analyse the Sustainable Revolution with the benefit of hindsight. Now, the owners of the revolution are few, but their numbers are increasing and their ideas are gaining credence. Many authors have contributed to building the foundations. Perhaps the first holistic green thinker was Fritz Schumacher in his book *Small Is Beautiful*.[4] This was written at much the same time as the Rio principles were first drafted[5] and was influenced by the attitudes of the 1960s. The book is now dated, but there is still a resonance with the issues of today. Other books that have helped to move the discussion forward include *Natural Capitalism*,[6] *Factor Four*,[7] *Cannibals with Forks*,[8] and *The Natural Advantage of Nations.*[9] Each book has contributed to the search for what sustainability means in practice.

For the developed world, I envisage the Sustainable Revolution leading to a zero-fossil-fuel economy and a range of sustainable practices. Many people believe that this will not be feasible without destroying our economies. It certainly will not be easy. There will be people who have to change the lifestyles to which they have become accustomed, organizations that have to alter long-established practices and businesses that need to replace processes that have been profitable for many years. We have achieved similar transformations in the past and society has been all the better as a result. I am optimistic that we in the developed world can achieve such an outcome, provided only that we find the will to do so.

It is far harder to see how the highly populous poor regions can adopt sustainable policies, in addition to the pressing problems they already face. It is, therefore, imperative that the developed world acts quickly and decisively. If the developed world can find a solution, then helping the rest of the world will follow. The underdeveloped world lacks power and influence; time and time again it has had to accept what the richer countries have decided, sometimes for the better, often for worse. This time the developing nations will again have to fall into line, but their needs and the needs of the world will coincide.

The Imperative to Act

The apparent stability of the ecosystems we observe in the natural world is the result of millions of years of adaptation. The adapt-or-die mechanism has eliminated elements that did not fit throughout the Earth's history. Some of the adaptation that has taken place has been dramatic. Our distant ancestors, the early mammals, survived the natural event that wiped out the then dominant life form, the dinosaurs. Like modern civilization, the dinosaurs must have looked invincible, but dramatic changes to the world's systems wiped them out. Scientists argue about exactly what caused the dinosaurs to become extinct, but how it happened is immaterial to my argument; the point is that the world's systems are dynamic equilibriums that can flip to a different state if the drivers change.

During the last few thousand years, prior to industrialization, the external drivers on the systems of Earth have been largely constant, and the system has been stable in response. There are long-term cyclical changes to the Earth's orbit which take place over hundreds of thousands of years. These have caused ice ages in the past, but the pace of change was slow. My ancestors in Europe migrated south with the growing ice sheets and then north again as the ice retreated. These were very slow and gradual changes. As observers, we could perhaps have watched the Earth continue with very little substantive change over many thousands of years. It is possible that, by chance, some of the activities adopted by mankind since the 18th century have delayed the onset of the next ice age. Over the centuries ahead, as our understanding of the workings of planet Earth become ever more precise, we may be able to make deliberate adjustments in policy to keep the planet just as we would wish. That is, if our actions in the present day, based on ignorance and arrogance, have not first undermined the stability of the whole system.

We are not passive observers, considering taking carefully targeted action. We are charging ahead, without understanding the repercussions of our actions. The scale of our activities, and our ability to affect the system, have risen exponentially over the relatively short period of the last 200 years. For example, we have driven the atmospheric concentration of carbon dioxide from a pre-industrial level of about 280 ppm (parts per million) to 379 ppm in 2005. This far exceeds the natural range over the last 650,000 years (180 to 300 ppm).[10] Another example is the emissions of mercury into the environment. This is predominantly from our coal-fired power stations, and ends up in our hydrology where it is absorbed into fish, concentrating in the larger and longer-lived species. The US Food and Drug Administration together with the US Environmental Protection Agency advise us – and in particular pregnant women – not eat certain types of fish.[11] Our society is now a significant internal driver acting on the system, pushing the Earth into a new equilibrium. But it will not be a static equilibrium. If the drivers continue to force change, the result will be continuing dynamic change. Instead of leaving our heirs the task of carefully tuning planet Earth, they will be struggling to reverse the damage that we inflicted during the 20th and early 21st centuries.

The changes we have already initiated should worry us. But of even greater concern is that the pace of change is continuing to accelerate. To use the example of carbon dioxide again, the growth rate of the concentration of this gas in the atmosphere was greater over the period 1995–2005 than it had been since continuous direct atmospheric measurements started in 1960. This is indicative of the fact that natural systems are under increasing threat.

Climate change is just one of the changes we have initiated – there will be others, such as the poisoning of our oceans (see Chapter 14). We would like to know the full extent of each change to help us to decide in a logical manner whether to adapt or act to prevent it. We must do both, of course, if our civilization is to survive intact. No part of our world is immune from the disruption. Our society, economy and business community will all need to respond to a different set of parameters, and to different priorities.

Sustainability in Practice

It is not easy for governments to adopt sustainability as the principle on which to build policy. An advocate close to the centre of political power should be able to make progress, but Al Gore had little effect in his time as vice president (1993–2001) to Bill Clinton. His book, *Earth in the Balance*,[12] published whilst he was in office, showed his environmental credentials, but despite his influence and power there was little discernible movement by the United States towards policy in support of sustainability. Now outside government, Al Gore continues to press his message in *An Inconvenient Truth*,[13] but, under the Bush presidency, there still seem to be a lot of deaf ears on Capitol Hill.

Business, too, finds it difficult to use the concept of sustainability to underpin its strategy. Companies are starting to report their results in terms of a 'triple-bottom line', incorporating performance against their social and environmental responsibilities, as well as financial results. This is progress, but a long way short of the wholesale shift in attitude required. Some businesses are starting to make more substantive progress; not through altruism but through a mixture of external pressure from government and society, together with business leaders spotting the commercial opportunities. Richard Branson, for example, is channelling the earnings from his portfolio of transportation businesses into renewable, sustainable energy sources.[14] As his business empire is privately owned, he can make such decisions unencumbered by the short-term nature of the listed equity markets. There will be those who are sceptical of his investment decision. However, I, and other believers in early action, should admire his stance. I believe that he has made a sound hard-edged business decision that will allow Virgin Fuels to underpin the profitability of Virgin Group over the decades ahead.

To get to the nub of the problem and start to identify a realistic approach, it is useful to consider the world as two separate but closely interrelated systems. These are the complex mesh of our society compared with the even more complex natural ecosystem. At the interface between them, society draws inputs from the natural ecosystem and sends back society's waste.

The natural system is blind to the pressure it is under. It has no executive authority or grand master plan; each element of the ecosystem will simply adapt or die as it always has done. The natural system is a follower, not a leader.

Society, as currently operated, is also largely blind to the effect it is having. The difference is that human players, although blinkered by the pressures of living and surviving in the modern world, have the ability to see, think and decide. We have foresight. Of the two systems, then, it is only society that we can hope to control directly. Nature will simply follow our lead.[15]

We can look at these two systems through the range of possible outcomes as shown in Figure 2.1 (see overleaf). For society, we can either carry on without constraint or we can adopt policies that show respect and understanding for the environment. The natural ecosystems can either be preserved or we must accept that they will be altered.

The scenario indicated by the bottom-left quadrant can be quickly eliminated: if society continues on the same path, without constraint, then it is not feasible that the world's natural systems can be preserved. The view that Earth's systems are stable and that they will cope regardless of what man does has been shown to be a delusion. We now know that, over geological time, the Earth has undergone major transformations. We also know that human activity is now of such a scale that it could precipitate similar major transformations. We do not know where the tipping point lies. Finding it by further practical experiment would satisfy our curiosity, but would be like searching for a gas leak with a lighted match. That leaves three scenarios, all of which are possible. Which one we arrive at depends on what decisions we make.

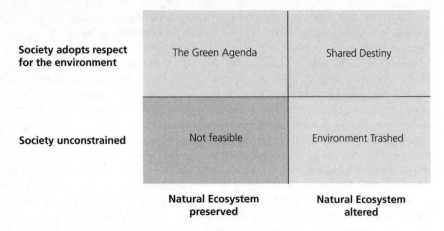

Figure 2.1 **Alternative Scenarios for Society and Natural Ecosystems**

If we do nothing, we will arrive in the bottom-right quadrant, with the environment trashed. There can be no dispute that mankind does not want this result.

That leaves two acceptable scenarios, both based on society adopting respect and understanding for the environment. I term the first scenario the 'Green Agenda' and the other 'Shared Destiny'. The first requires us to dramatically change our ways and eliminate actions that are driving change to the natural ecosystem. For many green activists, the Green Agenda is the only acceptable outcome, but the degree and pace of change required is enormous.

I have respect for the extreme green view and, on a personal level, could easily be persuaded to subscribe to it, but I recognize that its scope is too narrow. The tension between real-world economics and society and the aspirations of the green community are just too great. If we make an uncompromising push for the Green Agenda, we risk a breakdown of the process we are trying to start, and perhaps total failure.

The scenario that is both feasible and practical is that of 'Shared Destiny'. It requires society to work in harmony with the ecosystems of nature, coordinating our economic mechanisms, environmental controls and social policies. This will be immensely complicated. We will need workable theory and policies that can cut through the complexity to produce simple core concepts and levers that can be applied. Later chapters seek to explore how we can do this, leading to the final chapter in which I look forward to a shared destiny for natural ecosystems and society.

Current evidence indicates that becoming sustainable will not happen any time soon. It will not happen at all if the concept remains an idea that is continually refined by well-meaning experts, but is accepted by no one except committed greens. Our progress is stalled until the concept of sustainability moves from the liberal think tank into our real globalized world.

3   Our Globalized World

The state of the world today is in large part due to the drive of globalization: the free flow of goods and services between countries leading to the integration of economies and markets. Trade is the focus, but of course the flows of capital and the migration of people are closely interrelated issues. The United States is seen to be the leader, but many countries have opened their markets and reaped the rewards, particularly in East Asia where millions of people have been lifted out of poverty. China was a sleeping giant but has embraced the opportunities of globalization and is now becoming a major economic force. What becomes of a world in which every country embraces the challenges and opportunities of globalization?

Every country can aspire to the success of the United States as measured by economic indicators, up to a point. It is becoming clear, though, that the world cannot sustain such dramatically increased loads on the environment. There are also concerns that social structures are at risk. Many voices are raised against globalization, including politicians from both the extreme left, who want to protect social provision, and the extreme right, who favour nationalism and dislike seeing foreigners succeed apparently at their expense. Farmers, unions, environmentalists, the list goes on. This disparate group have only their dislike of globalization in common; they do not propose a coherent alternative.

As John Negroponte, when he was the US Director of National Intelligence, put it, 'Globalization has the look of a silent but titanic global struggle'.[1]

Globalization has brought substantial economic benefits, but a dark underside is becoming apparent. Fierce competition for energy, the growing gap between rich and poor, increased drug trafficking and the risk of pandemics, are all consequences of globalization.

The word globalization conjures up a range of reactions, from being over-hyped to unfairly maligned, depending on who you listen to. Recent US presidents and British prime ministers fall into the first category. They have encouraged us to embrace all aspects of the global economy. A contrasting group of people make up the latter group. They range from trade unionists in the old heavy industries of the developed world to Korean rice farmers, and from many concerned intellectuals to young people with radical views who have seized on globalization as the bogeyman of all the world's problems.

In a world of free trade, consumers get the best value and industry pays the lowest price for its inputs. Exports are facilitated through reciprocal deals to eliminate tariffs. The market economy is allowed to operate across borders, rooting out inefficiency and waste. Innovators are rewarded with a ready market. Unions might argue for protectionism, but their voices are muted and their political influence is reduced as fewer and fewer people are employed in activities that have migrated elsewhere.

Successful players in the globalization game need to be flexible and adaptable. The prize is growing GDP for all those who participate. Any country that is seduced by the attraction of protectionism and refuses to join the globalization bandwagon will find that, in a closed economy, prices to consumers are higher than they need to be; protected industries become lazy and inefficient; and exports reduce as other countries raise tariffs to match.

The economic argument is clear: globalization works. We should aim, therefore, to build on globalization and eliminate its negative attributes, rather than replace it.

The Historical Context

The heritage of globalization can be traced back over 200 years to the father of modern economic theory, Adam Smith.

> It is the maxim of every prudent master of a family, never to attempt to make at home what it will cost him more to make than to buy . . . What is prudence in the conduct of every private family, can scarce be folly in that of a great kingdom. If a foreign country can supply us with a commodity cheaper than we ourselves can make it, better buy it off them with some part of the produce of our own industry, employed in a way in which we have some advantage.[2]

This extract comes from Adam Smith's seminal book, *The Wealth of Nations*. In it, he argues that countries should specialize and do what they do best: exporting the fruits of their own particular expertise and importing whatever other countries can make at a lower cost. This remains the underlying principle of free trade. Embracing the theory was behind the building of the British Empire and it is why the United States is the powerful global power it is today.

For those who view Adam Smith as the originator of a selfish capitalist system, a quotation from his other great book, *The Theory of the Moral Sentiments*, might be enlightening.

> Though our effectual good offices can very seldom be extended to any wider society than that of our own country; our good-will is circumscribed by no boundary, but may embrace the immensity of the universe. We cannot form the idea of any innocent and sensible being, whose happiness we should not desire, or to whose misery, when distinctly brought home to the imagination, we should not have some degree of aversion.[3]

This shows that Adam Smith was a compassionate and principled man. His lasting legacy is to have described and explained an effective economic system on which to base society. There is nothing heartless or cruel in what he says. Where capitalism has failed to support sound and fair societies, it is a failure in execution, not a failure in the theory at the heart of economics.

The enormous changes that took place through the 19th century into the first decades of the 20th century were driven by free-market economics, and facilitated by technical advances in communications (the telegraph), transport (railways and steam ships) and machinery to automate production. This period was a golden economic age of growth and prosperity but problems were looming.

The depression of the 1930s and the two world wars before and after were disastrous for the world. Our experiences from that period meant that fascism and communism were discredited as ways to run society. It was not until the fall of the Berlin Wall in 1989[4] that much of Eastern Europe could return to the principles of Adam Smith. Another Scotsman, Michael Forsyth, MP, speaking on the bicentennial of Adam Smith's death, said:

> The basic principles of Smith's approach – the importance of free trade, putting consumers before producers, allowing and encouraging competition, rolling back state regulation and preventing politicians from trying to shape economic life in their own image – are clear enough to the new leaders of the post-communist countries, if not to some politicians in Western Europe.[5]

Many of the politicians and others who speak out against free-market economics and globalization are respected people whose intentions are good. There are parallels with the first half of the 20th century when the ideas of Karl Marx received considerable support from intellectuals across the world. Many of his followers were living in safe and largely well-run societies where they were free to debate the merits of communism. The reality demonstrated by the Soviet Union proved to be very different from the theory.

At the beginning of the 21st century, some of the anti-globalization lobby are self-deluding in the same way. Living in societies with sound economies that are benefiting from globalization, it is easy to discuss the drawbacks. They might be good people with honest views, but society had better make sure that the extreme elements of the anti-globalization movement are not allowed to take power. Their ideas should be listened to, and adjustments made, but the benefits of globalization and the free-market economy must not be thrown away.

The Current Status of Globalization

The state of globalization today is testimony to the foresight of those seeking to ensure that the world would not descend into yet another world war. Whilst the final stages of World War II were still raging, delegates from the Allied nations gathered at the United Nations Monetary and Financial Conference, held in the town of Bretton Woods in the United States. Its aim was to plan rebuilding the international economic system.

In July 1944, the Bretton Woods Agreements were signed. These set up a system of rules, institutions, and procedures to regulate the international monetary system. The International Bank for Reconstruction and Development (IBRD; now part of the World Bank) and the International Monetary Fund (IMF) were established, becoming operational in 1946. In 1948, the General Agreement on Tariffs and Trade (GATT) was agreed and was used to regulate world trade until 1995 when the World Trade Organization (WTO) was formed.

The WTO aims to increase international trade by promoting lower trade barriers and providing a platform for the negotiation of trade, and to resolve disputes between member nations. The world trading system is designed to provide open, fair and undistorted competition. The WTO has attracted considerable opposition from the anti-globalization lobby, some of which is plain daft. But the rational protesters have some justification: it is not a perfect institution. Even strong supporters of globalization acknowledge that reform is required.[6] For example, where countries have implemented high environmental standards, and have sought to extend these to imports from other countries, the WTO has ruled that a country cannot take trade action to enforce their domestic rules or law outside their own territory.[7] A country can enforce regulations on the quality or content of imports but not on the process of their production – even if the purpose is to protect animal health or exhaustible natural resources.

This problem has at least been recognized. At the end of the Uruguay Round of World Trade talks in 1994, trade ministers from participating countries decided to begin a programme of work on trade and environment, and they created the Trade and Environment Committee. The 2001 Doha Ministerial Conference kicked off negotiations in some aspects of the subject but progress is slow. The Earth is being put at risk whilst we endlessly discuss the issue. We need a coherent world approach that reconciles world trade policy and environmental protection, and we are a long way from achieving it.

The WTO is vulnerable to criticism, but it is the best system we have to regulate international trade, and a whole lot better than nothing. Without the WTO, countries would be free to behave to suit their narrow definition of national interest. There would be little to restrain the largest and most powerful countries. Objectors should be seeking to reform the WTO, not to scrap it.

We have become indifferent to the successes that flow from globalization. There is a danger that we take for granted the prosperous world of our time. But it is right that we be sensitive to the faults of globalization and try to redress them, whilst remembering that globalization is good economics and provides the context for good government. We should not fight globalization on principle, but should seek to reform it.

The Effects of Globalization on Countries and Societies

Globalization affects countries and societies in different ways, depending on their geography, history and stage within the process.

China is the biggest recent recruit to globalization and, like all new entrants, is basking in the glow of its benefits. China has moved rapidly from an isolated, largely rural economy, with limited access to the rest of the world, to a major world player that, if it continues its pace of growth, will rival the United States. On one hand, the world should welcome the opportunity for the Chinese people to lift themselves out of poverty. On the other, we should be concerned that the changes in China are adding hugely to the industrialization of our planet.

Opening up to world trade has been the prime driver behind China's rocketing economic growth. In 1992, the average tariff on Chinese imports was 40.6%; by 2002 this had dropped to 6.4%, closely comparable with the world's developed countries. Trade liberalization has led to a huge increase in exports, growing from $200 billion in 1999 to $600 billion in 2005. These exports are not matched by the same level of imports. China is running up huge foreign currency reserves, particularly American Treasury bonds.[8]

As the Chinese move from subsistence farming to manufacturing, and trade in their bicycles for cars, the load on our planet's systems will rise. At the end of 2003, China had 239 gigawatts of coal-fired electricity-generating capacity, predicted to rise to 546 gigawatts by 2030. China is commissioning a new coal-fired power station somewhere in the country almost every week.[9]

China's economy has done well out of opening up to world trade but, once the initial boom subsides, China will find that it is not necessarily an easy ride. For example, because free-trade agreements are reciprocal, the rural population will start to feel threatened by the importation of cheap agricultural products. If the Yuan rises to address the current-account surplus, then a cool breeze will blow through the export industries as they become less competitive. China is riding high on globalization, but the Chinese leadership may yet reconsider whether the rapid pace of social change and pressure on the environment is worth the price.

How China adapts and grows will have a significant impact on the world's economy, and the global environment. Having considered globalization's newest recruit, I will now turn to its oldest hand, Great Britain.

> *Complaining about globalization is as pointless as trying to turn back the tide . . . Success will go to those companies and countries which are swift to adapt, slow to complain, open and willing to change . . . We should have no reason to fear the challenges of globalization . . . We should relish them.*
>
> Tony Blair[10]

As a developed country, Britain has seen the cold wind of globalization blow through the traditional industrial base. Whole industries in textiles, mining and labour-intensive manufacture have been decimated. The process is not confined to the 'old' industries. For example, computer programmers now have to compete with a highly educated Indian workforce working over the internet from Bangalore, or workers from other third-world centres of expertise.

In the late 1970s, I studied engineering at Durham University in the northeast of England. Consistent with my choice of subject at that time, I marvelled at the legacy of the heavy engineering tradition, but I also noticed the beauty of the countryside that connected the industrial towns that dotted the landscape. Each town was built around a pit or steel works, with long lines of identical back-to-back houses to accommodate the workers; but these communities were coming under pressure.

There was no longer a market for coal from the industrial northeast. Imported coal was cheaper, and EU environmental legislation made coal a less attractive fuel. The social fabric of the mining communities was disintegrating. Regional aid was bringing in new high-tech industry, but the jobs were different. There were jobs for the well qualified, and for women (in the new clean factories), but the older miners with little education went on the dole. For a society built around the model of a tough male breadwinner, it was a hard transition. The unions of course resisted, but in the end Margaret Thatcher's government won out over Arthur Scargill[11] as the workforce – and its union – were becoming redundant.

The natural initial reaction by the miners had been to fight the changes to protect their jobs. Looking from a detached perspective, we can now see a picture of improvement and progress. Very little coal is now dug out from under the countryside of the northeast, leading to a cleaner environment. I returned to the northeast in 2000 to gauge the strength of support for starting and growing new business ventures. I found innovative and vibrant young businesses rising out of the heartland of the old economy, as the communities rebuilt themselves.

The pain of shutting down the old industries in the developed world is an example of necessary change. Globalization was not the cause – it would have had to happen sooner or later – but globalization was the catalyst that made it happen very quickly. Britain is in a better position as a result, and the affected communities are bouncing back.

Looking beyond Britain, we see the same shake-out of the old industries taking place across the developed world, and being resisted. Even in the United States – the world's strongest proponent of the market economy – lobbyists have been attempting to bend the government towards protectionism. The owners of the steel industry, the workers' unions and politicians with a large steel community amongst their electorate have used their combined political clout to get concessions. In the United States, such deviations from the forces of the market economy do not last long. Once a plant has closed, and the workers dispersed, politicians are drawn to other issues. This ability to accept change and adapt rapidly to new circumstances is a feature of those countries that have profited from globalization.

The United States epitomizes the rich developed world with a regulatory environment favourable to business. The country has a record of entrepreneurial activity and technological leadership, although other countries are now vying to take the lead. Many of the ideas might now come from elsewhere, but in terms of commercialization the United States still has the edge. The business community benefits from a huge domestic market. In an open global economy, this is also a vast market for other countries to sell into. The United States, the world's biggest consumer, sucks in goods and commodities from across the world. And, not least, it is also the world's biggest debtor, driving the world economy forward through continuing to spend rather than save. It is not surprising that many of the world's largest and most successful multinational companies (MNCs) have grown out of the United States.

The United States is one of the main beneficiaries of globalization and also the main target for those who oppose it, drawn from small segments of its own population as well as abroad. Ironically, the United States is one of the few countries capable of becoming self-sufficient, if globalization were reversed. It has a sufficiently broad geographical spread to be able to satisfy many of its needs from within its own borders. Major changes would be required, but the United States' outstanding ability for adaptation means that it could cope. If the world decided to turn against globalization, the United States would do rather better than most countries.

Mexico provides yet another view. It is a poor country sitting on the doorstep of the United States. I visited in the early 1980s and saw a country still based heavily on a rural economy. As an outsider, I thought much of the country was wonderful, and extremely cheap; foreign money could buy a lot of pesos. By economic measures the country was hopeless, but the people were hospitable and seemed very happy; this was clearly much more than just a brave face to please the tourist. My memory is of a laid-back, low-consumption and low-impact society, to be admired and envied in many ways, not pitied.

Since my visit, Mexico has ridden the wave of globalization, but it has not been a smooth ride. Huge capital inflows in the early 1990s were followed by huge outflows just a few years later, precipitating the crisis of 1994–5 in which the peso halved its value against the dollar. The North American Free-Trade Agreement (NAFTA), which took effect on 1st January 1994, gave Mexico a new opportunity to lift its economy.

NAFTA opened up huge commercial opportunities to manufacture, or more often simply assemble, goods for the US market. This brought considerable economic benefit to the north of the country, located closest to the US market. Foreign direct investment once again flooded in. The biggest complaint has come from small farmers who struggle to compete with exports from the United States' highly industrialized agriculture. Even so, many farmers in the north have also adapted and done well out of NAFTA by growing specialist produce for the US market.

The last two decades for Mexico can be likened to the growth that China is now experiencing. Mexico became the workshop for the United States, making all manner of things using the resource of cheap labour. In simple terms, US capital flowed in to build the factories and many Mexicans left the land to work in them. This was the easy first phase of globalization. However, the boom is faltering. Mexico no longer has the cheapest labour and investment is shifting elsewhere. It still has an advantage in its close proximity to the United States, but with freight costs low this advantage is relatively small for easy-to-transport durable products.

There are voices within Mexico questioning whether embracing globalization was such a good move after all. External observers cite corruption, poor education, red tape and crumbling infrastructure[12] as the factors that are holding Mexico back. This points to one of the problems of globalization: it only works if there is strong effective government. A free-market economy is not a free-for-all. An effective market needs a sound legal framework, appropriate and effective regulation, and honest and transparent mechanisms. Mexico has had the easy early wins from opening up to the global economy. It must now decide whether it has the discipline required to continue with globalization, unless, as I argue later, globalization itself alters to become more inclusive of a wider variety of economic models.

For yet another perspective, we can look into the heart of Europe. To France, the world's sixth biggest economy, permanent member of the UN Security Council, founder member of the EU and a driving force behind establishing the euro currency. Despite this global heritage, anti-globalization is shared by both left and right[13] of the political spectrum.

French workers have some of the shortest working hours in the world (a 35-hour working week), but also high unemployment. The beautiful French countryside is retained through traditional agriculture with many small farms, but needs considerable support from the Common Agricultural policy (CAP). France has chosen priorities that clash with the rigorous economic discipline that globalization requires. France wants to retain its unique rural structure and social support system, but struggles to reconcile this with losing competitiveness within the EU and world economy.

France is caught in a malaise of resistance to reforms that are clearly needed.[14] I believe the country has an opportunity to turn resistance to globalization into support for sustainability, garnering enthusiasm amongst its own population and using its deep-rooted French values to influence the future direction of Europe.

For Europe as a whole, we must decide whether to be fortress Europe, running our economy in a particularly European way; or open fully to world markets, taking the opportunities and accepting the constraints. How this debate develops amongst members of the EU will shape Europe's role within the world as we move beyond globalization. As a resident of Europe, it is my hope that we push the environment and social provision up to the top of the agenda, and play a leading role in shaping the new world order.

So far in this discussion, Africa has not been mentioned, because – with the notable exception of South Africa – Africa is not a fully functioning part of the globalized world economy. Countries such as Sierra Leone, which have valuable commodities to sell to the world, too often lose any benefit through corruption and conflict. In the poorer parts, such as sub-Saharan Africa, people are surviving on the edge. Food production is inefficient and subject to the threat of droughts. People are subject to nature's adapt-or-die mechanisms, breeding when the times are good and being wiped out by starvation when droughts continue. To Western eyes it seems inhuman, as if civilization has passed these people by. We also feel guilty, knowing that the increasing severity of droughts is caused by climate change, through no fault of the people affected.

The outside world tries to help by sending in aid to tackle the most visible problems. We set up piecemeal programmes to treat disease or improve infant mortality. We feed starving populations with the West's surplus grain, and excellent organizations such as Médecins Sans Frontières attempt to alleviate the suffering. But we are treating the symptoms. It would be far more useful to support Africa in developing African solutions to the continent's problems. It is in the interests of the world community to be prepared to help Africa reform itself, whilst being sensitive to the ways of Africa. The tribal roots and sense of community at the heart of traditional African values have the potential to provide the basis of sustainable societies. There are lessons the developed world can learn from the continent, as I explore later in the book. I have seen at first-hand well-intentioned but misguided attempts to provide external assistance. I believe that it would be better for Africa if the West did not force globalization upon the continent, and better for the world if Africa builds on its own heritage, bypassing the Western model of heavy industrialization.

Many parts of the world's economy have been kick-started by globalization. As a mechanism for economic development, the free-market economy has undoubtedly been successful. But globalization is showing some signs of becoming an economic bubble, which might become the biggest bubble in history.

Globalization relies on ever-increasing GDP and ever-growing consumption. But Earth's systems can only support so much destructive economic activity. The point will come when the systems are too overloaded and the bubble will burst.

4 The Sustainable Revolution

Embracing the opportunities of globalization has led to strong growth in many economies, with China as the largest and most recent beneficiary. Joining the club of globalized economies also means accepting that the world market is tough, highly competitive and unforgiving.

The multinational companies that invested in new facilities and plants in Mexico generated healthy profits for their shareholders, but better returns now come from moving production to China. There is nothing improper or underhand about this; it is the correct financial decision to maximize returns for shareholders.

As globalization matures and the immediate benefits work through the system, the downsides will become more apparent: the competition will become ever tougher, the fight over resources ever fiercer and the risks to the world environment ever greater. On the one hand, governments will urge on their local industry to be more competitive; on the other, they will attempt to maintain social cohesion and counter threats to the environment.

When governments find that reconciling these conflicting demands is becoming increasingly difficult, many countries will lose their enthusiasm for globalization and find that joining a Sustainable Revolution suits them rather better.

Revolutions happen when the forces for change exceed the capacity of society's normal adaptation mechanisms. Either the mechanisms are too cumbersome to cope, or the scale of the challenge is so great that they are overwhelmed. Vested interests are often at the root of this, such as an old guard defending its power base despite increasing pressure for reform. When change finally happens, it can be massive and rapid, shaking up the old order and ushering in the new. Revolutions are volatile and uncontrollable, until a new reality emerges and starts to coalesce into new structures and mechanisms.

The forces that we are failing to address adequately – and which will lead to revolutionary change – arise from the conflict between globalization and sustainability. The policy of globalization is sucking resources from the Earth at an increasing rate, driving activities to places with the lowest environmental and social standards. On the other hand, the policy of sustainability is seeking to persuade people, organizations and corporations to behave responsibly towards social issues and the environment. I am not alone in recognizing that global capitalism is in need of reform.[1,2] But I go further than many other commentators in my belief that our existing mechanisms of capitalism, as currently implemented, cannot handle these diverging forces.

The established order of how we run society and its institutions is set to be overthrown and the landscape reconfigured. Although we cannot know the results, we can try to predict how the revolution will develop and identify parameters that are likely to nudge its progress towards desirable outcomes. We should aim to hang on to the best of globalization whilst incorporating the principles of sustainability.

To reconcile globalization and sustainability at world level will be tough. First, it requires good global governance to oversee the standards and policies of the world. But national governments tend not to bow down to the authority of global institutions, except where it suits their interests. Second, it needs a concept of global citizenship that is established and deep-rooted, so that the world's population will accept constraints for the global good. But people do not behave as global citizens. If we expect action to be based on global governance and global citizenship, then we should not expect too much.

The key to understanding how to tame globalization and adopt sustainability is to look at mankind's common concerns. These are the resources we all share: the atmosphere, the oceans and the biodiversity of life, which knows no borders. The problems connected with our shared resources were defined two decades ago,[3] leading to the setting up of the United Nations Environment Programme (UNEP).

Under the auspices of the UNEP, the world is trying to sort out its environmental governance, seeking to persuade all of us to behave as responsible residents of the world. But the sum total of our action has been disappointing. Far from starting to solve the problems, we have presided over an acceleration of environmental degradation. This apparent inability to act – despite good intentions and the backing of the world's highest decision-making body – should be of deep concern. We should be pressing for action rather than forever restating the situation.

There is still time to sort out our pressing problems; but without the mechanisms to do so, we are like a rabbit caught in the glare of the headlights of a speeding truck. We can easily escape, but we are transfixed by the situation. Instead of leaping off to the side, we wait to see if the wheels run over us.

We can use an example to get a feel for the nature of the leap that we should make. Let us consider an area of common land coming under the sort of pressure that the world is now encountering. (The parallel with the whole Earth system is only partial, but the lesson we can draw provides a useful insight.) The land has been common as long as anyone can remember, and a number of families have grazing rights. To date, the common has been large enough, with an unwritten balance emerging through the generations that allows the common to support the community.

Now economic development is threatening the common. Many holders of grazing rights have realized that their incomes can be greater, their families larger and their lives materially better by maintaining larger herds of animals. Some families have already increased their herds substantially. Others see the benefits and decide to follow suit. It is only at this stage that the more enlightened holders of grazing rights start to see the risks. The common had been running well within its capacity, but it is now starting to show signs of overgrazing.

Over a protracted period, discussions take place to seek to manage the common. Some agreements to limit damage are agreed. For the main overall issue, that of overgrazing, a large group of rights holders agree to control numbers, but this agreement has little chance of success if other rights holders continue to increase their herds. The common becomes subject to an inevitable cycle of decline. If the cycle is not broken, the grazing will be stripped bare, animals will die and the returns to all will diminish. If we liken our world to the common in our example, then this is the decision point that the world has reached.

We can accept the situation and milk it whilst we can – before the inevitable decline destroys the resources of the world – or find another way. This is the classic problem described by Garret Hardin way back in 1968.[4] Hardin's proposed solution was through 'relinquishing the freedom to breed'. This was, and still is, a controversial statement. Where Harding was right was to identify that change is needed and that we might find aspects of it unpalatable.

In the example of the common, I see a way out, but it requires a break with the traditions of the past. A group of grazing rights holders decide to ensure their own destiny by breaking the spiral of decline. They take control of part of the common and limit grazing and numbers in that area. This group of people need to robustly defend their stance and keep others off 'their' area. They hope that over time the evident success of better management of their part of the common will be copied and replicated. They will need to work with and negotiate with the other rights holders to diffuse conflict, but must also be resolute in not allowing the cycle of decline to continue as far as their influence and power extends.

World society will respond to environmental problems in much the same way as the common rights holders. Sustainable societies will be built on a selfish determination to deliver a better life for a particular society's own members, moving to a situation where we are balancing economics, environmental protection and social provision. However, we should not underestimate the complexity of the challenge.

Balancing Economics, Environmental Protection and Social Provision

Which matters most? My instinctive answer is 'environmental protection', but this is based on my presumption that the resources for me and my close family are secure. Concentrating on protecting the environment when the population is dying of starvation would be inhumane and impossible to enforce without coercion. The general answer for what matters most has to be social provision.

Which is the biggest risk? This is where my instinct is correct. It is with the environment that we are taking the greatest risks. We can recover from financial crashes surprisingly quickly. Broken social systems can be rebuilt over a generation or two. But it is not so easy to backtrack on our environmental mistakes. Mankind now has the capability to wreck the environment so effectively that it would take thousands, or tens of thousands, of years to recover. This is not a risk we should be running.

Of the three elements, my brief analysis indicates that economics has the least direct importance. But economic measures are the ones that are most easily controlled, being specific, quantitative and measurable. They are also the prime tools we have been using to run society over recent decades, so we are familiar with them. Economic strength is the best starting point for building a sustainable society, and economic tools are some of the most effective methods we have to drive implementation.

A country, person or organization with sound finances can afford to look beyond economics. People who live in such countries have the luxury of being able to look at life in its wider context. Those of us with employment and secure finances in the developed world can afford to be tolerant, compassionate and fair-minded. It is the tough financial discipline under which our society and businesses operate which permits this. We can learn a sustainable approach, not by diluting our economic policies or blunting the mechanisms of the free market, but through bringing the same rigour to environmental protection and social provision.

Laying the Foundations

Setting the balance between economics, social provision and environmental protection requires power and commitment. Power is the capability to get something done and commitment is the willingness to do so. These two characteristics are distributed in different measures.

The government of a sovereign state is where the most power resides; in some countries, this is quite literally the power of life or death over its citizens. Paradoxically, power diminishes at the world level. The UN is, in principle, the most powerful organization in the world, but in reality it has a very loose grip on the levers of power.

Commitment is distributed according to a different profile. It is at the local level that a feeling of belonging, a sense of community and commitment to the common good are strongest. This then steadily weakens as we rise up through the administrative structures of society to world level.

At the lowest level, within a family, commitment is often absolute and the willingness to act for the common good is boundless. The influence of close personal relationships also extends out into the immediate local community of neighbours and families with same-age children. Local government and local organizations are less personal, but coordination is still through people who know each other, so the complex give and take of maintaining a healthy sustainable community has a high chance of success.

This close affinity with fellow citizens extends as far as the shared need to cooperate does. In the Australian outback, where the closest neighbour might be four hours' drive away, then the sense of community covers a large geographical area. Within a city, the sense of community is often confined to a small area such as one apartment block, a few shops and a bar.

A feeling of kinship can extend to the whole country if it is a nation state, as many smaller countries demonstrate. Larger countries, too, can behave as one community where commitment to shared values is strong, such as the United States.

The sense of community can also extend to groups of countries, leading to regions in which many values are shared. The Arab nations are one example. Europe is another; although the strength of the shared European identity seems to wax and wane. This is seen particularly during the process of enlargement as more diverse peoples and cultures are brought inside the structure of the EU.

At the global level, commitment is least. Very few people would regard themselves as world citizens with a moral responsibility to the world community as a whole.

This brief analysis of power and commitment leads to two important principles. The first is the principle of subsidiarity.[5] People understand their own environment, know the people around them, can take decisions for the collective good and take ownership of the result. The responsibility to run a sustainable society should, therefore, reside at the lowest possible level, with local solutions taking precedence of national solutions; national solutions taking precedence of regional solutions and regional solutions taking precedence of global solutions.

The second principle is the primacy of the state. This is where the combined value of power and commitment is greatest. Governments have power over borders, legislation and fundamental areas of policy *and* can call on a sense of nationhood, loyalty and pride. They, therefore, have the most influence over building sustainable society.

The reality is that the world has always been run in this way, but many aspects of the policy of globalization conflict with this natural order. In defining a policy that can take us forward and bring policy closer to people's needs, I find that a new term is useful. This will ensure our thinking does not slide back into familiar furrows that existing terminology conjures up. For example, I argue for an increasingly localized economy and society, but this is not the same as the 'localization' described by some green campaigners[6] – although there are a number of similarities. The new term I use is 'proximization', which I define as:

> *Proximization is selfish determination to build sustainable societies, aimed at social provision and driven by economic policy, whilst minimizing adverse impacts on the environment.*

Proximization is a natural rebalancing of the world order to return to a stable and effective world community. It will come about because of the determination of people to defend their communities and ensure a safe and secure livelihood for their family and the people around them. I propose that in order to implement proximization, the following principles should be adhered to:

- decision making taken on the basis of sustainability – balancing the economic, social and environmental consequences;
- subsidiarity – control left at the lowest possible level;
- the primacy of the state – where power and responsibility reside; and
- the use of market economics – the proven method.

Adoption of these principles will lead to localizing activities and closing off process cycles within the local area as the only sure way of being sustainable. There will still be loops of activity extending out to regional and global level, where this is the most effective and sustainable solution, particularly where this consists of know-how and expertise. There will also continue to be commodity flows, but on a smaller scale and operating under close oversight, as we seek to influence protection of the environment in places beyond our direct control (using the power we can wield to control what we choose to import).

Proximization is not without difficulty, and is likely to be a diffusion of ideas from the bottom up rather than the top down. It will take time for the changes in culture to evolve. It may not be until a significant cohort of countries adopts principles like these, and show that they work, that proximization gains widespread acceptance.

There are also risks; a half-hearted attempt at proximization could transform into that negative form of nationalism exploited by the far right. This is why we need to put a strong focus on the social element of the changes we make to ensure that we don't create an underclass within our society where extreme nationalist ideologies can take root. Proximization requires a robust coordinated approach to delivering social benefits for the entire population of a defined community or country.

Rebuilding Society

Under the stewardship of the state, a sustainable society consisting of cooperating communities can be built. Between countries, resistance to the movement of people, things and commodities will arise; but countries also have different climates, resources and skills. Countries that adopt sustainable thinking and respect collective arrangements to protect shared resources such as the oceans and the atmosphere will cooperate closely. Where it is sensible to exchange goods, services or commodities within a sustainable framework they will do so. Countries that decide not to adopt sustainable thinking should expect to be excluded.

Countries should continue to have the freedom to do what they will with their own territory, for better or for worse. According to the principle of subsidiarity, the residents of one country should have no right to interfere in how another society operates, except in so far as their actions threaten to damage the shared resources of the collective environment. It is only in this situation that one country would be justified in seeking to influence the behaviour of another for the common good.

If the countries of the world do not take close control of their own societies – in the way described here as 'proximization' – and rely on the open globalized world to deliver economic growth and wealth, then global governance will not be strong enough to prevent a trashed world environment that we will all have to share.

Proximization is the alternative. People living in counties that adopt it will have the luxury of observing how other countries are faring, whilst being insulated from many of their problems. Other countries looking in and seeing the evident success are likely to be converted, too.

A world in which proximization takes hold will reconcile global forces with sustainable policies derived from local circumstances. We should expect a variety of economic models in the same way that we will continue to have different social models and a variety of core values for each society. The world will continue to be a rich and diverse mix of cultures and nations.

The synergies and efficiencies available from the global market will still be useful, but the context will move from pure economics to a focus on building and supporting communities. Trade will adjust to match real needs in a sustainable manner between countries in which different economic and social priorities have been set.

Measuring Progress

Common sense says that overall world GDP would fall as policy shifted from a narrow focus on economics. For a government that is successful at delivering social provision for its population and safeguarding the environment, GDP may well drop. This should not necessarily be seen as a problem, unless our actions to implement sustainability stifle innovation and breed complacency and inefficiency.

This could be likened to a company shifting its focus from increasing turnover to increasing profits. This focuses management more closely on the desired final result. A reduction in turnover might follow, but no one should worry, provided the profit targets are reached.

There are examples of where measures of GDP are not that useful. The UN describes poverty in terms of an income figure.[7] This is derived from the GDP divided by the population. Although mathematically correct, it tells us little. Whilst working in Africa, I came across communities in which the paper money I carried had no perceived value. Some of these communities were exceedingly well run and seemed quite advanced in their social structures. One village I visited had no monetary income, so by economically based measures they were in abject poverty and in need of help. But it was I – with my Land Rover completely bogged down to its axles in a remote area – who needed help.

The whole village turned out to help pull me out. The only payment they would accept was a packet of biscuits I was carrying – which I supposed seemed different and exotic. I did not get the impression that this was a community in crisis. From the well ordered look of the village, they seemed to have sound administration. From the state of the beautiful natural scenery, I could assume that they were in tune with their environment. From their laughter as they dug me out, they were, I guessed, quite content.

Transposing Western economic measures onto all the world's communities does not provide a measure of the quality of life. Measurements of social provision and environmental conservation may be more appropriate. Ultimately, we should be measuring health, happiness and fulfilment, but this is hard to do on an objective basis. I leave it to others to work out what might be the best parameters, but we can be sure that GDP will be a poor measure of how we are doing when it comes to building a sustainable world. Governments should move away from using growth in GDP as their prime measure of success. GDP is, indeed, likely to continue to grow but it is the wrong measure and the wrong target.

The Sustainable Revolution is coming. The tension that is building between the opposing forces of globalization and sustainability will eventually be too much to hold. It is hard to predict when this will occur, but when it does many of the current mechanisms of society will have to change. The outcome will affect all aspects of our world as we rebuild the way we organize society.

Part Two

ISSUES AND OUTCOMES

5 The World's Natural Systems and Society

In mapping out the changes that the Sustainable Revolution will bring, we must consider the world's natural systems alongside those of society. Although we often consider them in isolation, for convenience and in order that we can comprehend them, nature and society are inseparable.

The Earth is like a spaceship in the vacuum of space with a few clearly defined inputs such as radiation from the sun, and with the only outputs the small high-technology devices we launch as we explore our solar system. James Lovelock – the originator of Gaia theory – explained the complexities of the Earth as a living, self-regulating organism,[1] with a myriad of systems and cycles interacting with each other. Over the relatively short period of the last 200 years, humans have invented and built the capability to cause fundamental changes to the life support systems of Earth. We are more than a passive resident of spaceship Earth: our society is an integral component of the living system. Society and natural ecosystems form one system. I call this concept the supra-ecosystem: natural systems and society interacting with one another, forcing change on each other and altering until a new equilibrium is reached that balances the competing drivers.

The fact that we live in a supra-ecosystem is an obvious observation (once it is pointed out), but the implications of the concept are not so intuitive.

We see nature's ecosystems as closed cycles of life. That is because over millions of years any open-ended activities have run to completion. All that remains are closed loops that repeat again and again and again. Until, that is, there are alterations to the external drivers, or some sort of internal perturbation, or perhaps mutation, which initiates change. Whatever the source, the change ripples through the system until stability is achieved once more. The open loop is closed off into a new pattern of closed cycles.

The players in natural ecosystems each behave to suit their own ends without a view of the whole system, without even comprehension that there is a system. Despite this lack of top-down coordination, the system finds equilibrium. Some players are predators, some are food at the bottom of the chain and some are in the middle as both predator and prey. The numbers of each adjust to the conditions.

Society behaves in much the same way, with each player behaving to suit its self-interest. For example, a new technology is invented which is at first disruptive. Society alters; the business landscape changes. New opportunities are exploited and old technologies and methods are eliminated. The open loop of the invention is hugely profitable at first, but over time the technology becomes embedded in the systems of society. It becomes a fact of doing business, with no particular advantage or disadvantage. The open loop of the original idea is closed off into the new pattern of commerce.

Any driver for change in the natural or man-made systems will force change in the whole supra-ecosystem. Likewise, any attempt to protect either society or the natural ecosystem has to take both into account. Our tendency to conceptualize the two systems as separate is in response to the sheer complexity of the supra-ecosystem; the only way to understand it is in manageable chunks. The following chapters of this book seek to do just that. But before disassembling the supra-ecosystem, it is necessary to drive home the point that our perception of society and nature as separate systems is just a mental convenience; there is no separation.

An example from history comes from Easter Island in the Pacific Ocean. The first Europeans to set foot on the island in the 18th century were amazed to find massive stone statues. It was puzzling how such a remote and bare island could have supported a society capable of their construction. Some time in the past there must have been a highly capable civilization.

Archaeologists have since pieced together the unhappy story. It appears that the society started expanding rapidly from about a thousand years ago. Over the next few hundred years, the civilization lived beyond the sustainable limits of the natural resources of the island (the building of the statues contributing to the drain on resources). Deforestation and soil erosion followed. The island could no longer support a population that had risen to many thousands.

Easter Islanders presumably still had the expertise to build boats, but no longer had the trees for the wood with which to build them. The ensuing conflict and fight for survival is thought to have included cannibalism. This collapse of the supra-ecosystem must have been devastating for the inhabitants: a time of turmoil, conflict and extreme misery.

When Europeans first landed on Easter Island, there was a small population scratching out an existence. It was a shadow of the civilization that had once lived there. Easter Island is one isolated example. We should reflect whether in our increasingly globalized world we are playing out the same storyline with the whole of spaceship Earth; charging ahead and forcing future generations to fight their fellow man for survival, in order to scratch out an existence from the ecological disaster of a ruined planet.

The world in the 21st century is subject to much stronger drivers for change than we have experienced in the whole of recorded history. The prime drivers are not just local, or regional, but global.

Global Drivers

One global driver is the widespread addiction to fossil fuels. The world's craving for energy is regarded as a demand to be met, not a habit to break. Increased consumption is facilitated by open energy markets served by the big oil companies.

These companies are scouring the world, seeking to locate and extract all the accessible reserves. Even national parks are coming under threat if significant hydrocarbon deposits are thought to lie underneath. Open global markets will ensure the exhaustion of the world's fossil fuels, over time, in an efficient and highly effective manner. This, in turn, will lead to greatly increased CO_2 levels in the atmosphere. Local or regional communities that stand to lose from the resultant changes in the Earth's systems will have little power to act.

The most powerful global driver is copycat development along the lines of the US and European models. Those of us who live in these societies see the success that they have brought: stable populations, established economies, good health care, ample food and reasonable comfort. If you have none of these, it looks like an ideal model to adopt.

If poverty is defined by financial income, then the Western model is the best way to alleviate poverty. The World Bank, the IMF and others champion development as the solution to world problems. This means that the model of a complex infrastructure, industry, increasing GDP, increasing consumption and greater material wealth is being rolled out worldwide. Low-income rural economies are regarded as failures to be rehabilitated. This is a very dangerous situation, where world-level policy is undermining the sustainability of many societies.

The increasing power and reach of global drivers, especially where there appears to be little effective control, is risking major changes to the global supra-ecosystem. The uniform adoption of the same policies and behaviours means that any ensuing problems are greatly magnified. One flaw in one society may have little impact on the world's systems, but the same defect throughout all societies of the world could have far-reaching consequences.

The world needs a diverse range of societies and economic models. This is not so as to take pleasure in the rich diversity of mankind (although that, too) but in order to have a resilient world system that will serve us well into the long future. This concept conflicts with much of mainstream economic thinking. It may not be economically efficient in the short term, but over the long term will be a good investment.

Society and Ecosystems in Equilibrium

The pressure that we are placing on the ecosystem is so great that it must find a new equilibrium. A scientist conducting an experiment with planet Earth would take a fail-safe approach, adjusting one parameter at a time and letting the effect ripple through the system. If the resulting changes were negative, then he/she could reverse that particular change and try another.

Mankind is not behaving like a careful scientist. We have hold of a number of levers at once and all of them are pushed up against the stops. Very few people are giving much thought to the possible outcomes. Even if the levers are pulled back to a more neutral position, it is likely to be decades or centuries before the full effects of 21st-century man's experiment have played out to a conclusion.

Climate change will be one of the relatively more predictable outcomes, but the full spectrum of changes to the supra-ecosystem is hard to anticipate.

There should be no dispute that the supra-ecosystem is vitally important and that we want it to continue to suit our needs. As we do not have direct control over it, we have to be very careful.

A business analogy is helpful here. For staff you employ, you can insist on how they behave; for factories you own, you can dictate how they are run. Relationships with organizations which are vital to your business, but which are free to choose their own course, must be handled carefully. In such situations, one must be sensitive to the needs of the other party and give, as well as take, to get a deal that suits both. We must be sensitive to the needs of nature as we negotiate a future for the world.

Within the supra-ecosystem, the only negotiator with foresight is man. We can do 'what-if' analyses to develop possible future scenarios. We have the ability to change our behaviour. If the other party is nature, then the negotiation is straightforward; there is no gamesmanship, hidden agenda or bluff. The natural world is complicated but also a transparent and reactive player.

It is clear that we do not want to destroy the system that supports us. Impassioned pleas for the protection of nature are becoming louder and more numerous. This book moves beyond the rhetoric to consider real-world practical policy options in order to ensure that the world system regains an equilibrium that is capable of supporting our children, grandchildren and their descendents into the future.

Balancing Needs and Resources

A sustainable society uses only those resources that the ecosystem can supply without suffering long-term damage.

The use of ecological footprints is a method that we can apply to define levels of consumption. For any activity, the area of the Earth's surface required to support it can be estimated. For example, the average American requires 9.6 hectares (ha) to support their consumption, compared with 5.6 ha per person in the UK and only 0.5 ha for each resident of Bangladesh.[2]

These headline figures are often quoted but it is worth digging a little deeper. I contend that the overall ecological deficit (or reserve) is a more important measure. This is calculated by comparing the demand for resources (expressed as a footprint) with the ecological capacity available (measured by the sum total of cropland, grazing land, forestry and fisheries). At world level in 2003, we were consuming resources at a rate which required 14.1 billion ha of ecological capacity, but the Earth has only 11.2 billion ha available.[3] At country level, the ecological deficit or reserve indicates how well its population is living within the constraints of its resource base. We should not be surprised that the figures show the United States as running an overall ecological deficit of 4.8 ha per person. The other large country running a big deficit is Australia, which consumes 5.9 ha per person more than its ecological capacity.

The world is in deficit by 2.9 billion ha. It is clear that we are living beyond the capacity of Earth, and that we must rein in consumption to achieve a sustainable balance. The question is how. In the previous chapter I discussed the dangers of relying on people behaving as world citizens. We should have a moral responsibility to the world community as a whole, of course, but this is a weak basis for action. Proximisation[4] provides a robust policy framework within which we can rebalance the ecological books.

The US deficit is driven by a whopping energy bill leading to a carbon footprint of 5.6 ha per person, but – interestingly – if the United States were to kick the energy habit, and reduce its carbon footprint down to the overall world average (1.1 ha per person), then its ecological deficit would be reduced to 0.2 ha per person. A further 5% reduction in other areas and the United States would then be running within its ecological capacity. Australia's deficit is more deeply ingrained; even if Australia reduced its carbon footprint to the world average it would still be running a deficit of 3.6 ha per person. The UK is another example of a country running well beyond its ecological capacity. Reducing its carbon footprint to the world average, the UK would still be running a deficit of 1.9 ha per person.

Bangladesh has the smallest ecological footprint per person of almost any country in the world; only the people of Somalia use less (0.4 ha per person). However, whereas Somalia runs a surplus of 0.3 ha per person, Bangladesh is in deficit (by 0.2 ha per person). It is hard to see where significant cuts could be made on what is already a low figure. For Bangladesh, policies that lead to a smaller population would appear to be the only viable option for being able to live within the ecological capacity of the country.

The figures for ecological footprints illustrate the range of lifestyles across the world. Some people argue that the richer nations should reduce consumption and the poorer nations limit their expansion to a global average footprint – that this would be equitable and fair.[5] In one sense, yes; but this is a distraction rather than a helpful proposal. Countries have different circumstances. In tropical regions with good rainfall, fertile soil, plenty of sun and temperatures that suit tropical animals like humans, living can have a very small ecological footprint. Where I live in Northern Europe it is different: there is a very short growing season and long cold winters. Food and energy supplies have to be gathered and stored. It is impossible to survive without wearing rather larger ecological boots.

In addition to constraints arising from geographic circumstances, governments make lifestyle choices on behalf of their populations in setting their policies. When this leads to a country grabbing a disproportionate slice of the world's ecological capacity, this is evidently unfair. But we should not object to a country which commits to live within its own ecological capacity, even if that country chooses policies that combine high consumption per person with a small population, in order to balance the ecological books.

Finland, at the northern tip of Europe, has a geography and lifestyle leading to an ecological footprint of 7.6 ha per person, more than the UK but less than the United States. If we look beyond this figure to observe how well the Finnish population is connected with its resource base, we find that there is a surplus of 4.4 ha per person. Finland has managed to retain the connection between the needs of the population and the country's resource capacity.

Changing Society

It would be relatively easy for affluent people in the developed world to adopt a sustainable lifestyle with the aim of protecting the supra-ecosystem. There is sufficient spare resource within our lives to make the transition. We have the time to consider what might be sustainable (which is not always obvious). We have the capital to invest in sustainable technology. All that is needed is a mind-set change to choose to live with nature's systems and avoid disrupting them too much.

This is a necessary first step on the route to a solution, but therein lies a fallacy. The potential trap is that such behaviour convinces people that the problem will then be solved. On the positive side, the negative drivers from one person, one family or one community will have been ameliorated. However, there are large parts of society without the will or the means to join in. These might be small sub-communities or entire countries. Our policies and actions must also coax them into playing their part.

The greatest value that derives from the developed world adopting a sustainable lifestyle, and building a sustainable society, is the example it sets. We have set the example of industrial development and it is roaring ahead, attracting more and more followers. It is now our responsibility to lead the drive to save our world and help others to bounce forward to a sustainable future.

6 Climate Change

Of all the possible planetary conditions that humans could encounter, the Earth is just right. Of course, the fact that it suits us so well is because we have evolved as an integral part of it. If we were to live our lives without upsetting the system, we could expect to continue to live in these ideal conditions for many generations, for thousands, tens of thousands, even hundreds of thousands of years.

However, mankind is upsetting the system. According to the Intergovernmental Panel on Climate Change (IPCC), by the year 2100 global mean temperatures will rise by between 1.1 and 6.4°C and mean sea levels will rise by between 18 cm and 59 cm.[1]

This could be much worse, if the fears of Chris Rapley, expressed when he was Director of the British Antarctic Survey (BAS), are correct.[2] He suggested that the West Antarctic Ice Sheet may not be as stable as had been thought. If it were to collapse, the resulting rise in mean sea level could be as much as 5 m.

Such a rise would not only inundate low-lying countries such as Bangladesh, it would also submerge much of a number of the world's cities, including New Orleans, London and many others. Professor Rapley is hardly a scaremonger; he is an eminent scientist pointing out that there are credible arguments for the possibility of much more dramatic changes than the sober and carefully considered predictions of the IPCC.

Whether the world is on a gradual path to a warmer climate or a major step-change we will discover in the decades ahead. The question is what we do about it.

The signatories to the Kyoto Protocol[3] believe that action must be taken and they have made a first step towards curbing the emissions that cause global warming. But this group does not include the United States, which for many years has been the world's biggest consumer of fossil fuel. Of even greater concern is that the Kyoto Protocol does nothing to rein in the carbon emissions of two of the world's fastest expanding economies, those of China and India. These are expected to use increasing quantities of fossil fuels to provide power to their growing economies.

Between 1994 and 2004, China's CO_2 emissions increased by 68% and India's by 53%, compared with an overall world increase of 25%.[4] These countries have started from a very low base; if the United States is their role model, they have a lot more catching up to do. In 2004, the CO_2 emissions per person in the United States were 5.5 tons; in Europe 2.5 tons; in China 0.8 tons; and in India 0.3 tons.[5]

We are living through a period of denial, increasing GDP year-on-year but letting the problem of climate change fester. Many politicians are happy to sign up to the Kyoto Protocol, but only because it has plenty of wriggle room with no binding penalties. The world needs to broker a much more robust agreement if we are to arrest change to our climate.

Predicting the Changes

The recorded history of civilization has been played out within a largely stable climatic system. Over the last few thousand years, changes from one century to the next have not been great. Perhaps the Little Ice Age between the 13th and mid-19th century is an exception. It was cold enough in Europe for the Thames to freeze over, allowing ice fairs to be held on the frozen river. In 1780, New York harbour to freeze, allowing people to walk between Manhattan and Staten Island. The Arctic pack ice extended so far south that there are reports of Inuit landing their kayaks in Scotland.[6]

The industrialization of the 19th century may have played a part in bringing temperatures back up to those we regard as normal today, but the 20th century was exceptional. Man's impact has grown to such a magnitude and scale as to be affecting the equilibrium of the climate system. History does not, therefore, give us an indication of the sort of changes that are coming.

In predicting where the climate might be heading, computer models are at the forefront. For weather forecasting, we are getting very good at making predictions about weather patterns accurate to five days or so. This is a big achievement, but long-term climate modelling is a hugely more complex task. Matching the true complexity of the Earth's systems requires more than just atmospheric modelling; it needs to include ocean currents, and not just surface currents but full three-dimensional flows. As our climate modelling becomes more comprehensive, we can expect that the results will become more reliable, but we will only really know how good the climate models are when we experience the reality.

The aspect of the climate system over which man has the greatest influence is the atmosphere. There are certain greenhouse gases (GHG) that enable the atmosphere to trap more of the sun's energy. Modern man inherited a situation that had settled into equilibrium. The stable GHG concentrations were maintained by natural mechanisms, producing and taking up the gases in balance.

Man has now upset this equilibrium. The IPCC assesses that the 20th century was the warmest century of the last thousand years: temperatures rose by 0.6°C and sea levels rose by 1–2 mm annually.[7]

The trend is accelerating: 11 of the 12 years between 1995 and 2006 rank amongst the 12 warmest years on record.[8] The changes observed so far are just the beginning; it is estimated that the full effects of changes in levels of CO_2 may take a century to feed through the system.

The low end of predictions for the end of the 21st century is an average rise of 1.1°C with mean sea level rising by 18 cm. This would not seem to matter much to most of the world. In Britain, the Thames barrier will need to be raised more often to protect London, but, on a positive note, English wineries may be able to produce rather better wine.

If the high-end predictions of a temperature rise of over 6°C and a sea level rise of over half a metre are nearer the mark, then these are significant changes. We should bear in mind that the IPCC estimates are by their nature conservative, only stating what they have the evidence to support. Mankind's experiment with the climate has not been run before, so no one really knows where it will lead. It can be argued that the Earth's systems are stable and that changes will be gradual. On the other hand, it may be that we are pushing the Earth so far outside its normal limits that it passes a tipping point and races out of control to a completely new equilibrium.

Scientists have, therefore, been looking back through geological time for examples that might assist our understanding. The task is complex, and the limited clues can be hard to interpret, but episodes of dramatic and rapid climate change have been found.

About 55 million years ago, an event called the Paleocene-Eocene Thermal Maximum (PETM) occurred. At that time, temperatures rose rapidly by as much as 10°C at high latitudes in the Arctic and Antarctic. Tropical oceans and deep ocean waters warmed by 4 to 6°C. These were accompanied by dramatic effects on plants and animals, as shown by the fossil record. Scientists think that the fast-changing climate was driven by a natural release of carbon-containing greenhouse gases comparable to what is occurring with the release of CO_2 and other gases since the start of the Industrial Revolution.

One hypothesis involves the release of huge amounts of methane gas that had been trapped in frozen deposits of methane hydrates. Methane hydrates are present in the deep oceans as frozen sediments, but some are associated with permafrost soils in the Arctic. Release of the methane can occur through natural processes, including warming of the oceans. Once released, the gas can induce atmospheric warming that has a positive feedback effect, releasing still more gas as ocean waters and permafrost regions continue to warm. The process can reach a tipping point where it starts to accelerate rapidly.

> *You may get a runaway greenhouse effect with dramatic results. Once the threshold is crossed, the climate may change very rapidly but recovery will be much slower, as we see in records from the Paleocene-Eocene Thermal Maximum, where recovery took about 100,000 years.*
>
> Ellen Thomas, paleoclimate scientist, Yale University[9]

This example shows that the Earth's system does have tipping points, which, when exceeded, can quickly run ahead to a new and different equilibrium. Exactly why these past episodes have occurred is subject to much speculation and there is no proof that we have initiated another. The point that should concern us most is, if we are pushing against a tipping point, and we find it, there will be nothing we can do to stop the runaway climate change that would follow.

Our Response

Primitive man, living as a hunter-gatherer, moved with the seasons and followed the ice-sheets as they expanded and retreated during the ice-ages. His lifestyle was able to adjust to climate change.

Modern man has staked out his place in the world with fences and boundaries, expecting to remain there from generation to generation into perpetuity. Post-industrial man will need to learn to become a nomad once more. Land that is now fertile cannot be expected to remain productive. The flood defences for low-lying land cannot be expected to hold. The new nomads will be those forced to move as their environment is no longer habitable.

Describing global averages tends to mask the fact that disruption to sub-systems could lead to dramatic changes in which the effect on countries or regions is much more extreme. This is much harder to predict with accuracy. For example, it is speculated that the Gulf Stream could shut down. This is the ocean current that carries warm water from the Gulf of Mexico to keep Europe warmer than its latitude would otherwise dictate. Scientists do not expect that it could shut down abruptly;[10] such changes would need at least a decade or two to enact but if this were to happen, Western Europe would have to contend with a climate more like that of Newfoundland, which is at a similar latitude to northern Europe.

There are other localized effects that are easier to predict. For example, the mean sea level at a particular place will conform to the global average – all our oceans interconnect. Although we cannot know the exact rise that will occur in the future, it is likely to be a gradual progression. A developed low-lying country such as the Netherlands can plan its defences against the best predictions of the scientists, and earmark a proportion of GDP to do so. A poor low-lying country such as Bangladesh could do the same calculation, but may not have the resources to prevent losing a significant part of its land area.

There are two schools of thought: accept climate change and learn to live with it; or prevent climate change through measures to curb GHG emissions. Which school to support depends on how worried you are by the effects of climate change. If you live on a low-lying island or in a coastal region of Bangladesh, then you will be a strong supporter of reducing emissions. On the other hand, if you are the US president facing re-election, you may feel you cannot take the tough measures required and stay in power.

Intuitively, the best option is to prevent climate change; if we can.

Prevention

Climate change is being caused primarily by GHG emissions including chlorofluorocarbons (CFC), methane and CO_2.

The world community can take pride in successfully tackling the worst of these, man-made compounds not found in nature, CFCs. The damage these can cause is more extensive than climate change and includes damage to the ozone layer, which protects us from the full strength of the sun's ultraviolet radiation.

Following the discovery of the Antarctic ozone hole in late 1985, governments recognized the need for strong measures to reduce the production and consumption of a number of CFCs and several halons. The Montreal Protocol on Substances that Deplete the Ozone Layer came into force on 1 January 1989, when it was ratified by 29 countries and the EEC.[11] Since then, several other countries have also ratified it.

The Protocol was designed so that the phase-out schedules could be revised on the basis of periodic scientific assessments. Following such assessments, the Protocol has been adjusted to accelerate these schedules. It has also been amended to introduce other kinds of control measures and to add new controlled substances to the list. Implementation of the protocol has had a dramatic effect in reducing the production of ozone-depleting chemicals. Scientists predict that the ozone layer will be fully restored by 2050.[12]

The success of the Montreal Protocol was possible because:

- the manufacturing process requires large and expensive facilities so that governments have the power to implement controls;
- there are viable alternative substances and technologies;
- the world agreed a united approach, ensuring that no one country or corporation could gain a competitive advantage through continued use of CFCs.

The problem of CO_2 emissions is harder to define and tougher to tackle. The carbon cycle underpins life itself and some of our renewable fuels, such as biofuels, emit CO_2. Carbon is not the problem; the problem is the release of fossil carbon leading to abnormally high CO_2 levels.

Way back in geological time, this fossil carbon was in the atmosphere as CO_2 and methane in high concentrations. It is hard to be sure, as we cannot directly measure our ancient atmosphere. The best direct measure we have is from the tiny bubbles of air trapped in ice cores drilled deep into the ancient ice of Antarctica, which go back 740,000 years,[13] but in terms of climate history this is not far enough. Despite the lack of direct measurements, it can be surmised that CO_2 levels were very high, and hot tropical conditions normal, until the CO_2 started running out (locked away in sediments). In comparison, our atmosphere today has very little CO_2. The Earth we see now has a much cooler climate and bands of vegetation appropriate to low CO_2 levels.

Whether man's current actions will return the Earth to a state like the hothouse of pre-historic times when the dinosaurs roamed the world, the experts will continue to debate. If we want to prevent it, we will have to stop releasing excess CO_2 into the atmosphere.

The Economics and Politics of Climate Change

The economics of climate change can be considered through the two possible responses: prevention or adaptation. We can attempt to put a cost to each of these and then compare which is more cost-effective. Both options will require investment; the former in reducing demand and developing renewable sources of power; the latter in the infrastructure to cope with the new climatic conditions. There needs to be a balance between these two types of investment.

In a closed system where the decision maker has control over the whole system, then a cost–benefit analysis could be carried out. Investment would then flow to the side of the balance where it will have the greatest effect.

Such a trade-off depends on two principal factors. First, there needs to be sufficiently reliable predictions of climate change appropriate to the locality to be able to put a cost against the infrastructure requirements of adaptation. Scientists will need to develop models of the climate that work at the regional level and are accurate out to an investment horizon of perhaps 40 years. Second, the decision maker has to have confidence that an investment in prevention is likely to succeed; in this case to be sure that preventive efforts are part of a global commitment backed up by an enforceable agreement.

Dealing with climate change through such a mechanism provides a logical basis for examining this complex problem. The review carried out for the UK Government by Sir Nicholas Stern[14] is one such analysis. It shows, based on carefully worked figures, that acting early to prevent climate change is cheaper in the long term than delaying.

National governments should heed this advice; but our governments have immediate budgetary decisions to take. In setting the most appropriate balance of investment between adaptation and prevention, they will have to take into account the circumstances of the country.

The United States, for example, is concerned about climate change, but is also a huge consumer of fossil fuels. There will be easy-to-predict negative effects, such as the submerging of coastal wetlands and flooding of low-lying areas of some cities, as sea levels continue to rise. Other changes will be less certain and, for a country with a wide geographical spread, these may be balanced by beneficial changes in other parts of the country.

The immediate costs of prevention, which need to be paid upfront, will seize decision makers' attention more than an uncertain bill for adaptation presented sometime in the future. So large countries such as the United States could decide to accept climate change and channel investment only into placating the minority communities that will be directly affected, such as providing help with relocation away from the coastal areas at risk. Other big countries such as China could also frame their policy in this way. I believe this would be an immoral position to take; but if the decision is taken on a short-term economic basis, it could be the outcome.

Many small countries will wish to strike a different balance. For a community living on the Maldives Islands, which are on average only 1 m above sea level, climate change is not merely an inconvenience but an execution warrant. The sea-level rises predicted by the IPCC signify that the Maldives will cease to exist some time in the 22nd century. Adaptation is not an option; prevention is the only way to survive. Such small and poor countries may not have much power, but they are drawing together to raise a voice loud enough to be heeded through the Alliance of Small Island States (AOSIS).[15]

Each country can calculate the balance between prevention and adaptation which would best suit their national interest. The Netherlands is an interesting example. It is an affluent developed country with substantial low-lying areas and considerable experience at keeping the sea at bay. The Netherlands has the expertise to calculate the infrastructure costs of responding to the anticipated sea-level rises, and use that information in their decision over whether to focus on adaptation or prevention.

This seems to be an obvious case where self-interest favours investment in prevention of climate change. However, for the Dutch government to invest heavily in prevention, in preference to the infrastructure of adaptation, which was not part of a comprehensive and enforceable global agreement, would be incompetent. For the Netherlands to end up with a zero-fossil-carbon energy system but no protection against sea-level rises would be morally worthy but economically and politically inept.

Bangladesh is a rather different case. Like the Netherlands, it is low-lying and stands to lose a lot of land area as sea levels rise. It is also a poor under-developed country. It is hard to envisage that Bangladesh could build the infra-structure required to adapt without massive external aid. Like the Maldives, Bangladesh has to put its trust in the international community to either coordi-nate prevention of climate change, or provide aid to the communities when the changes hit.

The world community might be shamed into providing a home for the relatively few Maldivians (300,000) as their islands are submerged by the sea. Whether millions of displaced Bangladeshis would find a welcoming home outside their own country is a tougher prospect.

A Realistic View

Climate change is an important global issue that has severe implications for some countries and places. There is now unanimous realization amongst scientists, politicians and the general public that it matters. Converting that unanimity into enforceable global action is proving elusive, despite ample sound advice about what is required to be done.[16] [17]

The main cause of climate change is the release of excess fossil carbon into the atmosphere; but the world economy is addicted to fossil fuels. Such fuels are cheap, even in Europe where fuel taxes are some of the highest in the world. Eliminating fossil fuels (as I discuss in the next two chapters) will be relatively much more expensive. This makes curing the world's addiction particularly hard.

The Kyoto Protocol is a limited first attempt, but without the United States, China and India, even its limited scope is toothless and near useless. It is also very dangerous to believe that an agreement like Kyoto is enough, on its own, to solve the problems we are facing. To understand this danger, let us assume that an agreement like the Kyoto Protocol is universally adopted and implemented across the world.

I will consider success in reducing fossil carbon release at two levels: a 20% reduction and a 50% reduction. The baseline I will use for this simple calculation is the fossil carbon that we will release over the next 20 years if we do nothing (without going into the complexity of estimating what this might be). If we broker, and implement, an agreement that achieves a 20% reduction, then the same total carbon release would take place but over a period extended by five years. An apparently massive 50% reduction would lead to the same level of CO_2 in the atmosphere delayed by 20 years. So, in this example, we would reach exactly the same point, but in 25 years from now (with a 20% reduction) or 40 years from now if we achieve 50%.[18]

The solution we seek should be to stop climate change; not just put if off for a decade or two. This means that our agreement has to ratchet down emissions to the ultimate goal of zero fossil-carbon release. Even then, there will be a time lag in the system until the effects of prior emissions have worked into the climate system. I leave on one side the issue that we may face in the future of having to embark upon a massive program to cleanse the atmosphere of excess CO_2 because much of the Earth has become uninhabitable for human society. I hope and trust that we are a long way from such a dire position, but, without a major shift in policy, this may be the situation that confronts humankind next century. An agreement like the Kyoto Protocol cannot, therefore, be an end in itself. Holding emissions steady at similar levels to now will not be enough. The Kyoto Protocol is only useful as a stage in the transition to a zero-fossil-carbon economy.

Whilst the debate continues, the effects of climate change will start to produce real graphic evidence repeated at regular intervals across the world's media. I have seen the beginning of this during the three years I have spent researching and writing this book. I believe that the rich developed world will be the home of a movement to finally take real action, as public opinion presses politicians to act. Like a reformed smoker who has kicked the habit, the countries that find the way beyond fossil fuels will be the most vociferous supporters of agreements to eliminate their use.

Climate change is happening and cannot now be stopped. The excess CO_2 that has already been released through the 20th and early 21st centuries will continue to alter the climate regardless of what we now do, but we can still prevent even greater change if we act quickly.

Climate change is a symptom of mankind's lack of respect for the ecosystems of planet Earth. Recognizing its significance[19] is important for starting the process of addressing the cause. The changes required are fundamental and go right to the heart of modern society.

7 Balancing Energy Sources and Needs

Global primary energy demand reached 446 quadrillion (10^{15}) Btu[1] in 2004, up a whopping 57% from 1980. This huge rate of increase is predicted to continue, with demand up by half as much again by the year 2030, 70% of the increase coming from developing countries, of which 30% is attributed to China alone.

The world does not have the ability to cater for this increased demand, while also preventing the environmental damage that its consumption will cause – two very serious and rapidly diverging threats. The International Energy Agency (IEA) predicted in 2006, in their Alternative Policy Scenario, that the increase in energy demand up to the year 2030 can be reduced by 10%.[2] This would be a marginal reduction, and the assumption that the IEA has used, that governments would succeed in implementing the measures they were then discussing (to enhance energy security and mitigate CO_2 emissions), may prove optimistic. The IEA also anticipates that the greater use of nuclear power will reduce carbon emissions, but, even so, by 2030, 80% of world demand will still be met from fossil fuels. This carefully considered view shows that we have a huge, deeply entrenched deficit between demand and sustainable supply.

At some point, much cleaner nuclear power will be available through the process of nuclear fusion. But even enthusiasts of this technology expect commercial development to take at least 40 years, and probably much longer. During this indeterminate transition period, if we do not make dramatic changes, massive quantities of fossil carbon will be released into the atmosphere. In addition, our current nuclear power technology will generate a large amount of radioactive waste requiring safe storage for many thousands of years – a disappointing inheritance for our descendants.

There is an impossible and unbridgeable dichotomy between our demand for energy and the increasing urgency with which we need to protect the environment. Clearly, we need to increase the amount of renewable energy we harvest, but this will fall short of the projected demand. We must reduce our craving for energy. This will require more efficient transportation, buildings and industrial processes, as well as better organization that eliminates many energy-using activities altogether. This does not have to be an imposition, or a regression to a medieval way of life, but a lifestyle improvement achieved by being much cleverer in the way we organize society.

Much can be achieved by altering our activities and learning to live in tune with local conditions and local needs. Shifting to smaller-scale localized operations reduces the need to move goods and materials around, and the need for people to commute to work. Designing buildings to suit the local climate can require far less energy than standard international designs. Reusing and refilling bottles within a local economy needs far less energy than recycling by smashing and remelting the glass. By adapting to local conditions, demand for energy can be reduced to the point where it matches the available supply of renewable power.

For this to happen, energy prices need to climb, as they will, in any case, when demand outstrips supply. There will inevitably be a period of general suffering across the world, until a new balance between consumption and sustainable supply is achieved. If we wait until this is forced upon us, we will also suffer severe climate change and environmental degradation. The only way to precipitate the process is by forward-looking governments deliberately increasing the cost of energy within their borders.

This is much easier said than done, and, as things stand at the moment, would be political suicide. Even if governments in the developed world were able to increase energy prices enough to stimulate the required infrastructural change, many developing countries would resist, resenting environmental restrictions imposed by the West putting a brake on their economic progress, whilst their standard of living trails far behind that of the developed nations.

The world must be weaned off its addiction to fossil fuels, regardless of the sensitivities of both developing and developed nations. There are difficulties and dangers, but it has to be done. This will require strong leadership from the developed world in transforming our societies if we are to persuade developing nations to curb their energy consumption, too. At the political level, this will require an unprecedented sharing of resources and technology. But, as I will demonstrate, there are numerous business opportunities in developing the new technologies and infrastructure required to implement the transformation.

The Energy Market

Energy is sold on the assumption that open markets are the best way to manage energy supply and demand. A market that is open and efficient will draw supplies from the cheapest source and deliver it to the consumer at the best price. If there are shortages, then prices rise, attracting investment to increase capacity – a self-regulating mechanism that maximizes efficient exploitation of all sources, including fossil fuels. Without additional controls, this process will ensure that all fossil fuels will eventually be burned, starting with the easiest (and cheapest) to extract before moving onto marginal or remote deposits as shortages in the market drive up prices.

Carbon trading and or carbon taxes can put a brake on the market and slow down exploitation. Such measures will be a vital component of the transition to the post-fossil-fuels era, but only if they form part of a larger plan. An open global energy market – even with a carbon-trading mechanism – will facilitate, over time, a massive fossil carbon release. Without radical change, the global energy market itself will remain a very large part of the problem we face.

Energy production and usage was once a local business, with its own sources, and people lived within the constraints of what was available. In electricity supply, particularly, local monopolies took hold: a power station had its own local customers, and consumers had little choice. The opening up of markets in recent years has shaken up these cosy monopolies, driving prices down, as customers buy their electric power from a range of providers.

The purchasing of electric power is now a purely financial transaction for most people and organizations, with little visibility of how or where it was generated. Further reforms to the energy market – to ensure effective competition – have separated generators of electric power from the operators of the distribution networks. While one party is working out how to generate power, another is plotting how to sell it. Although this reduces their ability to build monopolies – and keeps downward pressure on prices to consumers – there is no economic incentive to drive down demand. Quite the reverse: the more they can sell the greater the profits are likely to be. This separation of generators from distribution is also a barrier to implementing highly efficient small-scale fully integrated power generation (discussed below).

At the European level, the European Commission is a strong champion of open, competitive energy markets:

> In the past, national gas and electricity markets were separate 'islands' within the EU, where supply and distribution were in the hands of monopolies. Now, markets have been opened up to competition and national borders in energy markets are disappearing, though the European Commission would like to see even faster progress.[3]

The EU encourages competition through funding to connect isolated networks and improve cross-border interconnections, both within the EU and with supplier countries. For their part, all suppliers have guarantees under single-energy market rules that they can have access to the distribution grid and pipeline networks of other EU countries and that they will pay a fair price for access. In this open market, electricity ebbs and flows through the undersea cable connecting the UK and France depending on relative pricing.

This EU policy is a classic example of free markets being used to give the consumer the best deal, as defined by price. Although this is efficient economics, it does not lead to efficient (in an engineering or scientific sense) production and use of energy. There is also the risk of contradictions, with other EU initiatives aimed at reducing the environmental impact of energy production and use, such as the Sustainable Energy Europe Campaign 2005–8.

In January 2006, Europe was reminded of its vulnerability to external supplies when Russia cut off gas supplies to Ukraine, having the knock-on effect of reducing supplies to the EU. This influenced the EU's energy policy, published later in 2006,[4] which set three objectives:

- Sustainability
- Competitiveness
- Security of Supply

However, 'Competitiveness' remained the focus of this new policy, when the need was a major shift in favour of the other two objectives, 'Sustainability' and 'Security of Supply'. When the market fails to deliver more energy and European cities suffer major blackouts, it will not be reassuring to be told this was the cost of keeping prices down for so long. The current focus on competitive markets to drive down prices is undermining Europe's energy security and efforts to protect the environment. Competition for energy supply at a local level will be vital in ensuring that investment flows efficiently into the most cost-effective solutions, but making competition the focus of European policy is wrong over the long term.

The world energy market is now truly global. The United States was the largest user of oil in 2005, consuming 20.8 million barrels a day, of which over 60% was imported.[5] Europe imports 50% of its oil and gas, projected to rise to 70% by 2030. This gives oil-exporting countries considerable economic and political power. OPEC regulates the world oil market in a responsible way, taking into account political and economic factors. It is, after all, in its self interest to maintain world dependence on oil for as long as possible. For Europe, the influence of Russia is becoming increasingly important, as the EU becomes more dependent on supplies from there. Britain's near self-sufficiency in oil and gas has come to an end, as oil and gas production from the North Sea is starting to decline. Britain will increasingly be dependent on supplies from abroad.

In this open, global energy market, every unit of energy, every ton of coal, every cubic meter of gas and every barrel of oil, will be sold and used on the basis of matching cost of production with the ability to pay. When demand outstrips supply, those with the deepest pockets will continue to receive supplies, and the poorest will receive none. While people remain willing to pay the costs of extraction, every last reserve of fossil fuel will be pulled out of the ground and burnt.

The world has abundant reserves of fossil fuel, if we include low-grade deposits such as the oil sands of Alberta in Canada. The Canadian government estimates proven reserves of 176 billion barrels, second only to Saudi Arabia. These require effort (and energy) to extract the oil. Two tonnes of oil sand have to be dug up and processed for each barrel of oil produced. The processing costs were $18 per barrel in 2004.[6] As oil prices rise, this production overhead will become increasingly affordable. Once the world's easily pumped oil has been used, the global energy market will move onto the large-scale extraction and burning of these low-grade sources. It is not a question of when, as this is already happening now. In 2005, Canada was producing 966,000 barrels of oil per day extracted from its oil sands. In Europe, Estonia excavated and processed 14.9 million tonnes of oil shale in 2003, 26% greater than in 1999, and generated over 90% of Estonia's electricity from this source.[7]

In globalized markets, the fuels that are easiest to extract (cheapest) and cleanest (in response to environmental concerns) are burnt first. This has shut down much oil shale recovery (and Britain's coal industry) as they cannot compete. In the short term, the global market is therefore reducing our impact on the environment. This same market will then very efficiently move on to support exploitation of the less economic deposits. These oil-bearing sands or shale – and of course coal – are also less worthwhile in terms of the energy that can be extracted for each ton of CO_2 emitted. The world has vast reserves of these low-grade fuels. The consequence of this situation is that if we do not bring the global fossil-fuel market under control, in the years ahead we are heading for colossal carbon release over the globe.

With an open global energy market, buyers purchase from any source according to price. The associated carbon release and pollution belongs to the world; or rather belongs to no one, as no one accepts responsibility. There is no identifiable 'victim', except planet Earth. Without a change of direction, the global energy market will turn on us, accelerating the damage we are causing and then collapsing into a spiral of diminishing returns as we burn ever lower grade fuels that deliver ever less net energy output.

The Kyoto Protocol and associated mechanisms attempt to deal with what is a doom-laden and politically unacceptable scenario for everybody. But the problem is far too deep-rooted for this well-intentioned initiative to tackle. The unconstrained global free market will soon become part of the problem and must become part of the solution, but the energy market lacks a policy framework within which to agree appropriate regulation.

Proximization[8] of Energy Supply

What we need to do is reconnect people with their energy needs.
Colin Challen, MP, speaking in Helsinki, 2005.[9]

In order to make the world's energy supply sustainable, under some kind of control framework, we will need to take action at odds with the experience we have gained so far of the economics of energy supply in the industrial era. We are in new and uncharted territory here, and changes have to be made. First, energy should be obtained from as close to the need as possible, connecting people with the full consequences of their energy requirement, and encouraging the most efficient and sustainable solution.

At the micro-level, each building should be largely self-sufficient through energy efficiency, insulation, solar and wind power. City planners should design communities and set regulations that will minimize the need for external inputs of energy and make use of all locally available energy sources, including energy extracted from the city's waste. At country level, governments should balance the demand for energy, for example as dictated by climate, with the availability of energy resources, setting taxes and tariffs as appropriate. There will, of course, be enormous infrastructural implications; especially for transport, which is currently dependant on cheap fossil fuel.

When electricity is transmitted over long distances, power is lost. Today's large-scale electricity generation and transmission structure loses vast amounts of energy. If our engineers were given the task of designing electric power systems from scratch, in a climate of scarce fuel and energy insecurity, it would not result in the monolithic infrastructure systems we now have. Small-scale, fully integrated systems could be run far more efficiently, utilizing a number of savings. For example, many large electric power plants waste the heat they create as a by-product, whereas small power plants embedded into communities are able to use it to heat buildings, minimizing the environmental damage as well as saving energy.

It will be hard to initiate change to this deep-rooted structural legacy of electricity generation. But investment must be aimed at replacing it, not continuing to extend and adapt obsolete designs.

One idea to consider is to impose on the consumer a distance-to-use charge. This would help make local power suppliers more competitive, whilst forcing the power industry to reorganize into more sustainable localized energy markets. The bureaucratic overhead could be withdrawn once the required transformation was complete.

With each country running its own sustainable energy policy, some will become self-sufficient. Those with fossil fuel reserves might rely on them through the transition (and whilst there are still reserves to exploit). Many others will establish sustainable energy markets using other sources, buying energy from other countries as needed but looking carefully at the source of supply. The principles of proximization (outlined in Chapter 4) provide a context within which international agreements restricting the use of fossil fuels can have a real chance of success.

International agreements to limit fossil-carbon release need robust policing (which the Kyoto Protocol does not include). Breaking such agreements, or seeking to sell fuel derived from dirty processes, must be penalized by the imposition of high tariffs or trade barriers. Current economic thinking makes such action impossible. If, for example, some countries shun 'dirty' fuel, other countries that buy the cheap fuel gain an unfair cost advantage. Such short-term economic imperatives have to be resisted; pretending to be ignorant of the source of supply is clearly wrong, but it will take time to eliminate such behaviour.

The developed world must take the first steps towards the elimination of the burning of fossil fuels, by shutting down demand. This will then curtail worldwide investment in the infrastructure of fossil-fuel extraction and processing. As the world community finally makes this tough choice, countries that cannot comply, or refuse to, will find themselves increasingly marginalized. It seems impossible now that we would freely choose to refuse to import fossil fuels, particularly the cleanest ones such as oil and gas. I will show that this incredible about-face is possible and argue that it is necessary, but I accept that it will take a while longer before we are willing to accept the short-term impact.

In the short term, the total energy bill to consumers will be higher, but the overwhelming benefits of having sustainable supplies, and the accompanying environmental protection, turn this additional cost into an investment with a long-term payback. The Stern Report[10] indicates that accepting the true cost of becoming sustainable will be less expensive overall if we act now. This will not be easy, as people are used to the current artificially low level of energy prices, and so protesters are likely to make it hard for governments to act. However, once fuel shortages, blackouts and accelerating climate change make the reality of the situation obvious to everybody, it will be too late.

Business does not like restrictive economic policies, and will inevitably accuse government of destroying competitiveness. But this will be an ill-considered reaction. Forward-thinking businesses will soon understand that the rise in energy prices is inevitable, and act early to minimize the impact.

In arguing for proximization as the catalyst to deliver sustainable energy solutions, I accept that costs to industry will increase and put pressure on the economy. There is also the risk that restricted markets may make energy providers lazy rather than super-efficient. But these obvious drawbacks are very much better than the eventual alternatives, and, if faced early, can only stimulate and streamline business, by, for example, encouraging local competition between different players and different options.

There is no escape from this reality. Fossil fuels will run out, and countries will have to adapt. Leading the process of adaptation is likely to be very profitable. Forward-looking governments will realize this and impose policy such as energy-neutral buildings and regulations for localized energy markets, backed up by grants and other incentives. These measures will be the catalyst for radical new designs, processes and methods, stimulating local industries to supply local needs, and also placing them to profit from the world market in skills and expertise.

The finding and implementing of sustainable energy solutions will be forced upon us, and we will succeed. But the question is whether we will first inflict substantial damage to our environment. We can bounce forward to the solution, if we have the foresight and will to do so.

There are a variety of elements we can bring together to obtain access to clean energy that will not run out.

Solar Power

The main source of renewable energy is the sun. We can all plug into this universal power source directly and for free, but the energy is more intense towards the equator and less so moving north or south towards the poles.

One place this free energy arrives is onto the roofs of our buildings, the total global area of which would more than cover the entire state of California and Great Britain combined. Unfortunately, most of this enormous area serves no purpose other than to keep out the weather – including the sun. It could so easily be used to absorb solar power, using photovoltaic cells and other energy conversion systems. We can also allow direct energy from the sun into our buildings in a controlled manner, as heat and light. Currently, all the energy that falls on our roof areas where we do not have skylights is wasted, when it could be captured and used on the spot.

The business case for using solar power from roofs adds up, even at today's low energy prices and in the UK's northern latitudes. This is true in particular for solar water heating which, following the energy crunch, will become universal.

Solar Water Heating

In the UK, a solar water system can supply all the hot water a household needs from April to October. At its simplest, an old radiator painted black and housed within a frame with a glass front is all that is needed to trap the energy. Water flows through the rooftop collector to the water tank. If the solar collector is mounted below the water tank, then the system does not even need a pump, as convection can provide circulation. Some controls are needed to prevent the water overheating in the summer or the system suffering damage from freezing conditions in the winter, but these are simple refinements. As a young engineering student in the 1970s I designed such a system. Even then I was surprised that such solutions had not been widely adopted.

Solar water systems have developed considerably. Highly efficient collector tubes and advanced controls provide reliable and virtually maintenance-free energy with a life of 20 years or more. In 2002, I obtained a quotation for a good quality system for our house in southern England. The payback period worked out at 12 years based on the savings derived from lower fuel bills. That should be a cast-iron business case. Every new house should have a solar water system, and every older house should have one added.

Back in 2002, the perverse economics behind the lack of take-up was brought home to me. An estate agent I consulted advised that, far from increasing the value of our house in line within the capital investment, it might be seen as odd, knocking something off the resale value. At best, he said, it would have a neutral effect on price. We would, therefore, have to be sure of being resident for longer than the payback period of 12 years to recoup our investment.

House owners are not sure that they will live in the same house for as long as 12 years, so they need to be confident that the system will be valued by the purchaser, so adding value to the property. Perverse economics also affects the behaviour of landlords. They do not pay the fuel bills and tenants do not think that solar panels deserve a higher rent. So although the overall theoretical business case is robust, market attitudes mean that it only makes financial sense for owners who can be sure of being resident for longer than the payback period. This is set to change.

Solar water heating will become a standard feature of all buildings throughout most parts of the world. This is a huge market. It only takes a change of sentiment driven by significantly higher fuel costs for a rapid take-up. Once solar panels are fashionable and their value is accepted by house purchasers (and tenants), the companies delivering solar-heating systems can expect a boom in sales. In the short term, they should mark time by installing what will become a reference base of example systems, but have a business model that allows for a rapid ramping up of production and training of the required installation engineers.

Converting sunlight to electricity requires a more expensive technology called photovoltaic (PV) panels. In 2006 worldwide production of PV panels grew by over 40%, using more than half the world's purified silicon.[11] This expansion will grow exponentially as technical advances make PV panels cheaper,[12] driven by huge quantities of venture capital flowing into this area.

Now, we are at the crossover point when savings exceed the cost over the life of a system. Roof tiles that double up as PVs are certainly economic when building a new roof, or replacing an old one, but the current low cost of energy means it is still not economic to replace a serviceable roof with such tiles.

I believe all new buildings should be fitted with PV tiles as standard on south-facing[13] aspects, with roofs designed to maximize their effectiveness. When this becomes accepted practice, the panels will get cheaper. But the initial surge of demand following the tipping point will mean that companies making PV tiles can hold prices and move these savings to their bottom line before capacity in the industry rises to match the demand. Using the power from PVs also requires more complexity, particularly where the power is fed back into the power grid, but this is proven technology.

Of course, a fundamental characteristic of solar power is that the output follows a daily and seasonal cycle. Self-contained systems therefore need storage capacity. We may find that the sun-rich areas of the developing world lead in deploying robust, affordable self-contained systems, particularly as initially they would only need to power the prime requirements of a fridge, a radio, some lights, and, as incomes rise, a computer and a mobile phone charger.

The developing world has already shown how mobile phone technology can be used to avoid the costs of building fixed-line telephone infrastructure. These countries may also show that self-contained renewable power solutions allow them to avoid the need to invest in industrial-scale energy generation and transmission infrastructure.

But solar power is only one component of the future sustainable energy mix.

Wind Power

Power from the wind is sustainable, clean and does not contribute to global warming; but it does have the problem of intermittency. Not everywhere is as fortunate as the Falkland Islands in the South Atlantic, a notoriously windy part of the world, which is largely powered by wind turbines, storing electricity in batteries for the short periods when the blades are not turning. Even where wind is less consistent, the energy source is so benign that it is worth putting extra effort into designing ways to accommodate its vagaries.

The wind blows due to sun-induced turbulence in the atmosphere. Although wind turbines cream off some of its strength, as long as the sun shines the wind will blow, but not all the time. The weather may have certain patterns, but there is no guarantee of wind of a useful strength at a particular time or place. Wind turbines need to be spaced out to avoid the effects of wind shadow, so a typical wind farm consists of a regular but sparse pattern of turbines spread over a wide area of land. The actual footprint of the turbine tower bases covers a very small proportion of the area, so does not affect using the land for other purposes such as agriculture. There is, therefore, no need to make a trade-off between agriculture and energy. And wind farms located offshore have no effect on land use whatsoever.

There will be a limit to how much of our countryside we are prepared to see covered by a forest of wind turbines. It is also in the nature of wind that some of the best sites occur in our most exposed and rugged scenery. There are places we would wish to retain free of man's intrusion, even by so benevolent a technology. But many people, who say they are protesting against wind farms on environmental grounds, are failing to see beyond their own aesthetic preferences to the real environmental issues. There is no doubt that wind farms are better for the environment than nuclear or fossil-fuel burning power stations, and I would certainly prefer a whirring wind farm in my backyard to one of these.

Wind turbines can be noisy, and do intrude into beautiful countryside. But the wind itself is noisy, and engineers can minimize the swish of aerodynamic blades to be one of the least intrusive noises of the modern world. The most powerful models are imposing, but their smooth-flowing lines are derived from good aerodynamics so, as an engineer, I find them hard to fault. For me, their shape conjures up a strong wholesome image, portraying something essentially clean and environmentally sound. Opinions may differ. We will decide acceptability in relation to fuel prices, climate change and public reactions to nuclear power, with control exerted through planning legislation.

Wind is very different to other types of energy production, in which an input fuel is converted into usable energy, with a certain percentage of it – which we try to minimize – wasted. Most of the wind's power is 'wasted'; indeed, we expect much of it to rush past. The only way we can evaluate wind power is by measuring the amount of energy delivered to the point of use in return for the capital invested, the 'energy return on investment' or EROI.

A large offshore wind farm will require substantial investment to cover not just the turbines but seabed foundations and a transmission system to get the power ashore, with energy losses in transmission from the offshore site to the point of use. A smaller turbine fitted on the top of a building and feeding power directly into the building is less expensive in every way. An energy market structured as a national grid fed by large power stations is likely to suggest lots of large offshore wind farms. But if we calculate the EROI figures, we find that, in most cases, smaller turbines close to the point of use – on the roofs of exposed office buildings or high blocks of flats – have a higher figure. Relaxing planning restrictions and learning to tolerate the drone of wind turbines is more cost-effective than huge offshore or out-of-town wind farms. Of course, our need for energy will lead us to invest in both local supply plus large offshore facilities, particularly in places where offshore winds are strong and consistent.

The next challenge is to incorporate wind-power capacity into our electric power system. Even though our large grid systems are antiquated technology from an industrial age, they exist, they work and we will be reluctant to replace them immediately. The grid needs to balance two sorts of power: the baseload that runs continuously, providing steady power, and surge capacity needed when, for example, everyone in the UK makes a cup of tea during the interval of the soccer Cup Final. Nuclear power is one provider of baseload power, while other types of generating station are kept spinning and connected to the grid ready to supply surge demands. The total capacity of an electric grid should match the greatest expected power demand. But unless the wind is actually blowing, wind power cannot contribute; so investing in wind power cannot replace any of the existing methods of generating electricity. When the wind blows, its power certainly reduces fuel usage in other stations, but does not reduce the need for capital investment in other sources. (Some commentators point out that there is a correlation between peak demand and high wind, but for simplicity I have taken the pessimistic approach that this cannot be relied upon.)

So although wind is a useful contribution to the existing grid-based power system, its only contribution is to reduce the amount of fossil fuel burned – and only when the wind is blowing. With fossil fuel prices being so low, the case for investing in wind power is difficult to make. We must, therefore, design systems that match wind with other sustainable sources to overcome the intermittency problem.

Electricity is only a secondary product of wind power; torque is the primary product, turning the shaft that drives the electricity generator. Electric power is very flexible, but we can also deliver the torque direct to the mechanical need. This would be more efficient for power tasks like pumping water and milling grain, which do not have be done at particular times. This is a very sensible return to a previous age, but it would be greatly enhanced by using automation to run power-hungry bulk mechanical processes (like stone-crushing and waste-shredding) unattended and continuously, when the wind blows. In a world of realistic (high) energy prices, fuel bills will be a strong incentive to invest in all manner of technology to maximize the use of wind power.

Water Power

One way to counter the unreliability of wind is to use water power. Many hydro-electric schemes store water behind dams, so we can adjust the flow through the generator to suit our power requirements. This makes hydroelectric power an excellent source of controllable power on tap for when we need it.

We have been taking power from our rivers using water mills for many centuries. We are also drawing energy from waves and tidal flows, but these are more recent innovations. Hydroelectric power generated from water collected at a high altitude, and discharged at a lower level, is well established across the world. Once the facility has been built, it can generate power with no harmful emissions almost indefinitely. The only limitation is that the total power drawn over a period of time is limited by the average quantity of rainfall over the catchment area used.

There is one problem with harnessing water power that we need to be sensitive to. In expanding its use, we are altering the natural hydrology and submerging land which may have another purpose – for mankind or for the world's natural systems. I visited Tasmania soon after graduating as an engineer. Tasmania is an ideal place for hydro electric power. It has ample rainfall and high rugged terrain. The dams are wonderful examples of good engineering. Whilst looking at one such dam, I happened to meet a group of students from Melbourne University. They were there to campaign against the most recent proposed project: to dam the Franklin River. I did not hide my admiration for the engineering and my interest in this new project. A long and combative discussion ensued. They explained that Tasmania was already a net exporter of electricity, and did not need more. I disagreed, arguing that Tasmania could increase power-hungry activities such as aluminium smelting in an environmentally sound way. They then went on to explain that this was Tasmania's last free-running wild river. In the end I was persuaded. We should not be re-engineering the entire world's hydrology to satisfy our demand for power. I joined the students in wearing a T-shirt emblazoned with 'Let the Franklin run free!'.

Hydro electric power is one of our best renewable energy sources. But the generating capacity is finite, not all countries have the geography and climate to take advantage of it, and we do not want to trap all our wild rivers inside pipes for power stations.

Power from Garbage

Another source of largely untapped 'free' energy is biowaste. Landfill sites generate methane from the decomposing organic components of our rubbish, which on some sites is captured and piped out, but this exploits only a small part of the potential. The technology to produce methane from organic matter is well established. The next key development will be in collection systems, by which organic waste is fed into specially designed processing facilities.

Methane can be transported with little loss, so the location of the processing facilities is not critical. Methane production is most cost-effective when it takes place close to the source of the waste, or where it naturally collects, such as at a sewage plant. Where we live in Finland, we share a biowaste bin with a small group of other houses. Each kitchen has a separate bin for biowaste, which we line with newspaper (which is biodegradable) and empty into the communal bin, which is emptied weekly. The potential to achieve a balance between overall energy creation and consumption is lessened by the transport fuel needed for collection.[14] Extracting energy from biowaste much closer to the source would show a better energy balance.

Community sewage processing is the obvious place to incorporate methane extraction. Large community-based systems are likely to be more efficient and cost-effective, because the increased size justifies more advanced processes and controls. Alternatively, many households or sites may choose to retain their own methane-generating capacity rather than donate it to the community. Single-dwelling systems have advantages. If the system is designed to take the entire household's biowaste, including food and even shredded garden waste, then the methane potential of the household is maximized. The occupants are rewarded directly by lower fuel bills for taking care with their waste management.

The resulting compost can be a valuable fertilizer, replacing the need for fertilizer derived from fossil fuels. With larger community systems, there is the risk of pollutants, so until the tighter waste regulations anticipated in Chapter 16 come into effect, such compost may not be suitable for agricultural use. However, compost from single-dwelling systems, where the householder has undertaken to keep the system free of polluting chemicals, should have a ready market.

DESIGN CHALLENGE: SMALL-SCALE METHANE GENERATION FROM BIOWASTE

Design a small-scale biowaste processing system that is reliable and safe with the following characteristics:

- solids from sewage waste collected;

- shredding system for food and garden waste inputs;

- methane is produced and stored;

- compost extraction to be easy for a contractor to carry out without access to the dwelling;

- the system to be odour-free as far as the householder is concerned;

- a design that minimizes moving parts;

- the system to be made from materials that can be recycled at the end of the effective life of the system.

Some small-scale systems have been implemented by enthusiasts, and a few companies have developed products, but the market is tiny. As with solar power, we might find the developing world leading the way. Fuel for cooking is a scarce resource in many poor countries. Simple working systems that generate methane from biowaste could become universal, being much cleaner and healthier than burning scavenged wood, combustible rubbish and dried animal dung. The result in poor countries would be demonstrably better and take hold very quickly. In the developed world, the idea of cooking with gas made from biowaste may be harder to sell. Even though effective and clean, biogas might only be regarded as acceptable initially as a source for heat and power.

Households in many European countries have been won over to the concept of separating out their biowaste as the right thing to do. So, once energy prices go up, the scene is set for this market to surge, starting with new developments where the marginal costs of incorporating the required systems are much less than installation in existing buildings. For domestic biowaste processing to be acceptable, it needs to be out of sight, reliable and part of the overall design of the building or community. Current building practices and regulations will have to change.

I predict that there will be a huge market for small methane-generating biowaste systems in my lifetime, but the tipping point may be some way off. Attitudes will have to change, which will not be helped by the negative newspaper stories that are bound to arise. Domestic explosions caused by conventional gas are fortunately rare but not unusual enough to be newsworthy, so are reported only briefly on the inside pages. Gas explosions involving biogas will be equally rare but the comic impact of an 'exploding toilet' will be too much for editors to ignore, making headline news. Despite such possible setbacks, resistance will be overcome, and biogas generation distributed within our built infrastructure will become standard practice.

Embedded Combined Power Systems

Solar, wind and biowaste energy are each available to all people everywhere, and make environmental and economic sense to use on their own. When we plan to combine these renewable sources, the efficacy increases dramatically. Through clever design and taking a holistic view of how we live and work, these natural and renewable energy sources are, without doubt, capable of replacing fossil fuels for powering our living and working spaces.

The Beddington Zero Energy Development (BedZED) is a carbon-neutral ecocommunity in the UK, completed in 2002, with 82 residential homes.[15] Through effective design, high-grade insulation and maximizing solar gain, the need for energy has been dramatically reduced. The remaining energy requirement is provided by a combined heat and power (CHP) unit, generating electricity and hot water, which also provides a small amount of top-up heating when required. The BedZED CHP runs on waste from tree surgery work, and, as the source is renewable, is therefore carbon-neutral. We would need to go one step further and run the CHP on methane from the community's biowaste to move beyond carbon-neutral to energy-neutral, which in the temperate climate of the UK is entirely feasible. The BedZED design demonstrates that it is possible to replace fossil fuels using a mix of renewable sources and intelligent design.

Converting energy directly to heat is very wasteful, particularly using high-grade sources such as electricity and gas. If heating is the requirement, then there is plenty of heat available in our environment – but at the wrong temperature. Taking heat from an external source and then using energy to move it to a higher temperature is far more efficient. The principle is the same as a fridge, but in reverse and on a larger scale.

Heat pumps can be designed to pump heat either way, to heat or cool as required. The need for energy is least when the temperature difference is small, so in the winter the ground provides a relatively warmer heat source than the cold air outside. The reverse is true in the summer when cooling is the requirement and the ground is cooler than the outside air. Buried pipes are used through which a fluid is passed to transfer the heat between the heat pump and the ground reservoir.

Some heat pumps use the ammonia-water absorption cycle, which runs directly from a heat source that might be a fossil fuel such as gas; or solar energy, for example, which can provide a completely renewable method of cooling in the summer. Most pumps use electricity, compressing a refrigerant at one stage in the cycle to release heat; the refrigerant then flows to where it is allowed to expand, absorbing heat.

The overall energy balance of using a heat pump of course depends on the source of the electricity. One of the most efficient sources of electricity is a CHP unit in which the low-grade heat that remains after generating the electricity is also used for heating. If we link CHP and heat-pump technologies we can get impressive efficiency gains. It has been shown that, using gas as the fuel for the CHP, which then drives the heat pump, 35–50% less fuel is needed to deliver the same amount of heat compared with a conventional gas boiler.[16] Currently, in the UK, it is almost universal that gas is burnt for its heat content rather than its energy. This is very wasteful.

Our house in the UK is an example of bad practice. It is 20 miles from a huge coal-fired power station, which has enormous cooling towers that can be seen for miles, pumping low-grade heat into the atmosphere. The electricity is then sent over the grid to houses such as ours, incurring losses on the way. Conversely, our house in Finland is heated via a community system, which pumps heat, produced by a power station located close to the community, through insulated underground pipes. This is better, but not good enough. I propose that we use bio-derived methane gas to fuel small, CHP systems in each building, or slightly larger local community power systems.

When designing buildings, architects must make use of embedded combined power solutions. They should maximize the use of sunlight through windows and solar power from roofs. This should be supplemented by wind turbines, where the site is appropriate, and methane from biowaste. If we instruct architects to design a building that is largely energy self-sufficient, they have the technology to deliver. The occupants of the buildings will also have to become party to the design, adjusting their behaviour to balance the energy needs with sources. There are many times when I have felt cold visiting a corporate headquarters on a lovely warm sunny day, or stiflingly hot in the depths of winter. Instead of using energy-hungry systems to defy the seasons, we should allow seasonal variation into our buildings: cooler in the winter and warmer in the summer, but within a comfortable temperature range.

The Closed Carbon Economy – Biofuels

Carbon is at the heart of the cleanest and most sustainable cycle of all: life. Currently, carbon has earned a bad reputation because we run our society on fossil fuels, damaging our environment; but carbon is not the culprit. The closed cycle of growing plant material, taking in CO_2 and later releasing it again as the energy is used, is clean and sustainable indefinitely.

Where the biofuel is a waste product, there is no adverse impact. Finland is one of the leading users of bioenergy in the industrialized world, producing 19% of its energy from wood fuels,[17] mainly using waste from its forestry industry. However, many conventional biofuel crops replace other agricultural production, initiating a conflict between fuel and food. To replace 5% of the current fuel used for transportation (gasoline and diesel being replaced by ethanol and biodiesel) would require 21% of cropland in the United States; in the EU the figure would be 20%.[18] This would be feasible, but increasing biofuel production to replace food crops beyond this level would risk precipitating a crisis over food supplies.

Biofuels from a range of crops are now being made, but thus far only in small quantities. Production needs scaling up, not to large industrial complexes but to a myriad of small production facilities close to where the crops are grown, so we can minimize the costs and energy demands of transportation.

The change may occur very suddenly. Political instability in oil-producing regions, or a natural disaster that shuts down oil production, as happened following Hurricane Katrina in the Gulf of Mexico in 2005, could raise oil prices and trigger a switch to biofuel crops within just one growing season. The demand for biofuel-processing facilities would then outstrip the capacity of the companies capable of building them. The transition will be an extremely profitable period for such companies, which need to be ready to expand with the demand.

Agricultural land is finite, but fortunately biofuels and food crops need not be in competition for the same acreage,[19] because crops that act as feedstock for biofuel production need less exacting conditions. Switch grass, for example, can grow in arid conditions on land not suitable for most agriculture, needing nothing but good sunshine. This means land of little or no value for conventional agriculture can be used to grow crops for biofuel production. Good agricultural land should remain in food-crop production, but can also generate biofuel energy by using by-products such as straw or animal excrement. Biofuels need only to capture the sun's energy in a form that can act as an energy source. A liquid hydrocarbon (ethanol or biodiesel) would be ideal, but any biomass capable of burning can be used.

When considering biofuels, we need to be aware of one particular pitfall. Processing crops into a usable biofuel requires energy, which must be subtracted from the calorific value of the biofuel. Incentives to grow biofuel crops can lead to attempts to rig the markets and create perverse outcomes, for example producing biofuel that requires a similar amount of energy input to process. This processing energy can come from a low-tax fossil fuel, such as coal or agricultural diesel. The resulting biofuel can be used in transportation, side-stepping the heavy taxation applied to fossil fuels in this sector. The net result is profit for the producer, but tax revenue loss for the government with agricultural land taken out of food production – and at the end, the same amount of fossil fuel has been burnt. This situation is already happening, which does not help the promotion of biofuels.

Producing biofuels from desert areas is a huge opportunity with the scope to lead to a global sustainable energy market. As the UN reports,[20] deserts have ample and reliable solar radiation as well as land that is not fit for other purposes. As the land area is not already committed to agriculture, a trade-off with food production is not required. The problem is a shortage of water.

Many deserts are in poor regions, such as sub-Saharan Africa, and are short of investment capital as well as water. But the Middle East has deserts plus ample oil money to research crops suitable for desert biofuels, either a crop that can stand the arid conditions, or an infrastructure that conserves and recycles water – or a mixture of both. Scientists will find ways to bypass the plant stage altogether, using sunshine to produce a hydrocarbon fuel. Provided engineers can devise a way to make such a process practical and affordable, then we can replace oil from the Middle East with biofuel.

DESIGN CHALLENGE: RENEWABLE FUEL FROM THE DESERT

The challenge is:

1. To design an integrated system that converts sunshine into a transportable fuel.

2. This might be based on vegetation that is harvested and processed, but lateral thinking can be used for any method, provided it works in an arid environment at low cost.

3. The resultant fuel is likely to be a liquid hydrocarbon compatible with the current oil delivery infrastructure, but other fuels such as liquid hydrogen can be considered if costs can be driven low enough.

4. Define the oil price at which the proposed system becomes commercially viable.

Note: The energy input to the process must not come from fossil fuels, as the aim is to replace fossil fuels.

On the other side of the world, Australia has huge deserts, technical expertise and investment capital. It is a great country, but under the Howard premiership (1996–2007) it has risked undermining its standing in the world by not engaging with the world's efforts to reduce carbon emissions (at the time of writing, Australia had not ratified the Kyoto agreement). I believe this is very short-sighted. If the world turned against fossil fuels, then the economic barrier that prevents us from solving the challenge of fuel from the desert would be removed. I believe that it would be in Australia's long-term interests to switch policy and push hard to eliminate fossil fuels. Australia should act first at home and close down its coal mining industry in order to have the credibility to then support world efforts to close down the market for fossil fuels. In this way, Australia could become much more sustainable and establish a lucrative market for 'liquid sunshine' from Australia's vast desert interior.

The world would have enormous respect for Australia if it could put short-term economic considerations aside to pursue such a strategy. One of the first acts of Australia's Prime Minister, Kevin Rudd, when he took office on 3 Dec. 2007 was to sign the instrument of ratification of the Kyoto Protocol. This promises to be the start of a transformation in Australian policy. For a country without its own significant oil reserves, ideas such as producing biofuels from the desert will be listened to. But the idea that the Middle East could also become a centre of the world biofuel empire seems preposterous now, while oil can be pumped out of the ground at almost no cost. There is no medium-term economic justification for Middle Eastern countries to invest in biofuel production. But these countries must plan a future beyond oil, and biofuels should be part of it. The same tanker terminals built to take oil from the desert could switch to loading biofuels, so the Middle East can continue to fuel the Western world. Instead of ending up as a dead region at the heart of a dead industry, the Middle East could be at the heart of the revolution replacing fossil fuels with the closed-carbon energy cycle.

8 The Energy Crunch

Fossil fuels are short-term, finite energy sources. The fossil-fuel economy, and the industries that serve it, will only continue whilst there are still reserves, and whilst we remain willing to accept continued exploitation of them. It is clear that the reserves of quality fossil fuels such as oil and gas will be depleted. It is perhaps less clear, but no less certain, that we will eventually turn against fossil fuels, as the climatic effects of their use become more obvious and more damaging.

As our reserves of fossil fuels run down, oil and gas will be the first to run out. Gas is easy to transport and very clean when burnt, so demand for gas has been rising. In Britain, most new power stations in recent years have been designed to use gas. The North Sea gas fields have already peaked and will run down over the next decade or two. Other places have large reserves – for example, Russia and Qatar – but these, too, will be running down before we reach the middle of this century. Oil will last a similar time. Coal is the poor relation of the fossil fuels, hard to burn cleanly and best suited to static applications. We will still have extensive reserves of coal after the oil and gas have gone. Some argue that we will turn to coal to replace our petroleum supplies.

One way to look at this issue is to ignore the environmental impact and look purely at the economics and security of energy supplies. This is not a view this book subscribes to, but the argument is convincing. From a British government perspective, the following policy could be adopted. Gas is easy to transport through a mature infrastructure with little wastage and can be burnt cleanly at the point of use. Therefore, conserve all gas for the domestic and small business markets. This will postpone the day when the North Sea reserves are depleted. The best use of oil is probably for transport. So restrict the use of oil to that market. Use the long-term reserves of coal for all large static requirements, such as power stations or large industrial applications, using advanced technology to scrub flue gases to meet pollution regulation requirements. Following such a policy would revitalize the British coal industry. Add a general increase in taxes on all forms of fossils fuels, and there would be a policy to ensure security of supply for as long as possible. Energy prices would rise, but this would be a small price to pay for security of supply. Such a policy would put off the crunch day for Britain, ensuring energy security over the medium term.

This is logical and sounds sensible, but it comes from considering only the economic arguments – and ignores the environmental realities. Instead of leaving Britain's coal safely trapped under the ground, we would release the fossil carbon it contains into the atmosphere, further accelerating climate change.

As the world experiences the negative effects of climate change, accepts that the release of fossil carbon is the cause, and realizes that a world without energy from fossil fuels is inevitable as the reserves run down, then eventually I envisage a world agreement to leave the remaining reserves of fossil fuel under the ground. In 20 years' time, with high oil prices and other energy sources economically viable, OPEC's remaining reserves may become obsolete. This may appear a far-fetched scenario in today's oil-hungry world, but it is not inconceivable in the mid-term. As oil becomes obsolete, an energy economy that does not require fossil fuels must be created. This will either be by choice or simply because there is no more fossil fuel that can be economically dug or pumped out of the ground.

The world may find itself in a very difficult situation. Global warming and other alterations to climate will have accelerated, with a time delay between carbon release and observable weather effects. As we stop using fossil fuels, there will be very long delays of decades or even centuries before there is any discernible improvement. Companies responsible for running the fossil-fuel business are certain to be blamed, and risk being killed off with the industry. However, managing the running-down of fossil fuel usage is another enormous business opportunity for them, if they behave responsibly.

The big oil companies should use the cash flow from running the fossil-fuel economy to invest in developing the technologies surrounding the production, transportation and use of biofuels and other sources of clean, renewable energy. They should then act ahead of government and public opinion by campaigning for alternatives whilst minimizing new investment in fossil-fuel facilities, even if this restricts supplies and drives prices even higher. They should sit on remaining reserves, releasing only enough to satisfy the demands of governments, and justify-ing this with statements like, 'We can pump oil if you want us to, but we suggest not; we have other better technologies that we recommend, at a price.'

The fossil-fuel industry is already obsolescent. It will remain strong through the early stages of its demise as countries compete to get the supplies they believe they need. Then will come a tipping point, when everything turns against fossil fuels. Three primary factors are likely to work in parallel. First, steeply rising oil prices and taxes on fossil fuels reaches the point where other sources of energy become increasingly cost effective. Second, investment in fuel efficiency accelerates rapidly as the value of fuel savings increases. Third, climatic change turns public opinion against fossil fuels. In this very different political climate, international agreements to reduce then eliminate the use of fossil fuels will have a real chance of success, with rich nations taking the lead.

One way to ease the transition is through increasing the use of nuclear power.

Nuclear Power

Current nuclear reactors create power though nuclear fission, the process of breaking down very heavy elements into lighter elements, releasing large amounts of heat with radiation as a by-product. The heat is taken from the reactor core by either water or gas to power turbines producing electricity. Small amounts of radiation leak out as part of normal operating procedures, but stringent containment measures are designed to keep these below defined acceptable safety thresholds. However, despite a heavy emphasis on safety, the world has been shocked by a number of accidents, most notably the Three Mile Island accident in 1979, and Chernobyl in 1986.

Uranium is the main fuel source, and spent fuel remains radioactive for tens of thousands of years, but can be allowed to degrade safely in deep underground stores provided that the geology is stable. Uranium reserves will last for roughly a century, leaving future generations to manage the spent fuel long after it has ceased to be a source of energy. This spent fuel can also be refined to make nuclear weapons, and the more of it there is, the greater the chances of nuclear terrorism.

Although an operating nuclear-power plant emits no carbon and has no direct effect on climate, we need to balance this benefit with the risks, and with the long-term legacy of radiation waste.

> Good evening, comrades. All of you know that there has been an incredible misfortune – the accident at the Chernobyl nuclear plant. It has painfully affected the Soviet people, and shocked the international community. For the first time, we confront the real force of nuclear energy, out of control.
>
> Mikhail Gorbachev, Soviet President, 26 April 1986.

This one incident stopped the expansion of the nuclear-power industry in the Soviet Union, and curtailed plans for new capacity around the world. Thirty deaths have been attributed directly to the accident. So, at the time it appeared to be a relatively minor disaster; however, the long-term health effects are disturbing. The Chernobyl Forum 2003–5 (a collaboration between UN agencies and the countries directly affected) estimated that up to 4,000 additional cancer deaths should be expected amongst the 600,000 people most closely affected. It also reported that 4,000 cases of thyroid cancer have occurred amongst people who were children or adolescents at the time of the accident.[1] This is normally a very rare cancer, so it is thought many of these cases are as a result of drinking milk contaminated with iodine-131, which was one of the principal radioactive substances released.[2] The final death toll attributable to Chernobyl may never be known. The effects were not confined to Ukraine or even to Eastern Europe. Contamination was recorded as far away as the Welsh hills in Britain, leading to restrictions on the movement and sale of livestock.

It took some time for the nuclear-power industry to recover from the hard jolt of negative sentiment it received after the Chernobyl accident. However, following the 1992 Kyoto agreement on reducing CO_2 emissions, there has been renewed interest in the positive contribution that nuclear energy can make, helped by rising oil prices. Share prices in British Energy, the company that operates the UK's eight nuclear power stations, nearly doubled between January and December 2005, the same period when Hurricane Katrina shut down oil production in the Gulf of Mexico, sending the price of oil to record highs. Nuclear power stations have very high fixed costs, but the rising energy prices feed almost directly through to an increase in the rate of return. We can expect the share price of British Energy to shadow projected fuel prices.

Despite the huge investments made in nuclear power, it is widely acknowledged that such expenditure has not delivered high rates of return. Worse than that, there are significant long-term liabilities building up in terms of waste and the end-of-life decommissioning costs of reactors. Even so, there are economists who argue that we need conventional nuclear power to cover the shortfall until we can develop alternative sources of power.

Investing further in nuclear energy delays the inevitable and unavoidable move to the post-fossil-fuel era, leaving a major long-term liability. Future generations will not thank us for that. In any case, the figures for nuclear power do not add up. The huge costs of decommissioning, waste handling and accidents are left for the taxpayer to cover, and are left out of the calculations of the cost of the electricity produced. It might be reasonable to disregard such figures when deciding whether to continue to operate existing stations, but it would be wrong not to consider whole-of-life costs when deciding whether to build new nuclear power stations.

Europe's First 21st-Century Nuclear Power Plant in Finland

Finland surprised many people in 2002 when its parliament voted in favour of building the world's first new nuclear power plant in the 21st century (Finland's fifth). This came despite the country's sound environmental credentials. On closer inspection, it would be hard to imagine a safer location for a nuclear power station. First, Finnish society is strong and stable, so it is hard to envisage rogue elements taking control or security lapses leading to 'losses' of nuclear material. Second, Finnish engineers are some of the best in the world (although the company building the reactor is French). Third, Finland has remote, sparsely populated areas with stable granite geology in which to store the waste.

Nuclear power might be a sensible choice for Finland, in seeking to implement their Kyoto obligations, but can other countries contain the risks as well? I like observing building sites around the world as a barometer of a country's ability to construct safe facilities. You only have to stop and observe the precision and good organization of a Helsinki construction site to gain reassurance. In some other countries, I have observed sites that were downright dangerous: for example, piecemeal concrete pours, ignoring the quality of underground (and out-of-sight) infrastructure, and more.

Despite Finland's safety credentials, I believe that the country is wrong to invest in new nuclear capacity. As a model of sustainability, it sends the wrong message to the rest of world. However, of all the world's nuclear reactors, I would feel safest standing beside one built in Finland.

Whether to build new nuclear plants will be a major decision, when business and governments start organizing for the fossil-fuel crunch. Additional nuclear capacity might push back the energy crunch for a decade or two, but I believe it would be better to withhold investment in nuclear power, bringing forward the withdrawal from fossil fuel dependence. It would be better if these funds were channelled towards sustainable power generation that can continue operating after the crunch. Courageous politicians should be campaigning to get it right in the long term, accepting short- and even medium-term energy shortages by refusing to support more conventional nuclear power.

Nuclear Fusion

Fusion power has the potential to make energy an abundant commodity (as it is now), but the timescale for developing the technology is uncertain.

Fusion is the process by which our sun produces energy, in which light nuclei such as hydrogen isotopes are fused to release energy. Experiments to duplicate this process, in a controlled manner, have been going on for some time. In the UK, these started as secret Cold War experiments, which were later declassified, leading to the setting up of what is now the Culham Science Centre.

Fusion requires intense pressure and heat – as occur inside the sun. At Culham, fusion has been achieved within plasmas held together by strong magnetic forces for only fractions of a second. Huge amounts of power are sucked out of the national grid each time the tokamak[3] fires. To be viable, a fusion reactor must achieve a power output that greatly exceeds the power it uses to create fusion. Current research is a long way from achieving this.

The next project to take forward research into nuclear fusion is scheduled to last for 35 years and will be built in France at a cost of 10 billion euros.[4] This is expected to produce the first sustained fusion reactions and be the precursor for the first prototype fusion nuclear reactor to follow later.

If we can solve the technical challenges, fuel for fusion is easily found: the hydrogen isotopes required are plentiful in seawater. A fusion power station's radioactive waste materials will decay rapidly, presenting no accumulating long-term burden on future generations. Nuclear fusion is safe[5] and seems to be the ideal power source, but the earliest estimates of when the first fusion power plant might be operating is 2040.[6]

Even when the technology of fusion power has been proven, it is likely that it will be confined to large static installations requiring high investment for much of this century. We cannot rely on nuclear fusion to solve our energy problems.

Energy Efficiency

Reducing demand will be our first big success, through measures such as better insulation, fuel-efficient vehicles, less energy-demanding processes, improved energy reuse, and recycling. Each one of these areas of energy saving is directly equivalent to locating a new energy source. But, better still, these 'sources' do not suffer from losses in transmission, and can be considered as having been delivered directly to the point of need with 100% efficiency.

Our drive for efficiency must extend across all sectors. Figure 8.1 shows a high-level breakdown of energy use. The industrial sector is where we will see the earliest progress, as business responds very fast to opportunities to save costs.

Energy Use by Sector[7]	World	United States	EU
Industry	35%	35%	35%
Transport	40%	25%	35%
Households, Services and Agriculture	25%	40%	30%

Figure 8.1 **Energy Use by Sector**

Investment calculations for energy efficiency measures are based upon the price of energy. So the returns on such investments increase substantially as energy prices go up. Even at today's energy prices, there are many areas where the business case for better energy efficiency has already been made. However, energy is currently such a low proportion of operating costs that there is no incentive to put management time into finding out the figures. This will change when energy costs rise significantly.

Energy audits and carbon audits will become increasingly common. Initially, these will be regarded as fairly insignificant cosmetic measures so that organizations can demonstrate corporate responsibility. But when the energy crunch comes, attention will shift rapidly beyond audit to active troubleshooting. There will then be a shortage of the expertise required.

Our energy system, based on cheap fossil fuel, is a simple and comparatively crude system. Moving to an energy system based on renewable supplies requires much cleverer design and can be more complex to implement; although once in place can be much simpler to maintain and operate.

The escalating value of investment in energy efficiency will lead to improved efficiency across all sectors, where decisions are taken on a rational economic basis. However, in the transport and household sectors there may be resistance. The initial costs may have more visibility than the long-term savings. More effort may go into complaining about rising fuel costs than making the required adjustments.

Energy efficiency measures will reduce the imbalance between sustainable capacity and our 'need', but the only way to close the gap will be to eliminate many energy-hungry activities altogether.

Elimination of Energy Consumption

We built our industrial infrastructure on the basis of having limitless supplies of fossil fuel. This is no longer the case. We need to be just as robust and ruthless as we were during the Industrial Revolution in order to eliminate unnecessary energy demands and force through the transition to a sustainable infrastructure.

There are numerous examples throughout this book of how eliminating energy needs is the best approach, (although we currently seldom think in this way). Goods produced close to their destination do not have to be transported. People living near to where they work do not need to use energy to commute. These and other examples are explored further in my discussion of transportation and in my examination of the future of urban living (chapters 9–12). Surviving the energy crunch is not an isolated issue but will require wholesale change across society.

Surviving the Crunch

Our world is hooked on energy, an addiction fuelled by cheap supply as we pump out the easily accessed fossil reserves. But, soon, prices will rise steeply, transforming the energy sector. From our current perspective, we view this as energy becoming enormously expensive. A more realistic perspective would be to think of the present as an era when energy is ridiculously cheap. In the future, energy prices will simply rise to their true levels.

The business case for renewable sources (which, in many cases, is already sound) will be impossible to ignore. Management and decision makers will start searching for efficiency, and then move beyond this to options that eliminate energy-intensive activities altogether. Every aspect of society will have to adapt to the new reality.

The cleaner fossil fuels that are easy to exploit will be burned, over time, regardless of any realistic action we might try to take. Measures to regulate fossil-fuel usage, like carbon trading, will be valuable in helping societies to adapt. But if such mechanisms work too well, it may lead to a stable economic environment that encourages investment in the exploitation of more marginal fossil-fuel deposits, causing the release of even more CO_2 over the long term. It would be better for the health of the planet if the fossil-fuel crunch arrived sooner rather than later. Similarly, increasing nuclear capacity will delay the fossil-fuel crunch, but, in my opinion, the risks of building more conventional nuclear stations are too great. Nuclear power (based on fission) has an unacceptable legacy, and deflects attention, research effort and investment away from where it is most needed: developing the technology, processes and policies for a renewable energy market.

Nuclear fusion has enormous potential. We can expect governments to support accelerated research. Despite this, no one should expect early success in delivering clean cheap power from this source. The commercial sector will steer clear for now.

Investigating how to produce biofuels economically from desert regions is more likely to provide early success and indefinite sustainability. Desert countries should encourage the oil corporations to make seed investments in this area, in preparation for significantly higher energy prices and an environmentally led backlash against fossil fuels. We may well see Middle-East oil terminals shipping out biofuel, whilst the oil-heads (even though still capable of pumping) are shut down. These biofuels would be produced using innovative processes that have been developed by using money from oil revenues, as the oil industry plans its own demise.

The termination of the fossil-fuel industry may seem far fetched from today's perspective, but in a couple of decades from now it will be accepted as fact. We may not yet have reached the tipping point, but the players who will benefit are already preparing. Any business playing by the old rules will be wiped out.

Governments should be encouraged to adopt policies that drive prices up to the point where energy efficiency is vital for survival and serious investors move into renewable energy. Demand must be reduced, eliminating many energy-hungry processes altogether and dismantling the bulk-power distribution infrastructure in favour of localized solutions.

It will be a huge challenge to make the transition without major blackouts, power shortages or civil unrest. However, with the challenges come equally huge opportunities for the countries and companies that lead the wave of adaptation by developing low-energy systems, renewable sources and making the required infrastructure changes. Transportation in particular is due for a major realignment.

9   The Insatiable Appetite of Transportation

In our personal lives, the ability to travel is an expression of our freedom. We are not confined to one neighbourhood, one region or one country. We can travel to anywhere we choose, for a price; and that price is not too high. This feeling of freedom is epitomized by the car, which in the developed world is regarded as an essential possession. In the developing world, car ownership is one of the first aspirations of poorer populations as their economies grow.

In satisfying our demand for ever more transportation, we are sucking energy and material resources into building a growing fleet of vehicles[1] and their support infrastructure. Forty per cent of all the energy we use is for transportation, with the bulk of this coming from fossil fuels. Such fuels can cover our needs in the short term, but we will need to find alternative sources, or reduce demand.

The damage caused to the environment and our quality of life is becoming acute. We need to find a way to tackle the unsustainable appetite of transportation.

Current transport policies only exacerbate the problems. Although the decisions we take are logical responses within the narrow context of the problems we observe, we are dealing with symptoms, not causes.

Current Policy

One highly visible problem we face is that of congestion. Traffic jams (or gridlock) waste time for the people caught up in them, and delay goods in reaching their destination. It is also a waste of energy as engines idle away in stationary vehicles. Our solution is to build more roads and increase the capacity of the network we already have. This will save time, improve energy efficiency (in terms of fuel per mile travelled) and improve freight transit, so helping the business community to deliver economic growth. This is sound economics, but we do not pause to consider the other obvious solution of travelling less and moving freight shorter distances. If we make the effort to extend our thinking across society, and are prepared to consider an integrated portfolio of policies, then this solution also becomes economically viable.

Flight capacity at our airports is another bottleneck. London's Heathrow Airport, for example, can only handle a certain number of landing slots. The response has been to increase the capacity of other airports around London. Airbus is playing its part by designing the A800, the world's largest passenger plane, allowing airlines to maximize the number of people delivered into each landing slot. Further capacity is being spearheaded by low-cost operators flying point-to-point between regional airports, bypassing the main hubs. Air travel is becoming more affordable to more people leading to the opening of new commuter routes. We rarely pause to consider whether flying less would be a better way to reduce the pressure on our airports and the environment. Some people do accept this alternative solution, but their numbers are few and they tend to be on the margins of society. In the protests against the expansion of London's Heathrow Airport in August 2007, anarchists joined with green activists and others to make their point; but officialdom is not persuaded. And neither was I, until I examined the issues carefully with an open mind.

Other problems with transportation are starting to show. As fuel prices have risen, the relatively poor have been less able to afford to drive. They need to be able to live their lives: get to the shops, take their children to school, get to work or collect their welfare cheque. Politicians need the support of this socio-economic group. The result is that taxes on cars are kept at an affordable level so that every family can own one. In this way we support what is commonly felt within the developed world to be a fundamental right: to own and drive a car. Instead, we should be reviewing whether universal car ownership is such a good thing.

For the relatively better off, the problem is different. This group seeks to balance a nice place to live and the availability of good schools with a well-paid job. Companies can attract the best talent by locating close to good road access, providing a company car and free parking. Their workers can then commute to the outlying leafy suburbs. The alternative, which is rarely considered at present, is to think about building high-quality communities that integrate living and working in order to make commuting obsolete.

Excessive energy use by transportation is one of the problems we need to solve. We are making progress through improving efficiency with the growing use of hybrid power and a resurgence of interest in electric cars,[2] as well as better fuel-efficient aircraft. We can be confident our engineers will deliver further efficiency gains as rising energy prices make such developments increasingly cost-effective. But if the capacity of the transportation system continues to expand, our engineers are doing no more than swimming against the tide.

Another problem is the material requirements of our vehicle fleet and transport infrastructure. There are the vehicles of course, but also multilane roads, expanding container terminals at our ports and additional runways at our airports – all taking land and material resources. We will make huge improvements to our vehicle fleet. For example, as we adopt cradle-to-cradle production methods (see Chapter 13) we will be able to recycle all our old vehicles into new ones. But each addition to the total number in the fleet will need new resources pulled from the natural systems of the planet.

Fuel efficiency and better recycling, although important steps, are insufficient. No matter how efficient our cars become and how well we organize recycling, rampant expansion will strip the world resources bare. If there were seven cars per ten people (as in the US) throughout the world, then there would be seven times more cars on Earth than we have now.[3] The problem is more deep-rooted and the response required much more fundamental than we realize. We are slow to accept that limiting the size of the vehicle fleet is the only truly sustainable solution.

Transportation of People

We have always had to live within the capabilities of our transport, whether it is the distance a horse can be ridden in one day, or the fuel and oxygen on board a spaceship taking astronauts to the moon. I like the idea of taking my family to the moon for the day: bouncing around at one-sixth gravity like Apollo astronauts seems like great fun. This is not an option available to me, of course. My kids are perfectly happy with second best at the Heureka Science Centre near Helsinki, just a bus ride away. There they can simulate moon hops wearing a harness attached to a cable that reduces their weight to more like that on the moon. Our expectations need to match what is feasible and sustainable. Day trips to the moon are clearly out. Cheap holidays to the other side of the world, in our current generation of planes running on fossil fuels, should also be a non-starter, too, if only we stopped to think about it.

Another example comes from my childhood in the 1960s, when my family travelled from Australia to Britain by ship (the cheapest option then). We all had an enforced five-week vacation. To a child, it seemed a tremendously enjoyable way to travel, rather than a problem. My father, who was an academic, used the time to write a few chapters of the book he was working on. For some people, a heavy price premium to arrive quickly is appropriate, but, for many others, cheap travel at a more leisurely pace should be quite acceptable.

For shorter journeys we turn to the car, and then grapple with the problem of providing sufficient capacity in our road infrastructure. For most journeys, the need is to shift one person – a package of about 70kgs – from A to B. Adding in over a ton weight of car makes the problem far greater than it needs to be. Getting rid of the car can make the challenge of providing personal transportation easier to solve.

The ruling factor should be living within the sustainable capacity, allowing market forces to regulate our transport choices within a capped energy market. If that results in not being able to afford to commute from rural France to the City of London, so be it. If it means we cannot afford to run a car, it should not matter, as we proceed to design our communities around people, not cars, as I will illustrate in Chapter 11.

Freight

A key reason why globalization has been so successful is easy access to cheap transportation. Improving the transport infrastructure is regarded as a prerequisite for economic success. In a narrow economic sense, our experience shows this to be true; but the emphasis on growing capacity to shift more freight efficiently and cheaply is also one of the root causes of our environmental problems. I will show that the converse approach, of minimizing the distance that goods and commodities travel, would be more effective.

We care little how freight arrives, and the means and methods used, so long as it arrives safely within an appropriate time frame. The charges incurred are simply another cost of doing business. At global level, world merchandise exports continue to grow, exceeding $10 trillion in 2005.[4] Transportation is seen as a manageable and unavoidable overhead of this flow and not a barrier to further growth, but this will change.

We can be confident of achieving better energy efficiency expressed as energy per ton mile. However, increasing the total throughput of trade will negate such gains, and will undermine the good work of engineers in designing better cargo handling and transportation equipment. The expanding infrastructure will also take more land and resources: bigger container ships will need larger docks where they can load and unload, more trucks and motorways will be needed, and so on.

Globalization is driving increasing sophistication of the world freight system. Just-in-time manufacturing, supported by IT networks and tracking systems, is reducing the need for warehouses as more and more inventory is held in transit in containers or trucks on the move. Fresh, high value foods such as lobsters or out-of-season strawberries can be delivered swiftly by air between high capacity and efficient (in a logistic sense) hubs.

Our governments invest in infrastructure in order to keep the cost of freight transportation down, with the intention of supporting the economy. Business can then invest with confidence, knowing that transportation can cope. Bigger factories bring economies of scale and can be shifted to locations of lowest cost, nationally and globally. Shifting the output to the consumer is a cost, but not a high cost. We can be sure that the world's container freight infrastructure can cope at a highly competitive price.

This is the logic we understand and accept, but it comes from the old systems of globalization, which will soon be obsolete.

Government Action

Governments will eventually find that, in order to fulfil their broader responsibilities to society, they will have to change policy. They will introduce escalating fuel taxes and other freight overhead charges, driving up the cost per ton-mile. The British government brought in such a fuel tax escalator in 1993, when fuel in the UK was the third cheapest in Europe. This was set at a modest 3% increase in real terms, rising to 5% in 1995. By 2000, the UK had the highest fuel taxes in Europe (dramatically higher than the United States and Australia).

In autumn 2000, the price of crude oil rose to over $30 dollars a barrel (at that time, the price was seen as expensive), sparking protest – directed at the fuel tax escalator – led by the haulage companies. They complained that, with the open European market, they were being put at a considerable disadvantage by the policy. The protesters placed blockades on UK oil refineries. The fuel shortages that resulted caused considerable disruption. After a stand-off, the blockades were lifted, but the protesters set a 60-day deadline for their demands for lower fuel taxes to be met. One week before the end of the deadline, the British Chancellor, Gordon Brown, announced in his pre-budget report that fuel duty would be frozen for two years. This signalled the end of the fuel tax escalator.

Before the rebellion, the policy of escalating fuel costs was quoted as an example of best practice in efforts to reduce greenhouse gas emissions.[5] Despite this, in 2000 politicians did not have sufficient popular support to win the battle to retain the policy. They decided not to fight through to a conclusion. British politicians will be wary of picking this fight again soon, but after the energy crunch hits, governments will be forced to take such action.

There will inevitably be conflict, initiated by vested interests, but this time governments will have the backing they need to win. After the battle is over, companies will redo their calculations. They will find that smaller factories closer to the consumer are now a cheaper option. They may also like the fact that they can be more responsive to changing consumer preferences and that delivery is faster. As the altered parameters ripple through the economy, it will adapt to the new paradigm. With less freight shifting around, the government will need to maintain a smaller infrastructure. Tax receipts will be higher in the short term, until freight volumes fall and fuel usage decreases. The government is likely to find it politically palatable to share this tax windfall with those parts of industry that will be hardest hit, in order to persuade them to accept the changes.

I foresee many economists and commentators castigating this approach. They will argue that putting resistance to the transportation of goods into the economic model will be a continuous drag on GDP, and not just a short-term dip. I disagree. I believe that business is very good at exploiting new realities and that GDP will bounce back to a more sustainable position in terms of both the environment and profitability. In any case, it will be up to the politicians, not the economists, to decide when we adopt this approach.

The Future for Transportation

Transportation has to remain within the constraints of the sustainable energy supply, and the capacity of the Earth to supply material resources, without damaging the environment. We need to eliminate many journeys and reduce the amount of freight we shift, as well as increase the efficiency of our vehicles.

For industry, this will require a change in thinking. Plenty of opportunities will arise, such as production designed around responsive, small production facilities and marketing playing on national or regional loyalty. These opportunities will not be pursued because business has finally gone green. In a world in which the costs of transportation have risen to a sustainable level, business will exploit these opportunities because of the costs to be saved.

Personal transportation will also go through a major shake-up. In the following chapters, I argue that the car will lose its privileged position and antici- pate that the airline industry will go through a painful realignment. But, first, I will use the sector of sea transportation to give an insight into the future.

Ships on the international shipping routes are the least visible and least regulated of the world's transportation systems. There has been little concerted action to push for pollution standards or the control of carbon emissions, but rising fuel costs will drive change.

Ship operators will rekindle interest in renewable power, focused on the wind that blows with little impediment over the oceans. This will not be a return to the sailing ships of the past. These new ships will be high-tech, fitted with aerodynamic wings, rotors, sails or kites, all controlled by computers fed with satellite data to maximize the exploitation of weather systems. The engineers should be given free rein to experiment. Large commercial sailing-ship design has a hundred years of stagnation to overcome. Our engineers can deliver great solutions if given the brief to do so. But wind has one big disadvantage: it does not blow all the time. When a new ultra-modern wind-powered ship is stuck in the doldrums (the area of low wind around the equator), it will sit with the capital invested producing no return. Perhaps it will also need conventional engines, but there is another way. The power of the sun is likely to be greatest when the wind is least, so solar power could also be used. I issue a design challenge.

DESIGN CHALLENGE: A MODERN LARGE SAILING SHIP

The aim is to design a large commercial ship powered by renewable power sources.

The assumption is that wind – when it blows – is the primary power source, with solar as the secondary one. The structure to capture the wind's energy might also double up as a solar-power cell array to power electric engines. In addition, there could be huge fold-out solar panels, too delicate for more than very low wind conditions. Engineers should feel entirely unconstrained in the approach they take and can assume that the rules of ship design and safety can be rewritten. The key parameters are:

- power should be derived from sustainable sources such as the wind and the sun;

- biowaste should be collected on board for methane generation and eliminating the discharge of raw sewage into the sea (this applies particularly to passenger ships);

- construction methods should consider the ship's whole life cycle through to recycling on decommissioning.

An important aspect of the design challenge is to work out costs in sufficient detail to be able to estimate how high the price of fuel oil must reach before such a ship becomes competitive compared with conventionally powered new cargo ships (based on total operating costs).

On 8 May 2007, a 46-ft catamaran called *Sun21* arrived in New York Harbour to become the first solar-powered boat to cross the Atlantic. This small boat averaged 3–5 knots with a maximum speed of 9 knots.[6] A commercial ship would, of course, use wind when it could, but *Sun21* is proof that solar power can be a major component of ship propulsion. It is worth noting that solar power also powered all the onboard electronic systems, negating the need for fuel for generators.

Our engineers can undoubtedly deliver a wind/solar solution scaled up to full commercial size. The most interesting point will be the fuel price at which it is economically viable. This will indicate just how far the energy crunch needs to proceed for the shipbuilding industry to reach the tipping point. When it does, the shipyards that have invested seed capital in developing this new technology will have a lead that will be hard to catch. There is a very profitable opportunity waiting for circumstances to change.

Beyond this particular tipping point, there is another business waiting to launch: providing a global route-selection service with access to weather satellites, global computer models and expert meteorologists. Ships would pay a subscription for the service and receive in return navigation advice to minimize the time (and cost) of their journey.

My analysis of sea transportation may appear radical, but, when the time comes, it will not be resisted. It is clear that future restrictions on the use of fossil fuels and the escalating price of energy will lead to the sort of outcome predicted. My analyses of the future of the car and aircraft industries are much more contentious.

10 Icarus Air

The airline industry is soaring to new heights, with increasing demand driven by low-cost operators and new point-to-point routes opening up. But the expansion is not sustainable. It will come crashing down, destroying all but a few shrewd players who realize that a crisis is looming.

History records that the first sustained controlled powered flight was carried out by the Wright brothers at Kitty Hawk in North Carolina on 17 December 1903. That day must have been incredibly exciting for Orville, who was the pilot that day. Since then we have had a century of progress. Sustained flight is routine. Now the adrenalin does not pump even when we climb into an aircraft and fly non-stop from Europe to Australia. It is a bore, and uncomfortable, especially if you do not like airline food and the film is one you have already seen. How flying has evolved.

The Wrights' engine was a very basic one they built for themselves. It must have been both inefficient and polluting, but in terms of making history a little pollution hardly matters. Now, in a world of mass air transportation – powered by efficient engines – the fuel per passenger mile is many orders of magnitude better. However, the enormous expansion of flying means that the impact on our planet's systems is hugely greater than in the early days of flight. The increase in capacity is exceeding the valiant efforts of our engineers to further improve efficiency. Instead of reducing the impact, we are increasing it, despite good scientific evidence of the dangers.

Flying is an international industry dominated by big global players. Each nation has had its national airline, flying the flag as a symbol of national pride, leading to a history of subsidy and bailing out of ailing airlines. Aircraft manufacturing is also dominated by global players. Development costs are high, so you need to be big to enter the game. The aircraft manufacturing companies employ a lot of people, and crucially have defence-related importance, so have the ear of government. The biggest competitive battle is between Boeing and Airbus, with each accusing the other of underhand tactics. Boeing is accused of being subsidized through juicy contracts from the Pentagon. Airbus is accused of receiving soft loans from the EU. Both charges have an element of truth. The point is that governments do what they can (within international rules) to protect these strategic industries. So, to an extent, the aircraft industry is sheltered, but this will not be enough to bypass the sweeping changes that are coming.

In recent years the biggest change has been the emergence of low-cost operators such as Southwest Airlines, Ryanair and easyJet. They have brought entirely new business models to the sector, utilizing cheap hubs based on remote and underused airports. The service is no frills; operations are highly efficient; bookings are self-service over the Internet and the operators pioneered ticketless travel.

This has drawn new customers into flying as it becomes more affordable. The new and cheaper routes also support new long-distance commuter profiles, drawing in yet more passengers. In terms of running their businesses, I admire what the low-cost operators have achieved. In terms of the way they are reshaping our use of air transportation, we should be very worried.

The Unsustainable Stalemate

The market for air travel is expanding, but many of the new customers are highly price sensitive, for whom flying is a discretionary expenditure. If prices were higher, they would either not travel at all or use slower alternatives. The industry has to work very hard driving down costs in order to stay profitable.

One defining characteristic of the current air transportation industry is surprisingly low taxation. Most aviation fuel used on international routes is tax free, accounting for just 15% of operating costs, so it is not the prime focus of cost saving measures.

Fossil fuel, though, is the main reason the environmental impact of aviation is so high. Not only is carbon release affecting climate, but also the emissions are at high altitude, where other exhaust products may have additional effects, such as damaging the ozone layer. It is clear that taxes on aviation fuel should, therefore, rise; but if one country were to lead, then global airlines would plan their operations to refuel elsewhere. Raising taxes unilaterally would damage a country's own industry, hitting hardest the airlines operating from hubs within its own country. This would give foreign operators a considerable advantage.

We therefore have a stalemate of inaction, keeping aviation fuel artificially cheap. This is compounded by a history of subsidy and political reluctance to take appropriate measures. This leads to perverse outcomes where people commute weekly from Tours in the Loire Valley in France to Stanstead Airport near London at a price well below the cost of the environmental impact. Holidays on the Mediterranean coast are available at a cost below that of a holiday on a beach nearer home.

Let us consider how to break the stalemate. First, we should remember that flying is not essential to survival as food and clean water are. It is a luxury, albeit one we have come to expect. There is no case for exemption or special treatment. We should strip out historic baggage, re-engage free-market forces and let the business ecosystem shake out into a new and more sustainable equilibrium.

The Essentials of Air Transportation

Transportation by air is one part of the overall transport mix, used for the rapid transportation of people or high-value goods over long distances (for simplicity,

I shall ignore specialist niches such as military aircraft, small leisure aircraft and helicopters for police or search-and-rescue duties). There is not a distinct boundary between air and other options, but an overlap with other means of transport, such as city-to-city bullet trains that can compete on speed and price. Some passengers and freight will go by the overall cheapest route, whatever that happens to be.

The fixed-time overhead of travelling to the airport and checking in means that flying is more suitable for longer journeys than short hops. Flying has become the de facto standard for international and, particularly, intercontinental travel. For many passengers, speed may be a bonus, but they do not place a high premium on it. For other passengers, speed is essential and has value. If the price-per-distance charges were to rise significantly then the market would contract.

In other areas, there is scope for expansion. If fixed-time costs can be reduced, then shorter flights become a more attractive option. This means that demand for short-take-off planes able to operate from small-footprint sites inside affluent residential districts or commercial centres may increase. This will be a small premium market that requires planes that are low-noise, clean and efficient in order to win approval to operate.

Aviation Fuel Taxes

It is sensible and fair that fuel taxes should be set in line with environmental impact, leading eventually to the goal of the elimination of fossil fuels. The tax increases required will have a strong political dimension in all sectors, from heating buildings to car driving. When looking at the wide spectrum of the electorate, increasing taxes on aviation fuel will have less political impact than in other areas, so should be easier to introduce. However, the structural stalemate described above has to be broken. To do this will require global agreement from all countries to a tax floor that is universally applied.

Such an agreement may seem like a far-fetched green dream, but it just needs the right set of circumstances to become a reality. I have composed a fictional but realistic account that illustrates how this could come about (see box on next page). The compelling logic behind such an agreement will become so persuasive, and the groundswell of support from smaller nations will become so strong, that such agreement could be reached over quite a short period.

The enforcement of a global tax floor on aviation fuel is feasible. Effective sanctions would be needed, of course, against countries that step out of line, but this should be easy to enforce simply by the suspension of flights to and from such countries. A subset of non-compliant countries could emerge, but only flying between each other.

A Future for Aviation

Aviation is heading for substantial increases in fuel costs, over and above the cost of oil on the world market. For this not to happen would require that we continue

A FUTURE WORLD SUMMIT ON GLOBAL WARMING

Britain's Prime Minister (PM) has just started a new five-year term with a large majority in Parliament. The PM's landslide victory came on the back of an election campaign in which environmental issues were prominent. The PM had promised a win-win situation where he would hold down domestic taxes and take a lead in calling for international action to address climate change.

To follow through his manifesto pledge, he has called a summit of world leaders. The banner title under which they gather is 'Climate Change – Act Now'. Leading up to the conference the PM has asked for input and ideas. Science and politics have become entwined as the issues have been debated in the world's press.

Suggestions have been floated in the West that China's rapid growth and increasing use of its vast coal reserves is the main problem. China has retaliated by pointing out that the United States has been emitting high levels of carbon emissions for some decades. The question being asked by many delegations, including India, is why they should they take action that might hinder their development when the West remains the leading offender?

The US president counters in a televised address, in which he highlights the efforts being made by the United States to move to efficient, clean technologies. Just days before the conference convenes, the Chinese leader, speaking at a meeting in Paris before flying on to London, explains that China will not act unless the United States reciprocates with major cuts of its own. The scene seems set for deadlock. The British PM is searching for a solution – not only to the issue of climate change, but also to the political corner he finds himself in.

Britain's Chief Scientist and his US counterpart publish a joint article in which they provide a balanced analysis based on the scientific evidence. Although not central to their report, they comment that mass air travel is a major source of greenhouse-gas emissions but that disproportionately little has been done to curb it. They add that they suspect that aircraft emissions are causing damage to the upper atmosphere in other ways. The British PM's advisors spot an opportunity. After frantic diplomatic soundings behind the scenes, this issue seems to be one on which agreement might be possible. Without time for the leaders to consult in detail with their various domestic lobby groups, the PM opens the conference. His speech focuses on the impact of air travel and the amount of CO_2 that has been released to get the delegations to the table, and closes with the words 'Now is the time to act'.

Over three days, many issues are discussed but the one that shows progress is an agreement on taxes on aviation fuel. The smaller countries – without their own global airline or an aircraft industry – push the pace. After pressing for solid commitments, the British PM is pushed onto the back foot as the proposals to address aircraft emissions take shape.

A proposal from the Alliance of Small Island States (AOSIS) for an immediate tax applied universally by all governments of $5 per litre of aviation fuel is leaked by one of the delegates and makes headlines around the world. These range from an outcry from some business leaders to applause from green activists and sections of the left-wing press. This is going far further than the British PM had in mind, but he likes the headlines that praise such a bold move.

Under pressure to complete a deal, world leaders agree to tax aviation fuel at a common minimum rate to be phased in over five years. Each country agrees to levy the tax at the same rate or higher. A discussion over bringing some of the tax receipts together at world level does not progress. The final protocol leaves the tax receipts with the country to apply as it sees fit.

The British PM hails the conference as a success. The delegates return home, worried by the various interest groups who might now be upset, but confident that they are sheltered by the cloak of collective responsibility. Some quietly welcome the prospect of substantial additional tax receipts.

to deny that there is a problem. I can foresee, during what might be quite a long period, a reliance on the mechanism of carbon trading to keep our aviation business flying. The result will be the purchase of carbon credits by airlines to fund investment in carbon reductions elsewhere in the world economy. In theory, this is an entirely reasonable response. But in Chapter 21 I argue that although cap-and-trade market mechanisms can be very effective within tightly controlled markets, at world level market regulation is not sufficiently watertight. We will find that we cannot screw the carbon cap tight enough – and enforce global limits – to achieve the reductions required. We will then revert to direct taxation and the airline industry will be in the direct firing line. I may be proved wrong. Our enjoyment of the convenience of air travel may override our attempts to ratchet down the use of fossil fuel. But if we are to make real reductions in fossil carbon emissions, then we have to tackle the expansion of aviation.

To eliminate fossil fuels from the aviation industry will be difficult. A renewable fuel to replace aviation fuel has not yet been developed. When our scientists can produce such a fuel – or our engineers design engines that run on the renewable fuels we now have – then aviation may earn a reprieve. But until then, any real direct effort to reduce the environmental impact of flying will inevitably constrain capacity.

The economics of air transportation are going to be transformed, with flying becoming much less affordable. The core market of business people or government officials – who must fly – will remain strong. This market is not price sensitive (although the substantially higher costs will force administrators to consider other options and question the necessity of flying). Another small, profitable and secure segment of the market is the rich, who expect a high standard of service and are willing to pay for it. However, discretionary air travel will plummet. Many passengers who have become used to cheap flights will be looking at other options.

If I am right in my predictions, we will have finally started to address the problems of aviation's impact on the environment – and provide the incentive to search for real solutions. People like to fly and environmentally friendly flying will be a boom business in the future. For now, from the perspective of the current aviation industry, it will be a bloodbath. Airlines that have been struggling will file for bankruptcy. The second-hand market for planes will be flooded, and prices will dive. Older, inefficient planes will be sold for scrap, even though they have many flying hours left. The exemption will be owners of small, fuel-efficient planes that will be in demand and generate healthy returns.

From the perspective of those of us who have become used to hopping across Europe or the Atlantic and holidaying cheaply on the Mediterranean or in Florida, it will come as a shock. Our grandfathers may have been content to go by train to holiday in Blackpool or Brighton on the English coast, but we have become used to the reliable sunny weather of southern Europe and other holiday destinations.

The impending dislocation in the current airline industry will throw up an opportunity to satisfy demand for low-cost travel to sunny holiday destinations. Demand could be led by groups such as retired baby-boomers in Northern Europe or North America wanting to travel south. Before the Sustainable Revolution, drawn by low-cost air travel, the retired bought homes further away: British pensioners retired to Spain rather than Brighton, or Americans retired to South America rather than Florida. After the Sustainable Revolution, they will have to rethink their plans. If the parameter is to be within a few hours of the grand-children, then the radius of search for retirement homes will contract. If travel that is fast and cheap is no longer available, then there may be a good market for cheap but slow travel. Rail services may see increased demand. Ships powered by renewable power sources (along the lines proposed in Chapter 9) could take a share of the market. There will also be a niche for a zero-impact aircraft as outlined in the following design challenge.

Tackling this challenge would be a great job for ambitious and keen engineers and designers.

For those who have busy jobs and limited holidays, the extra travel time will seem a waste. But if we also succeed at improving our social economics in the way I outline in Chapter 20, then we may be able to increase our leisure time. It might then do us good to take a little of the pace out of modern life and start our holiday earlier, relaxing and enjoying a more leisurely route to the sun.

There are other hidden costs of the huge and rapid expansion of air travel. The world now has a mechanism for the efficient and effective transmission of

---

DESIGN CHALLENGE: ZERO-ENVIRONMENTAL-IMPACT FLYING

To design an aircraft to support low-cost transportation of large numbers of people with close to zero environmental impact. There are no other firm design constraints, but some ideas to consider are:

- large wing area covered in solar cells;

- design can include large volumes to be used for helium gas to enhance lift (not necessarily latter-day airships, but the designers should have the freedom to use such methods);

- relatively slow speed (set by the most efficient speed rather than any customer need);

- a roomy interior to allow for a great flight experience (it is anticipated that the design will be slow and large, so a spacious interior is unlikely to be a penalty);

- standard schedule built around a morning take-off so that the flight takes place through the middle of the day, maximizing solar power (the design can also assume a schedule that uses the natural wind circulation, especially for transatlantic flights);

- efficient conventional engines running on a biofuel may be needed for take-off and for safety (once at altitude above the clouds, the aircraft should cruise under solar power);

- design team can recommend changes to airports such as longer runways or towing systems to assist take-off if required.

---

disease. We already have well-researched evidence of the role of air travel in the SARS outbreak of 2003.[1] Global pandemics could be prevented or reduced in severity if only less people were whisked around the world each day. We cannot predict when the next pandemic might strike, but when it does, it might be the straw that breaks the back of the current global airline industry.

Leading Adaptation in the Aviation Industry

I have painted a bleak picture for the aviation industry. Even so, there are tactics that the airlines, plane manufacturers and airports can employ in order to profit from the opportunities that will arise. But it is important to note that not all players can play the same game; the advantage will be taken by the first to act, with the biggest gains going to those who buy into my concept well before it becomes accepted logic.

Airlines should continue their current operations but configure the owner-ship of assets and structure alliances to profit from the expected downturn in volume. For planes that are bought and owned directly, the aim should be a fleet of relatively small fuel-efficient aircraft. When buying conventional large planes, lease arrangements with an easy termination clause should be chosen, even if this means paying a premium. Whilst it is still possible, capital should be pulled out of the current fleet by transferring ownership to a leasing company.

For operations, the focus should be on a tight efficient core, serving the premium business sector, which will survive the downturn in volume. Airlines should start to use smaller planes against prime landing slots with the aim of cherry-picking premium business. The high-volume low-margin trade should be outsourced, or alliance partners should be allowed to take it. Finally, airlines should be poised to pick up assets on the cheap from distressed airlines, such as prime landing slots and routes. Going for profit, not scale, will be the new mantra.

The plane manufacturers' future plans should focus on small, fast, fuel-efficient planes. Boeing's 787 Dreamliner is a shift in the right direction. It is smaller than the old 747 and, according to Boeing, 20% more efficient than other current similarly sized planes. After the energy crunch hits, the Dreamliner will continue to be in demand whilst other aircraft are retired. Aircraft operators will then be looking for even better efficiency, so this is where aircraft development should focus. The plane-makers should also invest seed capital in the design challenge I have set to build a large, slow 'aircraft' running on renewable power.

With regard to selling current models, manufacturers should avoid any arrangement in which they retain residual ownership. They should be sold, not leased, either to airlines or leasing companies. This will protect long-term profitability even if the margin on the initial sale is less.

If the manufacturers and airlines both see the future I portray, there will be some tough negotiating ahead as both parties seek to defend their long-term position.

Airports will be faced with a tough business decision. The scenario I paint would suggest that they hold back or delay investment in additional capacity. However, it would be appropriate to invest in ensuring that core facilities are of a high quality that is appropriate to a smaller high-premium passenger throughput. Further investment in fast efficient ground transportation links would also be worthwhile. The other sensible move would be to earmark land for a longer and wider main runway, in case the result of the zero-impact challenge produces a plane that needs extra space to land or take off. Upgrading to take the Airbus A800 may be compatible with this; although the A800 itself is likely to go down as a last gasp in the old industry of mass air transportation based on fossil fuel.[2]

The huge rate of expansion of air transportation is clearly unsustainable in environmental terms. It is also unsustainable in business terms, but the industry has not yet woken up to this. Ironically, the profits will be greatest if very few players accept my analysis. In that case, those who do – and follow the direction I describe – will find little resistance to repositioning themselves.

There is a problem with my advice; the crunch may still be some years off. The actions I describe will hit profits in the short term, so inaction would be the sensible choice for chief executives with short-term profit targets or share options maturing in the next couple of years.

I hope that a core of the most capable and profitable players take a bet on the outcome I predict, and surreptitiously reorganize their businesses. Once this has been completed, it will be in their interests to see the industry decimated around them. They will then lead the campaign to lobby hard for governments to support a sustainable air transportation sector.

I can see my opinions on air transportation raising people's hackles. We have come to expect lost-cost air travel. Raising the costs to a realistic level will price many people out of the market. People may view this as unfair, whilst the rich can still afford to fly. But only the rich can afford to be space tourists, paying millions to ride into orbit. The rest of us do not aspire to follow them. It is the fact that something that we used to have will be taken away from us that makes us angry or resentful. We will need to think carefully about situations where there is no alternative to flying to make the changes palatable.

My opinions on the future for the car are even more contentious, and will be unacceptable to many when viewed alone. It is only when I explain the parallel changes required in the design of communities that my tough stance on the car makes sense. Our need for healthy, cohesive urban communities is therefore where I turn next.

11 Healthy, Cohesive Urban Communities

In 2005, the world's urban population was 3.2 billion, soon to exceed 50% of the world's population.[1] In North America, over 80% of the population are urban dwellers; in Europe the figure is 72%. Currently, 38% of Africans live in urban areas, but this is rising and is expected to exceed 50% by 2030. How urban areas evolve will be important in building a sustainable world.

Urban centres arose as service and trading hubs for the surrounding area. Small towns contain a market, a few shops and some sort of basic leisure or social facilities. Larger towns have a wider range of services and more specialist shops. Cities are fewer and have a full range of specialist services acting as the administrative centre for the region. Traditionally, towns and cities draw the food and water they need from the surrounding countryside. About 25% of the world's population, and half of the urban population, live in urban settlements with fewer than 500,000 inhabitants, which are small enough to work in this way. However, in an increasingly globalized world, some cities are becoming not just regional or national nuclei, but global hubs.

Some cities are growing together, merging into urban agglomerations such as Tokyo, Mexico City, New York-Newark, São Paulo and Mumbai (Bombay).[2] These megacities are drawing inputs of goods and supplies, and attracting people, from around the world. Their products are being shipped out to a global market-place and services, such as finance and insurance, are delivered to a global customer base over high-capacity data networks. These megacities are losing their close relationship with the surrounding area.

This seems to be urbanization running out of control. If this trend continues, we should be worried. We need to take a look at what is behind the evolution of the modern city.

Cities can be seen as living entities, in the same way that an anthill appears to have an existence that transcends the capabilities of each ant alone. Ants have adopted behaviours that natural selection has refined into successful model colonies. There must be some unwritten rules to which the ants comply, but, to an external observer, the anthill seems to be self-organizing.

Our cities are similar in that they have a dynamic that goes beyond any one person's control. We have laws and policy, but there are also unwritten rules and behaviours. It is not clear how much of our cities are planned and to what extent they have evolved. The dynamics of our cities are as hard to identify as those of the anthill, but we need to try if we are to influence the next phase of their evolution.

We can imagine the sort of city we would like. It would look like a healthy living organism, designed and built around the needs of people, integrated with its surroundings and operating in a sustainable way. Unfortunately, not many world cities fit this idealized model. Many have come to look more like a malignant growth, inflicting violence, stress, despair and loneliness on many of its inhabitants. Some seem to be growing out of control, sucking in ever more nutrients and polluting the surroundings. Such cancerous growth cannot be good for citizens or the environment.

It is evident that we need healthy cities, but cities do not respond easily to top-down command and control. We need to identify levers that can nudge their evolution in the right direction. These are none too obvious. Our attention is drawn to symptoms not causes: crime is tackled by increased policing and traffic gridlock is tackled by building more roads. This reactive response is short-sighted and ultimately ineffective.

In this chapter I will look beyond the manifest problems to identify some general principles around which our cities can evolve, seeking directions that are likely to lead to positive outcomes. Where I paint a picture of what the outcomes will be, this is conjecture: the precise form will emerge from adopting the principles I put forward. We should try it and see. I use Helsinki Metropolitan Area as an example throughout this discussion, not because it is perfect, or the only example of good city management, but because it does work very well.

I will start my search by proposing a universal definition of the ethos of a healthy city:

> *A healthy city should comprise a cohesive social community that is economically viable and works in symbiosis with the environment.*

Cities as Social Communities

Cities should be built for people and around the needs of people. An obvious point, perhaps, but one that is easily forgotten when looking at the complex systems required. At a basic level, people need shelter, warmth and sustenance. They also need work, not just to pay the bills but so they can feel a sense of worth. A community living on welfare benefit is bound to struggle.

Security is important; people should feel safe. The obvious approach is good physical security backed up by strong policing. The less obvious, but more effective, mechanism is self-policing communities.[3] Cities that are a checkerboard of small communities, each small enough for people to get to know each other, can largely police themselves. A police service is still required, of course, but within a cohesive community, people notice what is going on and can be the first level of response. The policemen employed by the city are a phone call away.

Health is also important, but focusing too much on the provision of treatment is, once again, being drawn to symptoms not causes. If we concentrate on the true need, we find it is better to ensure safe food, clean water and good exercise opportunities. Not just sport for the enthusiast, but activity designed into everyday living. Getting around using our own legs is good for us: it is efficient and it is clean.

Of course we need ramps and other access provision to ensure that the disabled, old and infirm can also get around, but there is no need to automate short-distance travel for the able-bodied. We tend to see motorized modes of transport as modern and necessary, despite the epidemic of obesity that the developed world is suffering. This is an odd attitude and is ripe for change. For longer distances, the situation is different. Here we do want fast, efficient and clean transport solutions, but for local journeys we need to be able to walk and cycle safely.

Cities should also instil a sense of well-being in their inhabitants. For example, a logical solution to the problem of expanding cities would be to burrow underground, leaving the surface of the earth for agriculture, leisure and nature reserves. To expand we would just dig deeper. But man is an outdoor animal. We need sunlight and access to fresh air and open sky. We want our cities to connect with the natural world, not hide beneath it. There are a myriad of issues we could consider when looking for what might help to provide this elusive sense of well-being.

The Balance between Public and Private Space

A person's fundamental needs are few: a bed in a secure place to sleep; somewhere to get food; a place of work and a place to relax. As prison governors know, these needs can easily be provided; but we want more space than this. We want our own bedroom. We also want a bathroom, sitting room and kitchen that we only have to share with the close family.

We continue to want more: a garden, a swimming pool or even a private golf course. This desire for more private space has a downside; the higher the proportion of private space within a community, the less space is available for building the community. An affluent resident with lots of private space has to make a specific effort to go out and interact with the community. There may be people who would like to live like hermits, but most people need a sense of community in order to have a sense of well-being.

Public space is needed for many things, including markets, parks, sport facilities and public buildings such as libraries. A balance is clearly required between public and private space. However, many urban areas have polarized into public or private space, and are missing the key component that is shared space. This is neither private nor public, but is owned by a community (I use ownership in the general sense of the word, without worrying about the legal exactitudes).

Shared space is, for example, an open area – with seats and play facilities where there is a natural interaction – which is 'owned' by a group of residents who live in buildings clustered around it. To each family, it is as if they have a large garden, but not for their exclusive use. In such a space, it is natural for people to look for and notice antisocial behaviour. It may be that the area has a secure perimeter and is, therefore, an exclusive shared area. It may be enough that the collective eyes of the community are surveying the area. If we follow the idea of increasing shared space – and if it is implemented well – people can be content with quite a small private space provided there is access to a much larger high-quality shared space close by. Sprawling suburbs of homes with gardens can be replaced by compact and vibrant communities.

It is worth considering one version of dense urban living, and noting why it failed, before we take the concept further. In 1960s Britain, many old slum communities, consisting of long lines of back-to-back houses dating from the Industrial Revolution, were replaced by tower blocks separated by large open areas. The intention was improvement, but in the UK these high-rise buildings became synonymous with urban decay, crime, drug use and loneliness. A main part of the problem was that ownership remained polarized between public and private space. The flats were private (in terms of use, if not in terms of legal ownership), but everywhere outside the front doors was public. There was no shared space in which to build community surveillance. You were either safe in your private space, or out in the fully public domain, which became increasingly lawless.

If we search to see how densely populated urban living can work, the concept of shared space seems to be the key.

Dense Urban Living

There are many examples of urban areas throughout the world which work well. The one I have observed at first hand whilst researching this book is within the Helsinki Metropolitan Area, and is typical of urban areas found across Finland: not a showpiece community but a normal living and working environment.

The area consists of groups of blocks of flats, five to eight floors high and located quite close together. There are also blocks of interconnected houses with very small gardens. This is not the only model used in Finland, but it is common, works well and is liked by residents.

At first sight it looks very ordinary and dull. If you look harder, you see that each flat has a balcony to give a small private space out in the fresh air and sunshine. The areas between the buildings are neat, with a good selection of trees and vegetation, much of which has been retained in its natural state from before development. This provides space for less shy wild animals and birds, as well as children. There is also play equipment for children and benches to sit on.

The design includes integrated publicly owned spaces that can be adopted as shared space. Anyone can use these spaces for sport or other activities. Schools use them during the day for their outdoor activities. At night, other sports clubs use them. There are floodlights, for which the key is easily obtained if you run a local club or activity. In the winter, some of these spaces are converted into ice rinks for anyone to use. Compare this with the waste in many other community models, where space is more polarized: for example, school playing fields that are fenced off for exclusive use by the school, or sport pitches that are built outside residential areas and are a car drive away.

In the centre of the shared community area, there is a small building surrounded by children's play equipment, including challenging but safe climbing frames, slides and swings. A small number of employed staff work in and around the building. Children can play inside the building as well as outdoors, but there is no clearly defined perimeter. Some activities are arranged, but the prime purpose is to act as a focus for the local children, so that there is an adult they can turn to if there is a problem.

In daytime, there will be children playing with no apparent supervision. During the working week, these are likely to be children as young as seven whose day at school is over and whose parents are still at work. The small team of government-employed workers (predominantly women) get to know the children and the children get to know each other. But there is no formal responsibility of childcare; children are not signed in or signed out. Parents and children make use of the facility as they see fit.

There are other areas between the buildings which are owned by the blocks of flats and shared by the residents. In many countries, this would result in no one taking responsibility for them and their becoming unkempt and strewn with litter. In Finland, the reason these areas are looked after is not just a realization that to do so benefits all residents, but also a consequence of the legal system of owning flats and apartments.

No one owns a flat or house that is part of a larger building. You own only a share in the company that owns the block, bringing with it a right of residence. The company has a responsibility to look after the building and its grounds, and the officers of the company are responsible for implementing it. As a resident, you can choose to get involved in running the company or be lazy and not even turn up at the annual general meeting. The company will still do its duty, levying charges as required, without the need to get unanimous agreement from the residents.

Cars are kept out of the central area, with parking spaces grouped in car parks at the periphery. Getting around to shops and schools does not necessarily entail crossing vehicle routes. Vehicles can use the footpaths and cycleways to load and unload but not as thoroughfares nor for parking.

Finland is a country with a lot of space; it is not forced into building very dense developments and people are not forced to live in them. These developments work because of the ideal mix between private space, public space and shared space, all of a very high standard. If residents were to insist on more private space, or local government were to put tighter control on access to public space, the model would collapse.

There is an aspiration amongst many of us in the developed world for larger houses and more private space. A beautiful village I know in southern England is a model of high-quality community living. It has a manor house in the centre which is now owned by a celebrity pop star. For him, it is a perfect place to live. He has large secluded grounds and close access to a vibrant community. However, if everyone had such large private space, the community would not exist. We all have to make decisions about where we live which are a compromise between our selfish desire for private space and our need for community.

In the 20th century, our desire for private space has been allowed to dominate urban development in the developed world, driving the growth of city suburbs, where every journey requires a car. When the Sustainable Revolution bites and other pressures come to bear, such as the escalating costs of car use and ownership, people will be forced to make a different compromise.

People's eyes will be opened to the advantages of living in cohesive communities with great shared spaces and facilities, such as good schools and shops accessible by foot or cycle. Properties in the best of such communities will command high prices. We might see many of the old suburbs razed and replaced by high-quality community living.

For all segments of society, rich or poor, our aim should be cohesive social communities, adapted to specific local circumstances.

Economic Stability

Cities need to balance their budget in delivering the required service infrastructure. In doing this, a complex mix of issues interferes with the core economics, ranging from power and politics to resistance from vested interests and concern for the disadvantaged. This leads to anomalies, some of which are damaging, yet so deep-rooted that we accept them without question.

We need to put people and communities back in charge. Whatever else we might wish for our cities, we must appreciate that they have to be economically viable. I propose two fairly uncontroversial levers: local people pay for local services; and full-cost charging. If we can stick to these principles – unless we have good reason not to and in full knowledge of the expected outcome – then we have a sound basis.

Implementing the first principle requires local taxation. This ensures that residents are engaged with running their community. People hold the management to account when it is their money being spent. Waste or needless extravagance is then not tolerated. The taxation locality has to be small enough that there is a sense of identity and ownership. Differences will arise. This should not be seen as a problem but rather as a strength of the system as communities grapple with their own set of circumstances.

Affluent areas will be left free to manage their own affairs but will receive little central government funding. At the other extreme, there will be areas where the average income is low, services are stretched and property is cheap. This is where central government will step in with additional support, funded by national taxation. Such funds will have considerable strings attached to ensure sound local governance and management.

The second principle is full-cost charging (unless we specifically decide to subsidize). In considering utility services such as power and water, this is important to ensure appropriate investment by customers and appropriate behaviour. When such full-cost charging hits vulnerable groups, we should resist the temptation to subsidize. Instead, we should invest in reducing their need, for example by paying for insulation, rather then subsidizing energy costs. There will be other areas, of course, where subsidy is appropriate, such as health care, education and sport. The amount will be a political community-based decision within the national context of what the state defines as public services.

Under the principle of full-cost charging, if we consider the services a city provides, then one glaring anomaly stands out. This is the infrastructure provided for cars. A huge infrastructure is provided, at huge expense, but the access charges are currently small compared with the full cost of providing it.[4] London's congestion charge scheme, which charges motorists who enter a defined zone, is an example of starting to fix this anomaly. Parking charges, car tax and taxes on parking spaces also contribute, but not enough to cover the full costs.

The Car Takes Over

Before the car, city streets were for people and horses and carriages. Streets were bustling social places where people met and sold things, as well as moving from one place to another. The horseless carriage (the car) was initially resisted on safety grounds, and a requirement was brought in to have a man holding a red flag walking in front of the vehicle. From this inauspicious start, it did not take long for the car to become accepted and then, over time, take over.

As streets become clogged with traffic, we react by widening existing roads and building new ones, keeping pedestrians out of the way on sidewalks. Streets were once communal areas for people, but are now owned by the car. We continue to maintain them for free and provide access for free as if they were still communal areas, but they now belong to cars and their drivers.

If you do not own or use a car, you are excluded from a large part of urban space. I suggest that car drivers are not a vulnerable group that we should be subsidizing. So, according to the principles I propose, we should charge full cost.

Roads take up valuable space but we do not put a value to the land because we do not intend that it is going to re-enter the market. Let us consider changing this by giving road space back to the community, not just as pedestrian precincts, cycleways, footpaths or parks but by allowing development to encroach on roads. Some of the wider roads would make substantial sites. If we are willing to think in this way, then we must put a value to the land that we decide to keep as roads.

A rental charge on the land, as well as the direct costs of maintenance, needs to be charged to road users. If we choose this policy, the technical difficulties in levying the charge are not difficult. We have technologies such as cameras supported by number-plate recognition, road-side sensors, Global Positioning

System (GPS) receivers and appropriate IT systems which can provide charging/paying services that can be integrated with the vehicle registration system.

In implementing this charging model, it would be tempting to exclude some road users such as fire engines and ambulances. But this would be a mistake. In these cases, the charge would be a closed-cycle financial transfer from one part of local government to another, but it would not be irrelevant. The fire service would then have a different set of figures to consider when deciding the number and locations of fire stations. It would strengthen the case for more small local fire stations. The same would apply to ambulances, strengthening the case for smaller medical facilities embedded into local communities.

The point is that a free road network is a distortion of the way our cities evolve; full-cost charging is more likely to lead to sensible solutions.

Reclaiming City Streets

Full-cost charging will not eliminate the desire to travel by car, and it will certainly not reduce the need for buses and taxis. However, as we consider how to provide the required road capacity, we will have a more realistic cost-benefit calculation to work with. In rural areas, surface roads will remain the economic choice, but in cities with high land values it will become increasingly cost-effective to put our roads underground. We already have some examples.

Tapiola is one of the satellite centres of Helsinki Metropolitan Area. It was built in the 1960s as a showpiece of modern urban design and was well ahead of its time. The town centre is carefully landscaped, attractive and is a very pleasant relaxed yet bustling environment, free of cars and buses. The main route for vehicles goes underneath the town centre, with bus passengers alighting directly underneath the central shopping area. The only danger of note when walking around is the minimal risk of being run over by a bicycle.

A more recent example is in the centre of Helsinki where a large shopping and leisure complex has been built on the site of the old bus station. It was a large open area with many bus stands where people would wait in the weather for their buses. The buses and their routes in and out are now in underground tunnels. The new underground terminus has over sixty sets of automatic doors, which equate to the old bus stands. These doors open only when the bus is about to leave, ensuring fumes do not enter the underground terminus where people are waiting. At an even lower level, there is a metro station to complete the transport hub.

Above ground there is now an open square that is used to attract people to a wide range of events, and a building with five floors of shops and restaurants. The top floor is used as a night club that has an open terrace with views out across the city. The city has reclaimed the road space (or in this case the bus space) and given it back the community. The city is a much more pleasant environment, and the buses are more efficient now that they do not fight for space in the heart of the city centre.

With our current vehicle fleet running on flammable fuels and emitting toxic emissions, underground roads are an expensive option. When driving clean vehicles – such as electric cars – becomes the norm, the construction overhead will reduce. For road users, there would be no weather problems with snow, ice or rain. For people and communities, the car would then be banished from their everyday local living.

The most valuable space in cities is that which is open to the sky. It can be used for parks and people or PV (photovoltaic) roofs to gather solar power. If we accept the principle that roads are a wasteful use of open-to-sky space, and implement full-cost charging to nudge the economics favourably, then we might find that we can afford to put almost the entire urban road network underground, returning cities to the people.

The changes required are not trivial but we might be surprised – once the principle has been adopted – at the speed with which developers could come up with proposals. When our forefathers designed the great cities of Paris, London or Washington, DC, it was before the car. The wide boulevards and impressive streets were planned so people could move around, of course, but it was not intended that they should be owned by the car. In the 21st century we can return them to their rightful owners – the people.

Symbiosis with the Environment

Cities as cohesive and economically viable communities also have to be in tune with the surrounding environment.

For energy, the city of the future will have to be zero-fossil-fuel-powered. This may seem preposterous now, but it is a simple statement of fact. The crunch will come sooner if we intervene, or more slowly if we wait until the Earth's reserves are expended. The only question mark is over timing.

City evolutions do not happen quickly unless we accept dramatic and traumatic change. City planners should, therefore, have plans for zero-fossil-fuel cities and should already be making long-term infrastructure decisions with that in mind, even if it is too early to be able to commit to massive new investment.

Some cities will be fortunate and have external renewable power supplies from hydro or offshore wind, but we can expect these external supplies to be limited, and, in a tight energy market, expensive. Unless, that is, we finally succeed in developing and deploying nuclear fusion, delivering abundant clean energy. We could then site our fusion reactors[5] under the city centres to maximize the use we make of the heat not converted into power. This would be the ultimate combined heat and power plant. However, I believe that ownership of this thought should remain with the science-fiction writers for now. It would be folly to avoid taking appropriate actions in the hope that fusion technology will rescue us.

This situation leads us into energy-neutral city design. This is a great 21st-century task for our engineers and planners, who I believe are capable of rising to the challenge, if asked. All roof areas should be used to harvest solar energy and provide foundations for a multitude of wind turbines. A new sound in urban life will be the whir of turbines whenever the wind blows. The city's dry biowaste will be burned in combined heat and power stations and wet biowaste will be processed to produce methane gas. These energy sources will be deployed either at building level (as owners seek to keep costs down) or at municipal level; an appropriate balance can be expected to emerge.

Building design will need to become much more energy-efficient. The concept of designing an attractive building and then bolting on a power plant to keep it warm or cool will be discredited. Energy-neutral building design requires rather clever holistic thinking but is perfectly possible. The best architects and engineers in this area can expect to command premium professional fees as the energy crunch hits.

The search for efficiency will spread into other related areas. For example, many office buildings have inefficient IT, which draws excessive power, leading to waste heat, which requires yet more power for air conditioning. Even when the temperature outside is sub-zero, some buildings still require cooling simply due to the excess heat from their IT. This is a ridiculous situation that management will no longer tolerate as energy prices soar. Energy-efficient IT will be a major growth business for IT hardware vendors.

I predict that we will see architecture returning to its local roots. What has become the international norm for typical office buildings of an impressive glass box with a large heating and cooling plant will become extinct.

For example, the traditional architecture of the Middle East has thick walls and small windows, often little more than slits. This has a purpose. Desert-region weather is typified by hot days and relatively cold nights. The thick walls keep the heat of the sun out during the day and slowly release the heat over the night-time, maintaining a pleasant temperature throughout the day and night. In northern Europe, acres of glass are a good way to maximize the solar gain, but buildings also need clever ventilation and fold-out sunshades to keep temperatures down on hot summer days.

We can take enjoyment from allowing our cities to return to their cultural roots, but the purpose will be to make our buildings energy-neutral.

Another aspect of tuning our cities to the environment is in terms of material needs. The principle – which we will discuss further when looking at manufacturing in Chapter 13 – is to separate biomaterial and technical material cycles. Biomaterial can be recycled in conjunction with the natural ecosystem, whilst technical material is extracted once from a natural source and then reused again and again indefinitely in new products (if this concept is new to you, then you will need to read Chapter 13 before the full implications become clear). A similar approach will be required for the management of our urban infrastructure: this has much more permanence than product life cycles.

Currently, we use a lot of reinforced concrete in our new buildings. It is a high quality, versatile material, and the associated building processes are easily automated. But it is very energy-intensive to make the cement that is the prime ingredient, and hard to recycle. Where we build the core of our structures with concrete, we should build them to last through a multitude of refurbishment cycles to make maximum return on the energy invested.

Many of our great buildings, which have stood for hundreds of years, such as cathedrals, were built from stone. The work involved was hugely skilful and labour-intensive, but not energy-intensive to the extent that our concrete and steel buildings are today. The combination of low energy input and a very long replacement cycle minimizes the energy requirement. This is how we should approach our core infrastructure.

We might even find that modern stonemasonry sees a resurgence. Careful use of rock in its raw state requires less energy but more skilled manual labour. This would suit our new world, either because we have intelligent robots to do the work or because we choose to provide constructive employment for people (this is discussed further under Social Economics in Chapter 20). Whatever choices we make about construction methods, the point is that our core infrastructure (including the shells of our residential buildings) should be built to last.

This is in contrast with all the internal fixtures and fittings. These should be totally biodegradable. Not only would this be good for the health of residents and workers (by eliminating noxious fumes), but also the interior could be stripped out at regular intervals to give the desired new interior. A partial refurbishment might take place every 7–10 years, with a complete gutting taking place every 20–25 years. Biodegradable interiors will serve their initial purpose for a decade or two before becoming an energy source, with their nutrients being returned to the land as fertilizer.

There would, of course, also be technical mass in areas such as plumbing and electrics, but these should be designed according to cradle-to-cradle principles (as with all products) so that they can be easily recycled. The monstrous hybrids we now come across on building sites, such as plastic laminates that cannot be recycled, will be outlawed.

Water is another fundamental urban need (Chapter 14). Cities will need to protect their watersheds, which might be at some distance. In dry areas where water is a limited resource, a fully functioning water market will be required to regulate the demand to match the available capacity. This will encourage water-saving behaviour, such as rain harvesting and reusing grey water to flush toilets. The processing of sewage will also change, not only to protect the environment but also to extract energy (as methane gas).

One of the biggest changes to city management will be in terms of handling other sorts of waste. Modern cities now produce enormous quantities of garbage containing a mix of materials that are hard to dispose of. Efforts at recycling are being made, but progress is limited. Most garbage either goes to landfill sites or is taken out and dumped at sea. This ignominious flow will have to stop. Although the problem is complex, we can solve it, as I go on to explain in Chapter 16.

Our Urban Future

Urban living is fast becoming the most common mode of existence for man. How we allow our cities to evolve is central to moving to a stable, sustainable world.

The complexity of the challenge is mind-boggling, though I hope to have shown that the levers needed to achieve sustainable cities are quite simple. If we adopt and stick to the principles outlined in this chapter, our cities have every chance of growing into healthy communities. If some cities continue to experience cancerous growth, we should try to identify the reasons, and then cut through to the cause rather than attempt to ameliorate the symptoms. All cities can and should be different; there is no single master plan for success.

Some cities may not respond to treatment: perhaps they should be left to die and their residents evacuated. New cities can be built on the brownfield sites of the old. If we start with an outline plan, build some core infrastructure and adopt the right principles, evolution will do the rest.

12 Putting King Car in Its Place

The car was the icon of the 20th century. The century opened with the first mass-produced car, which appeared in 1908 as the Model T Ford. The century closed with the stunning McLaren F1, capable of over 240 mph.[1] With the Model T, the car became affordable. The F1 is at the other extreme, a beautiful piece of engineering that epitomizes our craving for the ultimate car. It sits at the apex of a growing pile of over 600 million cars worldwide. Along with this vehicle fleet, there is an expanding infrastructure of roads, car parks, driveways and garages.

Like most people in the developed world, I am a car driver. I also enjoy going through car museums admiring the ingenuity, great design and engineering excellence we have invested in our motoring heritage. I feel an attraction to the best examples, and would delight in the exhilaration of being allowed to take the McLaren F1 for a drive. But I have come to realize that the way the car takes over is insidious, like some banned drug. I remember as a teenager that to drive was part of coming of age, giving freedom and the badge of adulthood. I then went through the phase of taking pride in a better or faster car, until I realized the negative effects the addiction was having. Both my wife and I were driving an hour each way to work. As parents, we were spending four hours each day in the company of our cars: time that could have been spent with our young children instead.

We have now chosen to live a short walk from the children's school and my wife's place of work. For my part, I use my home office a good deal. We all walk or cycle when we can. We still own a car, which gets out from time to time, but we have reimposed the proper master-servant relationship. We have taken back control of our lives from the demands of the car. I do not feel the need to sneak out at night to cruise the city streets listening to the CD-player. We have kicked the addiction. We have changed our lives by choice. When the energy crunch hits, the power of forced adaptation will pull many more people off the drug.

King Car

Before the Model T Ford, the car was a luxury item for the very rich. Since then, it has become so widely available and affordable that it is now seen as a necessity in the developed world. A car (or two) is the second-biggest investment a family makes – only the family home takes higher priority.

The love affair with the car continues. Adverts equate choice of car with lifestyle, love, family and prestige. The company car is more than transportation;

it is a statement of the rank achieved within the corporate hierarchy. The car holds a revered status and owning one is seen as an unalienable right. It is assumed that it is the responsibility of governments to build roads to accommodate demand. Taxes on cars and fuel are politically sensitive. They rise, but not by too much, because so many of the electorate would be affected.

In the poorer countries, owning a car is one of the main aspirations to be satisfied as disposable income grows. The potential world community of car owners is huge, as the poor seek to catch up with the developed world. There seems to be an enormous business opportunity for the car industry.

The car industry is already huge and the players are big – they have to be, in order to enter and stay in the game. They have a history, reputation and legacy from over a hundred years of development. Each model stays on the road for 20 years or more. If problems come to light in the design of a car that is built and sold today, the hit could be taken long into the future. This means that cars evolve, with each model being an improvement on the one before. Refinement upon refinement might be added, but nothing too risky that departs from a tested winning formula (in both technical and marketing terms). This is both strength and vulnerability as the industry enters the 21st century.

A key factor that has caught the attention of governments – and, to a lesser extent, the consumer – is the environmental impact of the car. Indifference on the part of the car owner is understandable. It is a truism that the impact of one car causes little damage, but, as those who live in big cities know, a million cars together can be a terrible beast, causing heavy smog and choking fumes.

Our governments therefore act by setting pollution standards to which the industry must respond in order to sell their product. The only time that the consumer need get involved is if the car fails its annual inspection and remedial action is required. Exhaust gases are a tangible negative and action is being taken. The wider environmental impacts – such as dealing with cars once they end their useful lives – are largely out of sight and are not given prominence.

One impact of the car, which is highly visible and which does not seem to bother most of us, is the increasing area of land dedicated to the car. This ranges from converting the front garden to a driveway to park a household's second or third car, to new motorways to relieve congestion. If a new road impacts a residential area, then resistance from the residents may be considerable. Where a new road crosses virgin countryside, the opposition is confined to a few farmers and environmental pressure groups. Some of these groups are radical and highly active, causing considerable expense and delay. The government – in fulfilling its duty to keep traffic flowing – eventually evicts the protesters. It is not long before the road becomes accepted as an integral part of the transport network, and the protest is soon forgotten. If we stop to think, we might find it odd that we let the car take precedence in this way.

When I used to go to Washington, DC, on business, I would stay at Tyson's Corner, a place with good access to freeways, plenty of restaurants and a good shopping mall. I would fly in and, at the airport, hire a car to use for the duration of my stay. This was the expected way to travel, and worked well, but the car-centric infrastructure of the city had its drawbacks. I like physical exercise, so I tried to go for a run, but found that there were no safe paths accessible directly from the hotel. I also tried to walk from my hotel with a colleague to a nearby restaurant for dinner (not for the health benefits, but so we could consume alcohol). I found that even a short walk could not be undertaken safely. It was as if pedestrians did not exist. In the United States, the car's voracious appetite for land has been allowed free rein. The car infrastructure works, but we must decide if this is what we really want for our communities.

A contrasting place is Venice, in Italy, a beautiful city crammed into a small geographical space. The streets are narrow and everything is close to everything else. Listening to the morning rush-hour traffic through an open window as you wake, all you hear is the clatter of feet punctuated by the odd small service vehicle. I also observed people going to the opera in the evening. They arrived on foot, wearing exceptionally expensive-looking coats. Perhaps this was just Italian chic, but the thought occurred to me that the coat was a replacement for a shiny expensive car and served exactly the same purpose: a show of wealth. The design of Venice derives from a shortage of space, but we should consider drawing our communities together in this way by deliberate design, even when we have acres of space to play with.

The car in the developed world is an integral part of our society and a major industry, but there are big decisions coming up over its future. We have to decide what we want from the car in the 21st century.

The Market

For the sake of this brief analysis, I will segment the market into three. The first is evident: those people who need to get from one place to another. Some random examples are travelling salesmen, specialists such as surveyors or estate agents, pizza delivery drivers, or people with no other way to get to work or to their nearest shop. For this market, reliable and affordable transport is required. Purchases can be based on a straightforward cost-benefit analysis, balancing running costs (including fuel economy) with capital outlay and residual value figures. However, this segment is small. Most car purchase decisions cover more than a simple need for transportation.

The second segment is where the car is seen as an extension of the personality. It portrays the image and status to which the purchaser aspires. The fact that the chosen car will get you from A to B is an underlying assumption, of course, but the decision is based on factors such as the comfort of the ride, the quality of the stereo and how you will look arriving in it. The cost – including fuel economy – matters, but in this segment it is more to do with the features you can get within the budget you can afford. A cost comparison with other modes of transport is rare when deciding whether to make a purchase.

The third segment is leisure. Perhaps the car is 'needed' here because of leisure pursuits such as driving along rough tracks, which requires a rugged

4-wheel-drive vehicle. Perhaps an enthusiasm for caravanning or sailing guides the purchase decision to a car that tows well. It might simply be that driving and being seen in an open-top sports car is the owner's passion.

The market could be segmented in other ways. For example, there is a small group of customers who want to be – and appear to be – green. Another is commuting (where there are other options) – a major part of car usage and an area where policy can have an enormous effect. The point is that the market is only partly about transportation. It is perfectly valid for someone to want a car as a personality extension or for leisure pursuits, but this should be recognized as a discretionary expenditure. It is not a need, but a desire. This insight is obvious but worth making explicit as we consider the future of the car.

What Is Wrong?

The car is having a detrimental impact on the environment. The effects of pollution and carbon emissions have been given plenty of exposure. The future of the car has to include reducing and eventually eliminating these negative effects. Some of the actions required are discussed later in the chapter. I am confident that we will succeed in producing a clean and fully recyclable car. So we can address the symptoms. But we need to go deeper and decide whether we are content that the car retains the status it has acquired.

The car uses land that could be used in other ways. The car is not only hungry for space: it also kills pedestrians, cyclists, passengers and drivers. Perhaps these are inevitable consequences, inconvenient but unavoidable. There are other more indirect effects that undermine human society. People do not cycle very much because of a justifiable fear of cars. People do not walk as much as they should because our built environment is designed for the car. The space that roads and car parks take up separates homes, shops, schools and offices by distances that we are reluctant to tackle on foot. Why have we let the car take over in this way? The answer is that the car is like heroin. It fulfils a need so well that we tend to ignore the negative side effects, even though the long-term impact is so negative.

The car is much more than a transit box on wheels. It has become an extension to our personal living space. We can fill it with all sorts of just-in-case gear, relieving us of the decision to select what we need to carry with us. We can travel without needing to engage with other people, play our favourite music and sing along without embarrassment. We can, in effect, remain 'at home' until we have to open the car door and step out. The car is also a status symbol and has gained almost revered importance: parked outside, polished, discussed and admired. The car you drive – its colour, the age, the make – says something about you. Best of all, the road network on which we drive is free. Once we own a car, we can go anywhere at any time. In our lives, the car epitomizes freedom and our right to choose our own direction.

But who is the master? A Martian looking down on Earth might presume that the car was the principal species as it crawls over the globe. Man could be observed building more roads, car parks and freeways, working as a slave to the dominant car. When the car arrives in a new area, its network of roads spreads insidiously like some sort of fungus. Like any successful parasite, the car does not kill its host, because without an owner the car cannot exist. For each owner the car is an object of pride; even if the sum total of all this gleaming metal is gridlock, pollution and degradation in the quality of community life. If allowed to continue, the entire globe will be tarmac and car parks, with areas of intensive agriculture in between to grow biofuels to feed the car fleet. This might be a sustainable world from the car's perspective, but not a desirable one from a human viewpoint. This is an exaggeration, of course: the car is only an inanimate object of transportation. However, if you notice car adverts, listen to pop music or watch road movies, you will see that the car has a cult following that transcends its material value.

The Essential Need

Getting at the essential needs that cars satisfy is difficult. We easily become confused between the needs of humans and the requirements of the car. We have to clarify the human requirement and be uncompromising in eliminating the concept of a car having needs. A car is an inanimate object; full stop.

Humans have a need to get around. This is the transportation of a rather special package of biomaterial in safety and in comfort. Within our immediate vicinity, we can transport ourselves by walking. For the locality, there is the highly efficient machine of the bicycle. For longer distances, we need a transport infrastructure. Roads to carry motorized personal transportation (the car) are best for unique point-to-point travel. For regularly repeated journeys, such as commuting to work, it makes sense from a systems viewpoint to design the infrastructure and influence location choices by employers and employees in order to produce an efficient model in terms of fuel, time and land use. Collective arrangements are required to suit 70 kg cargoes, such as buses and trains.

If we define the need in this way, we get to the essentials of the need to travel. Policy can be used to satisfy this human need in an environmentally friendly and human-centred way. The issues of the car as a personality extension, status symbol or leisure pursuit should not be ignored, but taken as secondary. If we insist on getting the provision of the essential need right – and do not allow the secondary needs to get in the way as we do so – then we have a recipe to put the car in its rightful place.

A number of people will feel threatened by my definition of the essential need. Proud car owners will feel under attack, car commuters will be wondering how they will get to work, and parents will be wondering how they can get their children safely to school on time and do the weekly shopping. These are very real concerns that need to be addressed, but unless we can first loosen the stranglehold that cars have on urban society, we are prevented from making real progress on developing the alternatives. We have to endure the cold turkey symptoms of withdrawal before we can appreciate the benefits of cities with fewer cars.

Taxes

Taxes will be an important mechanism in smoothing the transition to clean cars. Taxes on fossil fuels should rise as high as politically acceptable until, eventually, such fuels are eliminated. This is only part of the adaptation required. There is a wider role for taxation in regulating the future of the car.

Instead of increasing road capacity to counter gridlock, we can adopt policies that will solve the cause, escalating the costs of motoring way beyond the modest increases that the rising cost of fuel brings. The combination of taxation and stringent environmental regulation will reduce the number of discretionary and wasteful journeys. In the longer term, lifestyle choices will be influenced. More people will choose to use the car less, or not at all. People will be cajoled off the streets and onto the trains, buses, trams and cycle paths, and, if our policies are carefully framed, we will come to appreciate the healthier lives we will live as a result.

One result will be that the relatively poor will not be able to afford to drive. We should resist the demand for subsidized car ownership for the most vulnerable and invest in effective mass-transit systems. The choices people make about where to live will be influenced by the issue of transport provision far more than they are now. In selecting sites for affordable housing, proximity to transportation should be a prime factor. The business case for small local shops also starts to look stronger (and will look even better when we change our policy towards food distribution along the lines outlined in Chapter 15).

Bringing in heavy taxes on cars quickly and in isolation would lead to ghettos that are car-free for no other reason than that the residents cannot afford them. This would be unacceptable. We have to ensure our policy uses the tax receipts to invest heavily in better public transport. A delay in delivering these better services would be politically and socially dangerous. To establish the required infrastructure in parallel with increasing taxes will require borrowing heavily against future receipts, or even over-investing from other budgets.

There is a very real danger of a subculture of the car-less arising, which feels disenfranchised. This need not be so, if changes occur across all levels of society. The more affluent will be able to afford the increased costs, but they will also see changes. As local government levy escalating taxes on car parks, businesses will find it is cost-effective to reduce the size of their car parks and wean staff from cars to other options. Companies will locate their facilities near to good mass-transport links and be proactive in influencing community design that integrates commercial and residential areas connected by safe cycle routes. Even those who do not choose energetic ways of getting to work can enjoy the pleasure of reading their favourite magazine on their way to work using good public transport.

If the road network remained free and the car parks remained cheap, then the rich who continued to drive on the less congested roads would be envied, and resented. If they pay heavily for the privilege – and clear action is taken to divert investment into alternatives – then using cars less can permeate across society without being divisive. We have a choice: to stay a slave to the car, or put it in its rightful place through carefully targeted investment and taxation.

The Future

The energy crunch will force us to act. As environmental damage becomes more evident, I predict that the 'cool' image of many cars will be undermined. Like the cigarette, which once was a fashion accoutrement, the gas-guzzler car will become a socially unacceptable habit. Driving a green car will become the fashionable thing to do, but the changes will go deeper than this. Governments will have a pressing need to act and the mandate to do so. We can expect the position that the car holds in society to change.

Driving up the cost of motoring as a single-strand strategy would be divisive. We need to add in a commitment to other transport options and policies that reduce the need to travel. These include more bus lanes, more road charging for city centres and peak periods, larger car-free zones, better cycling networks separated from car traffic and high taxation on parking spaces.

Where I live in Finland, I have observed a new roundabout being built. This could have been a simple piece of road construction but has been complex and time-consuming. The reason is that a complete network of cycle paths has also been built underneath, requiring a series of bridges and subways. These separate the cycles from the cars in well-landscaped routes that are safe and pleasant to use. The solution looks more like a cycle network to which a roundabout has been added than vice versa. The roundabout will help the flow of cars, but the main time, effort and expense has gone into improving the safety and utility of the cycling network. Finland gives the bicycle the priority it deserves. If such policies are widely adopted, then the car will become less attractive and the alternatives will become more attractive.

Whereas lifestyle gurus now exhort us to take up sport (by driving to activity A, B or C) their message will change to using the energy of our own muscles to take us from one place to another as an integral component of our lives. It will not happen quickly, but the more people rebel against the dominance of the car, the less support there will be for car-friendly policies. The focus of transportation will shift from cars to people.

It may become almost impossible to own a car if you live in a city, and unnecessary if you live within a community. Rambling suburbs built around cars instead of people will lose their appeal. As the fashion shifts, other community models will become more appealing, forcing us to make a conscious choice about modes of transport.

Having separated us from the need to own a car, I predict that governments will be supportive of door-to-door buses, taxis and hire cars and that these will remain strong businesses. The car as a leisure pursuit or status symbol will, on the other hand, become an expensive luxury.

There will, of course, continue to be people who live in remote locations, such as farmers, who are beyond the reach of collective transport provision.

These people will need personal transportation but our future car fleet will be running on renewable fuel sources. We can assume a farmer, or anyone with a remote property, will have, for example, the space for an additional solar array large enough to charge up an electric vehicle capable of moderate journeys. Such investment will be a necessary cost of living in remote locations.[2] But when rural residents enter urban areas, they should expect exactly the same restrictions as urban residents.

Perhaps I am being reckless in my predictions and allow wishful thinking to intrude, but if we adopt the approach I propose, the potential benefits to society will, I believe, be worth the pain of the implementation. However, the ingrained mindset we have from a century dominated by the car will be hard to overcome.

I recognize that the views I express are extreme in comparison with the general attitudes of modern society across both the developed world (where car ownership is widespread) and the developing world (where owning a car is a common aspiration). When our engineers deliver a truly green car, the pressure for reform may abate and we allow the car to retain its place in society. This is a debate in which we must decide the future we want for society. I have made my views plain and will campaign for a society that regards the car with less veneration. Meanwhile, I will continue to use my car – where the journey requires it – but I will also support collective measures that restrict my use of it and reduce my 'need' to have one. If, despite this, I am to continue owning a car in the future, then I want it to be a truly green model.

Leading Adaptation in the Car Industry

There is a difficult period of transition looming over the car industry as the Sustainable Revolution gathers pace. In the developed world, I predict there will be a fight over market share in a contracting market. The costs of car ownership which are outside the control of the car companies will rise substantially. Fuel prices will rise, due both to increases in the price of oil and the escalating taxes that governments will impose. The tax burden will extend beyond the annual licence to expanded road-charging schemes and parking restrictions and charges. To compound the car industry's problems, regulation on emissions and responsibility for the whole life cycle of products will get progressively tighter.

For an industry already saddled with a legacy of liabilities this will be tough. The dinosaurs of the 20th-century car industry may not survive, but there are great opportunities for companies that can adapt quickly and exploit them, but not without taking risks. I suggest that breaking free from the legacy of the existing models and production methods is where the greatest potential resides.

The cars of the 21st century will need to break with tradition. We already have the technology, but putting it into an affordable mass-produced car will take a huge effort. Ultralight, strong bodies made from carbon fibre are standard in racings cars; this needs to be scaled up to the mass market. The core automotive components need to be fully recyclable, or designed to be reconditioned and reused in new models. All the internal trim and detailed ergonomic features should be either recyclable or totally biodegradable. Biofuels, electricity or even hydrogen (provided we can overcome the handling problems) can provide the power. A hybrid between biofuel and electricity is, perhaps, the current favourite to win, using electric motors and either an engine or fuel cell, but all options should remain open.

DESIGN CHALLENGE: A CAR FOR THE 21ST CENTURY

Design a low-emission car that is fully recyclable and powered from renewable energy sources with the following characteristics:

- carbon fibre as the main structural component;

- hybrid power using electricity supplemented by a liquid biofuel;

- standardized basic operating parts;

- simplicity of the final product in terms of maintenance and use;

- a manufacturing process designed for small production facilities and which can be easily replicated;

- cabin fittings to be fully biodegradable and easily changed or updated;

- ease of customization to the body and internal cabin designed into the production process, where this does not compromise function; and

- a whole lifecycle model where refurbishment is simple and core components can either be reconditioned or recycled.

The situation has some parallels with that which Henry Ford faced a century ago. In the early 20th century, an affordable car did not exist. In the early 21st century, we do not have a truly green car. For the existing car industry to take the lead, it will require the allocation of considerable capital. The investment will also need to be ring-fenced into a separate division that is insulated from the ingrained habits of the past, and which operates under a new brand. Initially, this will be to attract the early green adopters, but it will also shelter the main brand from the inevitable teething problems. Later, as the models prove to be effective and reliable, they can be rebadged with the famous marques of the past.

We will also see new enterprises, backed by venture capitalists, entering the car business. As the Sustainable Revolution takes hold, a huge flow of funds will be chasing a limited number of good opportunities. As in the dot.com era, these funds will not be risk-averse (unlike the bankers supplying investment capital to the old car giants). It might require an alliance of venture capitalists and specialist investment funds, because the amount of capital required will be substantial. A half-hearted attempt will be doomed to failure. However, the surge of interest and sales that Toyota has enjoyed from its Prius model will be magnified ten times over for the corporation that delivers the true 21st-century green car.

The leader will, of course, be looking to build and then defend its position. An extensive family of patents is likely to be key. Production equipment that is highly specialist and complex (but also easy to operate) will provide a barrier to other companies. There could be a small number of high-value components – such as a central-process controller – over which tight control of the technology and manufacturing can be maintained. Otherwise, the design should be suitable for local production with a look and feel that can be customized for the local market.

The opportunity needs investment in the development of new processes. The focus on innovation will be in the scaling up of existing leading-edge capabilities and driving down the production costs of capabilities not used so far in the mass-production car market. Marketing should focus beyond the energy crunch, initially picking up the small premium green market, but poised to exploit the surge of interest following the Sustainable Revolution. Early sales will be at low volume, but the ability to scale up quickly will be a crucial part of the business plan. A model of multiple smaller production facilities that are clones of the pilot facility would support this strategy well.

The green sales pitch will apply not only to the product, but also to applications for government support and permission to enter foreign markets. Considerable support and cooperation can be expected, perhaps including grants, soft loans and even subsidies. In terms of accepting these, companies must be careful not to cede control or release technology except under robust licensing arrangements.

In today's market, the opportunity described above looks lukewarm. The product will appeal to a small segment that is willing to pay a premium for a green image. This will not give a sufficient return on investment. The early sales will build image, iron out defects and reduce the cash-burn rate, but will not deliver profits. Waiting for the Sustainable Revolution will require prudent investment in the technology and processes, patience and deep pockets. After the energy crunch, sales and profits will boom. The lead will be unassailable for many years. Henry Ford dominated the mass-production car market for perhaps 15 years before his competitors became a real threat. I suggest that a company with the ambition, foresight and capital to develop and launch a truly green car may be able to dominate the 21st-century car industry. Whether this can last for as long as 15 years in our fast-paced world, we will have to wait and see.

13 Global Manufacturing Renaissance

Globalization has squeezed manufacturing to deliver ever more cost savings. Advances in technology have been immense, but any commercial advantage is soon eroded as the improved capability diffuses quickly through the industry. The current intense rivalry means that manufacturing appears to be an unattractive industry. As the Sustainable Revolution takes hold, I predict it will go through a renaissance.

A superficial look at manufacturing in the developed world indicates a model of production excellence. Factories have become increasingly automated and ever more efficient at the linear process of converting inputs to outputs. They have also become bigger, as companies exploit economies of scale; and leaner, with supplies arriving according to just-in-time models, all facilitated by advances in IT systems.

One way to continue the relentless search to reduce costs is through acquisition, with multinational corporations taking over national companies. This can lead, for example, to production concentrated on one site to serve the whole European market with the same generic product, rebadged as required. The acquired national brand becomes just a badge stuck on the final product as it comes off the production line. Choosing where to locate these huge production facilities is a complex mix of economic and political issues. Multinational companies are looking for the least-cost package, balancing factors such as cost of labour with government grants and transportation costs.

Automation is another way to reduce costs. In a well-known joke, the factory of the future is described as being staffed fully by robots and machines apart from one man and a dog. The man is to comply with legislation, which says that there must be a person on site in case of an emergency. The dog is there to stop the man touching anything. I first heard this amusing quip many years back, but it looks less like a joke now. Manufacturing facilities without human workers will become commonplace in my lifetime.

In this overview of manufacturing, the environment has not been mentioned once. It is a point of detail; a body of legislation to be complied with; hardly worth noting at the strategic level. This is how it should be.

Living within the constraints of the environment should be an accepted fact of doing business. Unfortunately it is not, at least not yet. This means that manufacturing will enter a transitional period as the Sustainable Revolution bites. We can expect this to be highly disruptive and challenging for management. It will also be highly profitable for the businesses that place the right bets early and invest for the future beyond the transition.

During the transition, the environment will be prominent on the corporate radar, but it will then drop back to the operational level as the new reality beds in.

Manufacturing in Tune with the Environment

Pre-industrial man did not know it, but he used a system that has been called by those who have rediscovered it 'cradle-to-cradle' production. This is closed loop processes in which the product is recycled when it finishes its useful life into materials that can go into building the next product.

For early man, he derived all the inputs to the things he made from the natural world. These were returned to nature when the product came to the end of its useful life. The only lasting physical evidence of his presence is a few tools made from flint, some bones and perhaps monuments such as Stonehenge – a stone circle in southern England built over 3,000 years ago. He would not have recognized the significance of the fact that he lived a sustainable lifestyle. It was innate and natural. The environment did not need managing; it was just there.

Industrial man carried on doing what he had always done and continued to ignore the environment, operating on a much larger scale and introducing substances alien to nature. As we enter the 21st century, we are starting to really notice the impact. Our first reaction is to legislate against activities proven to be harmful. We will have to move beyond this first primitive step to a society that is in tune with the environment. Cradle-to-cradle is a good metaphor for the way we will manufacture products in our future industrial society.

In cradle-to-cradle production, the aim is to eliminate waste through good design. The core concept is that our modern world should contain two manu-facturing cycles. The first runs on biomass. The other cycle runs on technical mass.[1] The former has existed as long as life has existed; the latter includes all those substances produced by man and not found in nature (or not in the form we use them).

The key principle that gives the model such power is to retain a separation between the two cycles. Goods that are made fully with biomass can easily be recycled by natural processes. Goods made from technical mass can be recycled back into other goods. Finished goods may contain components from both cycles but at the end of the product's life they can be dismantled and separated. There is a crossover, of course, between the cycles in that there is an initial extraction process for technical mass from a natural source, such as metal extracted from a naturally occurring ore. However, once a material enters the technical cycle, the expectation is that it stays there.

Products that contain an inseparable mixture of materials from the two cycles have been aptly named 'monstrous hybrids'.[2] In the early 21st century, such products are commonplace. We do not see them as monstrous because we are not tuned into the new way of living. When we have had enough of them, we just put them out with the garbage to be transported to a landfill site. Their monstrosity will only become evident as the actions proposed in this chapter start to shape our attitudes.

Cradle-to-cradle production is a complete change of attitude. It is not pollution reduction; it is the total elimination of waste. It is not down-cycling (where a product has a second, less valuable use before ending up in landfill); it is genuine recycling of materials in a way that could go on indefinitely. It also need not be a burden for industry; cradle-to-cradle production makes compliance with regulations irrelevant.

As an engineer, I was taught to deliver solutions in terms of a working product, bridge or building. The concept of cradle-to-cradle solutions was not in the curriculum. It took me some time to accept the concept but – like so many profound insights – once I did, it became obvious. I expect many others to have an initially indifferent response, so it will take time before it is regarded as normal practice.

The transition period will be challenging. Successful businesses will need to understand the concept and look for a safe (in business terms) way ahead. When an opportunity arises to make progress, and which reduces costs, clearly it should be taken; but even where costs increase (provided the increase is not too significant) that, too, should be taken for the future advantage it will give. Moving too fast might be dangerous if it risks undermining the current business with respect to unreformed competitors. But those 'blind' players who are simply responding to increasingly tight environmental regulation are taking the greatest risk, and may not survive the Sustainable Revolution.

Eventually the linear model of production and supply will be replaced by cradle-to-cradle recycling with few exceptions.

Searching for Enduring Value

In addition to cradle-to-cradle production, there will be other changes coming through, such as a drive to close down the global trade in waste which I predict in Chapter 16. For multinational manufacturing companies, an advantage based on the exploitation of lax regulations (with regard to the environment or work-force) in some countries will become increasingly difficult to defend.

As companies search for ways to deliver enduring value (and enduring profits), there will be a change of emphasis. Patentable innovation and good design will remain important, and will be coordinated at global level, but the commercial dynamics will favour smaller localized production.

This will have the additional benefit of improving responsiveness and bringing the company closer to the customer. The ability to respond to changing needs and customization to suit the local market will be valuable attributes. It will also be profitable to cement the relationship with the customer by drawing the customer into the production process, much as Valtra currently do with their tractors.

Valtra is the leading tractor manufacturer in the Nordic countries, with operations extending worldwide. Part of the company's philosophy is to custom-build tractors against a customer's order and to an individual specification. The customer, together with the sales person, decides on the tractor's specification, choosing from up to half-a-million different combinations.[3]

Valtra also offers customers the opportunity to visit their Suolahti factory in Finland to observe their own tractor being built. Thousands of customers accept this invitation each year. Such close customer contact engenders very strong loyalty to the company and the brand.

Where globalization and the Internet have commoditized many products – making sales an impersonal transaction based on price – the new business landscape will make it easier to build long-term relationships with customers.

Global activity should focus on innovation in both products and production methods. Design should also be sourced globally, looking for the best concepts from a diverse range of social contexts. This will be the new economy of scale, leveraging innovation and design. It will also be defendable in the markets of countries with good governance using patents and copyright.

Production facilities should be small and easily replicated so they can embed into customer localities. They need to be designed to be responsive and flexible to allow adaptation to local vagaries. Although the output will appear to be highly differentiated, there will be considerable economies from standardization of the underlying technology. In a physical and marketing sense, these will be local products for the local market, but the intellectual know-how will be global.

As the transition to cradle-to-cradle production gathers pace, there will be many 'blind' players acting in a responsive manner. There will be huge opportunities to step ahead of them and trip them up in ways that will not be seen as underhand.

Manufacturing Based on True Recycling

So far I have outlined revolutionary change in production processes, but this is just the start. The whole concept of production of goods and their consumption by customers is set to change.

The premise I use in predicting this further transformation is that the recycling of all goods has become the norm. This is completely out of step with today's throwaway society, so it may be too radical for early and quick adoption, but understanding it will ensure that the limited action we take now is compatible with the future envisaged.

Current methods of disposing of unwanted goods include taking it to the dump, dropping it off at a charity recycling centre or paying someone to take it away. If a new appliance is ordered, the old one can be taken away by payment of an additional fee. The system has a natural inertia that hinders recycling. The consumer incurs additional expense to get rid things at the end of their useful life. Regulations require that it is disposed of diligently, but the market says to lose it as cheaply as possible.

Compare this with the lifecycle of a beer bottle in Helsinki.

All domestic Finnish beer is bottled in identical bottles; only the label is different. A deposit of 10 cents is charged on each bottle at the point of sale. At every supermarket and sizeable sales outlet there is a machine that takes the empty bottles. The process is totally automated. The customer puts the bottles (which can include wine bottles, certain standard plastic bottles and aluminium cans) in the machine and a slip of paper is printed out with a bar code. This can either be claimed for cash in the shop or scanned at the checkout and the value subtracted from the shopping bill.

This system is so ingrained in Finnish society that social mechanisms have evolved to take advantage of it. One of these is an army of bottle collectors who can be seen walking the streets and checking public places (including waste bins) and gathering up the bottles for the extra income they provide. These people are not looked down on, but are simply accepted for the part they play in society. I assume that they are the less well off, old or unemployed but they do not look desperate: many look well dressed. Many are retired people who enjoy the activity and take pride in doing something that is useful, as well as welcoming the extra income.

In Finland, there are many events when drinking outdoors is part of the occasion such as midsummer and the first of May, but it seems that every Saturday night can be such an occasion. There is an associated behaviour that – to a foreigner – looks odd. Empty beer bottles (or champagne bottles for that matter) are put neatly on the kerb or in doorways. They are not thrown or tossed, but carefully placed.

Before the morning these bottles will have been gathered up by the deposit collectors. If you look carefully you might spot, whilst the party is still in full swing, the bottle collectors sliding in like ghosts to gather the crop before anyone else. No one employs these people or organizes them. They exist because the system exists. It has become socially acceptable to leave an empty bottle in the street as part of a highly effective system of recycling.

The market mechanism applied to Finnish beer bottles means the bottle is reused again and again and again. The system is complex but the key to implementation is easy to find. Setting a residual value to the bottle, which can be claimed by anyone, is all that is needed.

The same system could apply in principle to all our goods and products; all that is needed is a system of setting a residual value. The rest of the system would then arise as a consequence.

The Residual-Deposit Model

A model we can apply to all goods sold is based on the principle of a residual deposit reclaimable when the item is returned. At the end of its useful life, the owner has an incentive to put the unwanted item into the recycling system. If the owner is too lazy – or the amount set for the deposit is an insufficient incentive – others can step in to claim the deposit.

It is necessary to define in outline the elements of how such a system could operate before the implications become clear. We need to set a value to the deposit, have control measures and ensure that the system is not just an overhead, but provides an incentive or commercial advantage to all those taking part.

The amount of the deposit should offer sufficient incentive and reflect the cost of recycling. It could be charged at the point of sale, increasing the sale price, or recorded as a liability against the manufacturer. My detailed proposal is based on the latter, with a government agency setting the residual liability and acting as the deposit-clearing service.

Each product would be recorded on the agency's database with the agreed deposit and serial number. When the product is returned to one of the recycling players, the value of the deposit is paid to whoever returns it, reimbursed by the government clearing service, which, in turn, invoices the manufacturer for all the deposits claimed over a given period (plus a service charge). It would be in the interests of the manufacturer to ensure that the correct details of all products sold are entered into the agency database to prevent fraud. The control process may seem cumbersome but can be almost totally automated, and once established, should be easy to operate.

A further control would be needed to guard against manufacturers who go out of business. It would be a requirement to take out an insurance policy to cover the residual liability of products still in society. For imported goods, the importer would have to guarantee the deposit through insurance or bond. An incidental consequence would be resistance to the importation of goods, particularly low-quality goods with a short life and hard-to-recycle components. These will attract a potentially expensive liability on the importer, thus further reinforcing the market for goods produced locally.

Recycling would be carried out by government centres, independent operators and the manufacturers, with government centres given the mandate to accept anything offered. If they built up a store of hazardous or hard-to-recycle products, then action could be taken against the manufacturer to claim such additional costs over and above the deposit. A government agency, with an overview from a network of recycling centres, would spot systemic problems with a company's products and have the evidence to take appropriate action.

Commercial players would enter if they believed they could make a profit through more efficient recycling. The output from the process of true recycling would be useful and valuable material, much more so than the output of our current valiant efforts to extract useful material from the appalling mixed waste we produce. Independent commercial players may offer more than the deposit for some items in order to secure the material content.

Not-for-profit recycling organizations may find advantages that go beyond the profit to be made. The disassembly of a wide range of products is likely to be harder to automate than the manufacturing process; so recycling centres are likely to be labour intensive and, therefore, may usefully employ disadvantaged people as a direct social benefit. This would be a progression from today's charity recycling centres and would be much more effective and profitable.

Another link in the system would be an army of freelance deposit collectors, formed spontaneously, which would fill in any holes between the customer and the recycling centres. We would just need to leave our unwanted items outside for them to be spirited away.

The main recycling player to emerge from establishing such a system is the manufacturer. They would be in the strongest position to make best use of the discarded products. Parts could be reused or refurbished, especially if this is kept in mind during product design. The manufacturer would also avoid the administrative charge levied by the government centres. They would simply pay deposits direct, and update the records in the government database. The benefits of good cradle-to-cradle design will be palpable. It is also likely to produce a very close relationship with the customer where the company can seek to use deposit reclaim in order to sell a replacement item as one linked transaction.

The New Manufacturing Environment

Having defined the residual-deposit model, we can identify a new relationship between manufacturing and consumption with a number of important behavioural changes.

The deposit will be set at a higher value for products that are hard to recycle. To reduce this liability, business will have to design for recycling. A fixed deposit will lose value over time. So products that remain in useful service for decades will incur a minimal liability on the company. Products designed to last just a few years before needing to be replaced will be penalized (unless the business plan is built on refurbishing/recycling on a regular basis and the product is designed accordingly).

Old products will have real value for the technical mass they contain, particularly for the manufacturer, who knows exactly how to get back the material with the minimum of effort (because the product has been designed that way). For quality well-designed products, the residual value will exceed the deposit, so increasingly the state-sponsored deposit system will contract as cradle-to-cradle production becomes universal. In a world of tight commodity markets, we can expect payments that are higher than the deposit to be offered for many items in order to secure access to the materials they contain.

The residual-deposit model rewards good cradle-to-cradle methods and penalizes inferior production. A manufacturer who stays with 20th-century production techniques producing monstrous hybrids will attract a high deposit, incur high recycling costs and high insurance premiums.

A further point of interest arises if we compare a sale in this system with a lease. We see that the two are not so different. With a lease, the leasing company has to consider what to do with the product after the customer has decided to terminate the agreement or upgrade. A sale with a residual deposit is very similar. More customers will be drawn to leasing, instead of owning, items, such as home appliances.

If leasing takes over from sales, then that would give companies a completely open agenda to work out the best refurbishment or recycling plan. The 'best' would be the balance between customer satisfaction and profitability. I have omitted to include environmental impact. This is deliberate. The future manufacturing industry will have zero environmental impact embedded as an operational constraint. This constraint will apply across society, including water supply, agriculture and the handling of waste, as the following chapters explain.

14 Our Thirst for Water

Water, water, every where,
Nor any drop to drink.

The Rime of the Ancient Mariner, 1798[1]

The Ancient Mariner could see the huge quantities of water we have on our planet but the salt water in our oceans was of no help in slaking his thirst. Fortunately, planet Earth has a very effective system of evaporating this water to fall on the land as fresh, clean rain. We can find the water we need in the nearest lake, river or stream. If we need more, then we only have to sink a well or borehole into the ground – except in the driest of places – to find clean water.

However, we are now going further than using the water provided by nature; we are remodelling the hydrology of the Earth. Impressive civil engineering projects supported by powerful pumps are extracting, diverting and using increasing quantities of water. As an engineer, I marvel at what we can achieve, but as a geographer I worry that there will be repercussions from this destruction of the natural hydrology.

We are also returning more and more water to the natural system in a state that nature finds hard to handle. This polluted water ends up in rivers, lakes, ground water and the Earth's ultimate reservoir, the ocean.

In researching this book, I had no intention of writing much about the oceans. As I put my ideas into words, I came to realize that I had fallen into the same trap as most of mankind; I was not giving them the attention they deserve.

The oceans are largely out of sight and out of mind, a huge area from which we pull out fish to eat, and the edges of which we use for holidays. But if we allow the 20th-century attitude towards the sea to follow through to its logical conclusion, fishing and swimming will no longer be safe. We use the oceans as a place to chuck anything we no longer need and want to get rid of, slowly converting our oceans from a biodiverse reservoir to a cesspool.

The oceans are a free resource that belongs to us all. That means that no one takes, or accepts, responsibility. Very little real effort is made to protect them.[2] If we were fish and breathed through gills, it would be different. As land animals, we are not in any imminent danger. It is enough to be confident that our drinking water will be clean through protecting our watersheds. We can also rely on the natural flow of water to clean our waste away. If nature cannot process it, it ends up eventually in the world's oceans.

An easy 'solution' is to claim that the oceans are self-cleansing; they certainly seem to be. For any one incident, dilution means that it soon becomes undetectable. The oceans are so vast that an entire year of effluent discharge by the industrialized world can be shunted off without causing measurable problems. Over 10 years, such pollution is still hardly detectable in remote parts of the ocean.

However, over 50, 100 or 200 years the sum total of the myriad discharges of substances alien to nature becomes increasingly apparent. At first, it is detectable but not a danger to human health, as we see with plastic particles spread widely across the oceans.[3] It then becomes a concern to health, as it is in the confines of the Baltic Sea.[4]

We are reaching the stage when we will ban fishing for human consumption across the world's oceans, starting with fish higher up the food chain, such as shark, swordfish and marlin, soon to be followed by tuna.[5] Logically, fishing bans will end up applying to the entire ocean, unless we drop our food safety standards.

Swimming in the sea will become a universal danger to health; as it already is in close proximity to some centres of population and industrial activity.[6] Sailing will still be a safe leisure pursuit but falling in will require emergency medical attention.

This dystopian description of the oceans is not fantasy. It is where we are heading, ever so slowly but ever so surely. It will be beyond our lifetimes when the problems become as bad as I have portrayed in the picture above, but that should not be used as an excuse for inaction.

When we stop polluting the land, we can wait a while and our hydrology will cleanse it for us. The oceans are different; there is not some other place the pollution can be shunted off to, unless we have patience. Over geological time, the Earth might well be able to cleanse the seas, confining the legacy of the 20th and 21st centuries to narrow toxic bands within the profiles of sedimentary rocks. However, we might need to wait many thousands of generations for that.

It is the fact that we cannot backtrack on polluting the oceans that is so dangerous. Link this with a time frame that will not hit hard anyone alive today, and we have the ingredients for an unstoppable disaster. We have to change our ways.

Water and Society

Water has always been vital to civilization, with wars fought over access to supplies. But, in the modern world, we have come to think that technology can deliver all the water we need whenever and wherever we need it. We are wrong; our thirst for water has to be satisfied by respecting the natural hydrology, connecting those who use water with its source and the place to which it returns.

The world's hydrology has always fluctuated: dryer years and droughts; rivers meandering along a slightly different course; the odd lake in very arid areas disappearing and reappearing from time to time. Man used to move to live where the local hydrology could support him, and then live within the constraints of the supplies available.

In dry areas, this meant adopting careful conservation measures supplemented by sinking a well and extracting the water needed for the family, but the method was a rope and bucket. Man borrowed water for his purposes on a scale that left the overall hydrology intact.

We started rather more fundamental interventions in the hydrology a long time ago: the Romans were adept at moving water to where it was needed by building aqueducts. The benefits of cleaner and healthier communities were the result, and any changes to the hydrology were localized and limited in scale.

Waste and water has been a recurring problem. John Snow deduced that water was the method of transmission of cholera, discovering that the London epidemic of 1854 was centred on one public water pump. He made the observation that separating clean and dirty water was vital to good health. An obvious and intuitive point perhaps, but scientific rigour was required to prove it. However, biopollutants such as human faeces are very easy for nature to deal with. A local problem with waste water soon works its way out of the system with distance and time.

So pre-industrial water use was an important issue and at times a source of conflict, but the overall system was not under threat. The industrial age started to dump large quantities of pollutants into the environment but also improved public health by eliminating many of the problems of the past. Abundant clean water could be provided by pumping out ground water using high capacity pumps from deep boreholes.

Sewers were also built to carry dirty water away from direct contact with the population, to be discharged somewhere downstream or into the sea. Thomas Crapper became famous for popularizing the flush lavatory to move our waste on the first leg of its journey into the sewage system. (Now, however, we should rethink whether using clean potable water to flush away waste is a sensible system.)

In the modern developed world, our capacity to control hydrology and obtain the water we need appears limitless. If we need more water, we simply invest more in infrastructure. If we find that our water is polluted, then we invest in transporting water from further away and/or install better filtration equipment. If all other options have been exhausted, we can fall back on desalinating sea water (using energy to do so). The strangest behaviour of all is society's demand for bottled water.

Bottled Water

In a country where the population does not have access to clean water, a market for bottled water makes sense. But the market for bottled water is mainly in developed countries with good water-supply systems. It is based on fashion, taste and perceived health benefits.

This business consumes considerable material resources and energy in terms of bottles and transportation. It is estimated that 154 billion litres of bottled water are sold globally each year, with US consumption alone requiring 1.5 million barrels of oil.[7]

Like most major Western cities, Helsinki consumes bottled water, including brands imported from France, but modern Helsinki does not have a water problem. In the late 19th century, Helsinki suffered from excessive use of the local groundwater, with wells drying up in the summer, and the ingress of pollution. Throughout much of the 20th century, water was pumped from the Vantaanjoki river using infrastructure first put in place in 1876. Now Helsinki gets its water from Päijänne Lake through a 120-km tunnel (constructed in 1982). The watershed is well protected and the water is clean. Helsinki has solved the problem of sustainable water supply.

In a blind tasting by some of Finland's top chefs, Helsinki tap water came out top, beating a number of brands of bottled water.[8] One Finnish company (Nordwater) has seen the potential but in a very unsustainable way, shipping 1.4 million bottles of tap water from its bottling plant in Helsinki to Saudi Arabia.[9] For Helsinki's own consumption, there is the potential to launch a truly sustainable brand of bottled water. Empty bottles with a well-designed logo could be sold to restaurants and consumers emphasizing the Finnish source. The bottles could be filled up from the tap and, after the initial production run and delivery, then they could be recycled indefinitely, incurring no further transportation overhead. Tourists would be reassured that the water is clean and – with clever marketing – the Finns might also take pride in drinking their own water.

Governments can be expected to wake up to the evident oddness of selling bottled water from distant sources. It is a prime target for increasing taxation revenue. This need not be a bureaucratic difficulty; perhaps water imported from abroad could be reclassified with low alcohol beverages and subject to the same taxation regime. Such a tax would only hit the more affluent and reflect rather better the total costs to society. It would have an additional effect of making people rather more concerned about the quality of their own local water supplies.

Water Supply

Nature's wonderful self-cleansing system, driven by the sun, warms the oceans causing evaporation. This later disgorges from clouds as rain. Provided that we keep our atmosphere clean, then the rain will be clean.[10] On hitting the ground, the water rejoins man's world, and whether it remains clean or not depends on us.

Some runs off quickly to join our surface hydrology. Where man has caused deforestation, this can happen too quickly, leading to the washing away of topsoil and flooding. Provided man retains a good balance of vegetation, it will flow off under control into our lakes and rivers and eventually back into the sea.

Some of the rainwater takes the slow route, draining down into the ground to replenish aquifers. This water may take hundreds of years to reach the sea, and is filtered through layer upon layer of permeable rock in doing so. Provided the water steers clear of man's activities, it remains clean and potable.

The best way that we can ensure that we have clean water to drink is to protect the watersheds that feed our reservoirs. This is an obvious point, but it is easily forgotten if our investment focus is on water treatment. We have learnt this lesson well in many places. US cities have estimated that every dollar invested in environmental protection could save between $7.50 and $200 on the cost of what would otherwise have to be spent on filtration and water-treatment facilities.[11]

The city of New York provides a good example. The city gets most of its water from the Catskill Mountains. In 1997, the city adopted a watershed management agreement. It had realized that it would need to act to preserve the quality of the city's drinking water. New water filtration plants would have cost $4–6 billion and incurred running costs of $250 million annually. Instead, under the agreement, the city decided to spend $250 million buying land to prevent development within the watershed and to pay farmers $100 million a year to minimize pollution.

The other easy source of clean water is groundwater. If the watershed is our water current account, then the aquifer is our deposit account. The level of the water in the aquifer has stabilized over thousands of years, with payments in matching payments out, averaged over the long term. In dry years, a net outflow from the aquifer keeps our rivers flowing. This is balanced by relatively wetter years when it is replenished. In this way, the aquifer has been providing resilience against short-term periods of low rainfall.

However, mankind is drawing excessively from the deposit account. The more we pump, the lower the levels of groundwater. In the 1960s, when London still had a lot of water-intensive industry, the groundwater level had dropped to 88 m below sea level. This clearly could not continue. Changing abstraction patterns have allowed much of this drop to recover. Ironically, one of the problems London now faces, as the water table returns closer to normality, is the threat to the foundations of buildings built during the era of excessive draw down.[12]

So if we overpump our aquifers, and then stop doing so, they will recover to former levels. But this is not a complete solution. One of the most important attributes of groundwater is its cleanliness. The natural filtration process that occurs as the water travels through the ground means that it is usually clean and safe as we draw it from the borehole. High up in the mountains and in our protected watersheds, the water entering the aquifer is clean, but much of the land that feeds water into the aquifer is occupied by man.

Water and Waste

Waste water also requires investment, but our focus is on removing it from our immediate environment, away from our living places, streets and local rivers. If the coast is nearby, then the cheapest solution is often to pump it out to sea through a pipe long enough that noticeable chunks do not arrive back onto local beaches. It is soon dispersed and gone.

Natural systems can eliminate man's biodegradable waste but long-lived pollutants, such as some chemicals and pesticides, pass into the aquifer. The legacy of man's lack of care takes time to appear in the borehole water, but when it does – prompting us to take action to stop the source pollution – it may take tens, hundreds or thousands of years for the aquifer to be washed through.

Often, it is tempting to put off long-term water-management issues such as aquifer degradation to another year, another decade or another generation. Fortunately, there are sensible ways forward that are feasible in the real world. Not making the extra effort to define them would be stupid. If we look at the alternatives carefully and decide not to act, that would simply be selfish, trading off less effort or investment now against the health of future generations.

I put forward three principles to ensure the sustainable use of the water, meshing the needs of man seamlessly with those of nature:

- live within the natural hydrology;
- do not put anything into the water system that nature cannot break down; and
- use market mechanisms to ensure that investment flows to where it can have the most effect.

Living within the Natural Hydrology

In the developed world, our expectation is that our house is connected to a water supply. We expect that it is reliable and that we pay for what we use. We have become disconnected from a feel for what water is available. This is illustrated well by a suburban response to a long spell of dry weather. The grass starts to go brown and the plants show signs of distress. Our response is to use the sprinkler and a watering can to keep the garden looking green and lush. Water from the tap is seen as a right, and the water company is responsible for keeping it flowing. If the water available to us was a finite quantity, then our attitude would be different.

Imagine a house standing alone on a rocky hillside without access to a municipal supply. Its only water supply is from a large tank that collects rainwater coming off the roof. There is no underground water available as the house is on solid granite that is not suitable for a borehole or well. The resident household needs to balance needs with the water available. When the tank is full – and rain is expected – then water can be used with gay abandon. During dry spells, more care is required. The priority is water to drink and cook. Grey water from washing is used for secondary purposes, such as watering plants and flushing toilets (or dry toilets are used, conserving yet more water). There are people who live like this in remote and arid locations.

With consumers out of touch with the source, the natural conservation response has been turned off. It is left to the local authorities to impose hosepipe restrictions and other measures. It is seen as their responsibility as suppliers, not ours as consumers. If we accept the principle of living within our natural hydrology, then we need to turn this around. We need to behave more like the resident of the isolated house on the rocky hill.

Being aware of the amount of water available should become second nature. In exceptionally dry weather, we should only water vulnerable plants, and then only in the evening when it will have most effect. If such dry periods became a regular occurrence, we should examine our plumbing, taking measures such as removing the bath and fitting a shower, collecting rainwater and recycling water from a primary to a secondary purpose. Where there is a swimming pool, it should only be filled when there has been plenty of rain and then should act as a reserve for use in exceptionally prolonged dry spells.

The example chosen is domestic, but the points raised apply to business, too. It is not sustainable to use greater quantities of water than the local hydrology can support. Eventually, nature or local government will force a reduction in consumption that could have a direct impact on the business. As local water supplies become stressed, the big industrial users will come under attack. This is a risk that business can avoid.

Coca-Cola is a good example of a water-intensive business operating in all corners of the globe. Water is the prime ingredient, requiring copious quantities of it, more than double the amount that ends up in the product due to bottle washing and pipe cleaning. Commercial economies of scale favour large production plants. This means that each plant has a heavy thirst for water.

Coca-Cola has been on the receiving end of accusations that it is aggravating the problem of scarcity of fresh water in arid areas such as parts of India. It is accused of depleting the local hydrology, thus depriving local residents of the water they need.[13] One response the company made was to improve efficiency so that less water is needed for every litre of product, but the effect is marginal.

In hindsight, Coca-Cola should have taken more care in designing its plants to fit within the local hydrology. Plants should have been located in areas with ample supply or, better still, smaller plants serving a local market. Smaller plants place less load on the hydrology and are seen to be using the water for local needs. Such plants also exploit other benefits of localizing production that will become increasingly valuable, such as minimizing transportation costs.

Coca-Cola has promised more effective action in India by building large rainwater storage capacity at existing plants, collecting rainwater during the monsoon to reduce its need to draw water from aquifers. There are many businesses that should consider this option. Rainfall harvesting could become widespread in any area where the capacity of the local hydrology is being stressed.

If Coca-Cola had fully embraced the principle of living within the local hydrology from the outset, then this would have influenced decisions over the size and location of bottling plants. Such an approach would have reduced risks to the company, ensured sustained long-term profitability and helped to burnish the company's image. Other water intensive industries should take note.

Protecting the Natural Water System

The second principle, that of not putting anything into the water system that nature cannot break down, is a sound way of protecting the natural hydrology. The challenge is how to enforce this in our world of chemicals, which are used widely in activities such as manufacturing, farming, cleaning and pest control. Our everyday lives in the developed world are full of chemical inputs.

Imagine we want to repaint the garden shed. We buy a tin of brown liquid and complete the job. There is a small amount left in the tin, which sits on a shelf in the shed for a while, but it is taking up space so we want to get rid of it. We could pour it down the drain; but, being conscientious, we read the label. It advises us not to empty it into watercourses or drains and that it must be disposed of properly (without saying what this means). We consider pouring it away behind the shed – but then that would pollute the garden – so we chuck it out with the garbage to go to a landfill site where it will eventually corrode and leak its contents. I wonder how many of us would take the tin to a specialist solvent recycling centre to seek their advice; and, if we did, whether they would know what to do with it.

Over time, the garden shed starts to rot and two or three decades later it, too, ends up in the landfill. The whole contents of the tin have ended up in the environment.

When we use chemicals and substances in our modern world, we must assume that they end up in the environment by one route or another. Strict regulation is one way to ensure proper disposal through processes designed to break them down into components that nature can handle. There might be some chemicals for which the only solution is a closed cycle from which they never escape. Such an approach is prone to failure and subject to the temptation of cutting corners if the costs are high and the unscrupulous or lazy can avoid being caught.

The only truly safe, sustainable solution is to eliminate such chemicals from society. If none are for sale then they cannot end up in the water system. This principle may take some time to gain wide acceptance, but its truism means that it should eventually prevail. There are other reasons for adopting this principle. For example, generating energy from sewage (Chapter 7) is easier in the absence of strong chemicals, and the resulting solid waste becomes a safe and saleable fertilizer.

There will be a number of apparently 'irreplaceable' substances and processes that will need to be exempt and subject to intrusive and rigorous inspection. In reality, these should be very few. I have enormous faith in the ability of our scientists and engineers to find alternatives, but we must be robust in countering the accountants who say it will cost too much.

Market Mechanisms

Water is usually provided either by a state utility or a private company. In both cases, water is seen as a need that must be met. It is left to other government departments to urge reductions in use in order to reduce the impact on the environment. The regulator of a privatized water industry will also take a wider view of the overall impact of water usage. There will be many cases when investing in reducing demand is more cost effective than investing in increasing supply, but if it is the customer who has to make the investment, then there needs to be an incentive.

In considering the situation where demand outstrips sustainable supplies, the initial reaction is to consider investing in more supply infrastructure, such as additional reservoirs. An alternative is investing in efficiency measures for users which will close the imbalance, such as fitting all houses with short-flush toilets. An easy way to start would be to insist on improved water efficiency in new developments through the planning system. The water company could also seek to persuade the regulator that investments that the company makes in supporting efficiency measures by customers can be recouped through higher water charges. Such thinking is part-way to a sustainable solution; however, we can set up a market to do the job for us.

For a water-supply market to work, we should separate charging into two components. The first is delivery of the service of water supply. If a state utility is the agent, then it is given a budget. If it is a commercial company, a contract is agreed to operate and maintain the infrastructure. As for the customer, this part of the charge is fixed.

The second component is the water, which is charged at a price that is allowed to float. If there is more water available than demand, the market price of the water will be zero. If there is a shortage, the price starts to climb. If there is a severe shortage, the price could rise substantially. This water income should be ring-fenced for investment in either the water supply or efficiency measures, such as helping the poor to invest in more water-efficient plumbing. The main point is that there is a clear market signal and incentive to behave like the householder in the isolated house on the rocky hill.

In order to operate, the market would need a figure for sustainable water usage within a particular network. This would not have to be set in real time but be changed in steps from month to month or season to season. An independent committee, including expert hydrologists, could set the water-extraction limits, meeting for each decision and publishing minutes to show transparency.

The behaviour that would follow would make a direct linkage with the water available. For example, someone owning a swimming pool would be forced to consider the timing of when to fill it; the market would push towards doing so when water is free and the reservoirs are full: clearly the right outcome.

Like all efficient markets, investment would flow to where it would have the most effect. In wet regions, people would not invest in rain harvesting or water recycling; where water is in short supply, they would. Markets can be quite sophisticated in looking forward and investing early when shortages are likely. A bureaucratic planning process relying on rules and regulations would find this very hard but, in theory, a market can do this with ease.

Where a private company is contracted to supply the service, a clause could be included in which leaks belong to them. When the price of water is zero, they pay nothing. When the price climbs, they pay for all the water they leak. This is a sound commercial basis for making decisions, balancing the cost of fixing leaks with the benefits.

One assumption for such a market to operate is that water usage is being metered reliably on a regular basis. If the metering system worked in real time, it could also be used for automated and rapid leak detection, saving yet more water. Affordable water meters that can be read automatically and remotely is a business opportunity waiting to be exploited.

We need to get used to thinking about our water needs in relation to the sustainable hydrology: our water bills will be the stick and the prospect of lower bills the carrot.

Connecting us all to our local hydrology, ensuring we do not put it under too much stress or pollute it, is the basis for sustainable water supply.

15 Safe, Sustainable Agriculture

Agriculture will become increasingly important as we move to a more sustainable world. Not only is the world's hunger for food rising as the population continues to expand, but the demand for non-food agricultural products, such as biofuels, will soar. Crops are also the source of a range of perfect manufacturing materials for a sustainable world, such as timber, cotton and flax, which combine excellent characteristics with easy recycling.

As we build a sustainable society, we will become more dependent on agricultural produce. The pressure to convert more and more natural land to agriculture will increase. This will be exasperating, as we will require yet more agricultural capacity to replace fossil fuels used within the agricultural industry itself. Farm machinery will require biofuel and we will have to grow crops without being able to increase yields using fertilizers derived from fossil fuel. We will have to find a balance between protection of the remaining natural land and satisfying our increasing demand.

The prime agricultural product is, of course, food. When food supplies are tight, short-term needs will always win out over long-term considerations. This makes sustainable agricultural solutions particularly hard to implement in many countries or regions. But it is imperative that we do so, or the long-term damage will lead to even greater hardship in the future.

There has been a tendency to regard agriculture as a stand-alone industry, forgetting that agriculture is an extension of the world's natural systems. We therefore focus on economic efficiency, selecting crops using profitability as the main guide, and maximizing yields with huge fields devoid of hedges to minimize 'wasted' productive space. A short-sighted, short-term profit focus is afflicting agriculture. We see land that is exhausted from single cropping or which has been destroyed because the local ecosystem or hydrology has been disrupted, and health problems from diseases such as BSE.[1] The farming methods that cause these problems have derived from 20th-century industrial practice. This lack of respect for our relationship with nature can be expected to fail over the long term.

Fortunately, many farmers do connect with the natural world. They understand the value of mixed agriculture, crop rotation, and appreciate the role of hedgerows and natural habitats. They can avoid the impact and expense of insecticides through leveraging natural processes, such as influencing the distribution of natural predators. They can use nitrogen-fixing crops in rotation with other crops to replace the use of fertilizers that are derived from processes based on fossil fuels. Research will continue into cereal crops that we plant once and then harvest each year without ploughing and replanting, thus preserving the soil and reducing the use of energy-intensive machinery.

It is not only farming operations that need to improve. The whole supply chain for agricultural products will have to change. The Sustainable Revolution will cause disruption in, but also strengthen, this important sector.

The Global Market for Agricultural Produce

The way that markets operate has a strong influence on how we manage agriculture. At world level, there has been considerable discussion over agricultural trade liberalization. This issue has taken particular prominence during the Doha Development Round of the WTO negotiations, which commenced in 2001. An open world agriculture market, devoid of barriers or restrictions, would be a major force for change and is worth a close examination.

In an open market, food will be grown where the conditions are most suitable, taking into account the cost of transportation. In a world of cheap transportation, the distance between producer and customer can be considerable. For example, fresh roses are flown from Africa to sell in capital cities across Europe from London to Helsinki. If transport costs were to rise significantly – as they will when the fossil-fuel crunch hits – then the economics of the trade would be undermined. The consumption of agricultural products will become much more localized. This is what many green campaigners argue for. They will find that, after the Sustainable Revolution, hard-edged economic reality will support their case.

Another attribute of open global markets is that they disconnect the producer and the consumer. The producer is inclined to see farming as a commercial enterprise to make money from faceless consumers. The consumer trusts that the quality of the food matches the cleanliness of the supermarket where it is purchased, with very little knowledge of the source of the food or the conditions under which it is produced. It is this disconnection that allows industrial practices to enter the food production process, leading to problems that are discussed further below.

One of the main perceived benefits of open markets is cheaper food for the consumer. We should reflect on whether this should be the prime driver behind agricultural policy. In the developed world, food is a low proportion of a family's budget. Overconsumption is a problem, leading to obesity and significant health problems. Other priorities should take precedence over a narrow focus on driving down prices.

Another reason to question the wisdom of open global markets for agricultural produce is the effect these have on poor countries with economies based on subsistence farming. Their economies could be destroyed by an influx of cheap food produced by large-scale mechanized farming. This would force them down an industrial path to rebuild their economies. I suggest that it is not in the interests of the developed world to force such change on these countries. If they have a low-impact sustainable system that they are content to retain, it should be their right to do so, without suffering penalties.

Subsidies

The biggest source of distortion in world agricultural markets is subsidies. These are commonly applied and lead to anomalies. Subsidies are, in almost all circumstances, counterproductive and often perverse. Europe's Common Agricultural Policy (CAP) is an example. It is one of the underpinning policies of post-war Europe, designed to ensure that Europe would be self-sufficient in food. It achieved the aim and Europe is now a net exporter.

Europe is a different place in the 21st century, and calls for reform to the CAP are growing louder. Just under 50% of the EU budget is expended on it, amounting to 0.43% of European GDP in 2004.[2] It has become common practice for European farmers to manage their businesses to manipulate the subsidies, rather than supplying consumers.

A subsidy is paying a farmer to produce food that the market would not otherwise want. Simple intuition says this cannot be right. So let us consider outlawing subsidies in Europe and see what effect this might have. First, food production would alter to match market forces across Europe and so would be more efficient in economic terms. Second, the rural economy in France and some other countries would come under pressure to change, leading to major alterations to the natural landscape.

For a French president or prime minister to agree to this in isolation would be political suicide. There is, therefore, deadlock. A way out of the stand-off is to apply tariffs to food being imported (in addition to removing all subsidies). This would raise the bar to producers outside the EU and allow a free market between European farmers, who would be protected from competition from abroad. (Let us put on one side what current WTO agreements might require.)

If we replace subsidies by tariffs then – from a governmental perspective – we have replaced a drain on funds with import tariff tax receipts. This will be one attraction of the proposal. But there would also be a damaging tit-for-tat response from non-EU countries. Every other country would put up the tariffs that it believed were in its best interests. This would lead to:

- each country protecting and retaining its own local agricultural capacity;
- exports flowing freely to countries that need the food (a country is not going to erect import tariffs if its people need food);
- imports and exports continuing to take place where the cost advantage is so great that the hurdle provided by the tariff is exceeded; and
- prices to the consumer rising to match the true cost of production.

It is hard to identify anything wrong with the first three of the outcomes above. It is only the fourth that is negative; consumers are likely to pay more. I suggest that resistance to this particular outcome should not be allowed to drive European agricultural policy.

The transition to a subsidy-free Europe would not be easy. The political complexity is so great that the debate is likely to run and run. It may be impossible to reconcile the conflicting views. If so, the debate may re-examine whether the EU behaves like one country with completely open internal borders or remains a club of separate countries retaining national restrictions.

Rewriting the Rules for Agricultural Markets

World agriculture has become embroiled in a complex mix of politics, economics, pseudo-economics and protectionist measures. Let us clear away these issues and start again.

Food is a fundamental need. Countries require the security of continuation of supply; populations need and demand guarantees that the food on sale is safe; and agriculture needs to be sustainable indefinitely. This leads to self-sufficiency, at all levels from local to national, as the natural default option.

Market forces are the main control mechanism, playing off the costs of production and transportation between competing producers. Local producers therefore have an advantage that increases as the cost of transportation rises. When food is bought and sold, it must come from a trusted source (a prerequisite of supply). We also expect rare or exotic foods to command a premium.

Governments will want some control over the market to ensure that their country is self-sufficient in staple items and to protect the health of their people through setting standards. This will, in effect, be a barrier to some sources of supply until they can prove compliance. So we should expect that national borders will produce discontinuities in the market.

Let us consider what levers the government should have. First, a lever they may be tempted to try – but which they should not have available to them – is subsidies. These would undermine the market forces at the heart of the market and are almost always counterproductive. This leaves three effective levers:

- adjusting the cost of transportation (a tax on distance-to-market);
- putting up tariffs (to retain capabilities); and
- erecting barriers (to protect health).

Let us look at each of these in turn, starting with transportation. Taxes on transportation, weighted according to environmental impact, are sensible when applied to all sectors. Such taxes would give advantage to local producers. Increasing the tax on transportation and/or fuel might be sufficient to improve the performance of our agricultural markets, and would be easy to implement.

In addition, there is a more focused way of applying the distance-to-market lever. A tax could be levied that is proportional to the distance between purchase and production. At first sight, this looks like a bureaucratic nightmare. However, comprehensive computer systems are the norm at all the big supermarkets. The biggest change required would be to ensure the incorporation of 'location of source' within the product-coding system. The location of each supermarket is constant, and the calculation is just a few lines of computer code. A tax could be applied per unit of distance. This would a very small percentage, set by government, and adjusted as required. The tax would be applied automatically to each item as it was purchased.

Despite their protestations, the supermarket chains would not find this to be a big overhead. Local markets for fresh produce would, for practical reasons, have to be exempt, reinforcing their competitive position. Small local shops would also need to be considered for exemption, so reinforcing their role in reducing the need for people to travel by car.

Such a fundamental change will produce anomalies – some of which can be foreseen. Consumers will travel to purchase items with a high value (as opposed to weight) from an outlet closer to the source of production, expending fuel as they do so. Remote communities will complain that they are unfairly penalized. Local political representatives can argue over this point. Overall, taxes on transportation or distance-to-market taxes are alternative versions of the same lever, and can be very effective.

The second lever is tariffs. This assumes that there is a border through which goods pass that provides the opportunity to levy the tariff. I suggest that this should only be used to protect agricultural capabilities that the country wants to retain. It could also apply where the country has placed environmental management requirements on its own farmers which have a cost attached. Politicians may, of course, come under pressure to use tariffs for other reasons, such as simply protecting their farmers from competition. In this case, the political decision may require balancing the power of farmers against that of consumers. Of course, where a country does not have the capability to grow a particular crop then there would be no need to set a tariff. The country would simply buy on the world market at the best price.

The third lever is barriers. Again this assumes there is a controlled border. I suggest these should only be used on the grounds of health, but again a political dimension may intrude. On the precautionary side, food should only be allowed to be imported from countries where safety is guaranteed. Some foodstuffs, such as meat, will come under stringent controls; others less so. The receiving country has responsibility for the health of its people so only it should make the decision.

Outcomes

Governments will recognize the multifaceted advantages of locally produced produce and will seek to influence the market in that direction, using the three levers of a distance-to-market tax, tariffs and barriers. Farmers will be reconnected with the consumer, providing a transparency that has been sorely lacking in the developed world.

Farmers who produce quality, safe food and protect their environment will command a premium. Farmers who use industrial or dubious practices will be exposed by the local press and their produce shunned by the market. The main negative effect will be an increase in prices to consumers.

The poor and less well off will find that the price of those foods that cannot be produced locally will rise. Seasonal local produce will be their cheapest choice. Those on a tight budget, who buy by price alone, will find their choices naturally steered towards items that can be sourced locally. We should expect that prices in general will rise, but the big increases will be on the more expensive and exotic items. This will have a greater effect on the affluent and those who are better off. In the developed world, adopting this new mindset with regard to agriculture will increase prices to the consumer but will be skewed towards those who can afford to pay – and will have the welcome side effect of leading to a healthier diet as people have better access to fresh, locally sourced foods.

There will be political difficulties in implementing the changes. Even in the developed world, governments have electorates that contain the relatively poor, the old and others who are less well off. They may not be starving, but they do have the power to overthrow governments. Changing agricultural policy to a more sustainable, better-managed and fundamentally sound system may not be their prime concern. Prices are likely to be their pivotal interest. This is where politicians will have to use their skills in order to find a solution. Assuming that the government will have eliminated spending on subsidies and increased revenues through pulling the tax levers described above, there should be funds available. This net improvement in government finances could be used to alleviate some of these concerns. The measures used could include increasing the budget for school meals, or raising pensions for the elderly. Once the changes in agricultural policy have bedded in, they will become integral to our domestic spending habits, but transitional arrangements like those outlined above will be a political necessity.

The Changing Business Landscape

Higher transportation costs and a market skewed in favour of local produce will affect the supermarket chains who dominate the market. They will need to alter their distribution networks to smaller hubs. They will need to negotiate contracts with a wider range of dispersed farmers within their geographical region. Forward-looking retailers will reconfigure their property portfolios and distribution plans, thereby pre-empting and even driving the changes. The concept of 'fresh and local' could be used to differentiate them from competitors who do not understand the coming changes.

With transport costs high, there will be opportunities to grow out-of-season or unusual produce at a location close to the consumer. There will be renewed interest in greenhouses. Not ones that use expensive fossil fuel for heating, but ones with state-of-the-art technology that makes maximum use of natural solar energy. Bioenergy from farm waste could be added to the energy mix. The opportunity will be there for the farmers, but companies that can produce relatively cheap greenhouses, using renewable energy sources, may generate the biggest profits.

Another area may be the re-emergence of the local abattoir. Stricter rules in Europe, which are costly to implement, have been putting smaller operations out of business. Animals are transported long distances to large facilities. The issue of improving animal welfare will provide one impetus to moving to more local facilities, but the more persuasive argument is based on purely economic grounds. Increasing the cost of transport will move the competitive advantage back towards the smaller operator.

These changes will ripple through all sectors of agriculture.

Sugar

Sugar is an integral part of our diet, although efforts are being made to reduce consumption in order to improve health. Currently, the sugar market is an example of the negative effects of subsidies. It is perverse that funds are expended to subsidize sugar production, whilst other funds are used to champion the health benefits of reducing consumption. The EU produces more sugar than it needs, spending 1.3 billion euros in 2003 on supporting its production. The excess sugar is sold abroad, leading to accusations from other sugar-producing countries that the EU is dumping its excess sugar. Under pressure from the WTO, reforms to the EU sugar market commenced in 2006, reducing subsidies considerably. This is the first stage in allowing the market for sugar to work in a more sensible manner.

Being non-perishable, sugar is easy to transport but it is also of low value for its weight. General increases in transportation costs or distance-to-market taxes would discourage the transportation of sugar if it can be grown closer to the consumer.

As for tariffs, a country could choose to preserve a national capability as for other staple foods. Tariffs could be raised until home producers could produce the sugar profitably. It is unlikely that consumers or their representatives would object strongly to modest rises in price. After all, it is acknowledged that encouraging lower consumption has proven health benefits. Politically, the farming lobby could be supported with little risk of a consumer backlash.

The use of barriers to the importation of sugar would not be defendable. Doubts about the safety of sugar from any particular source have not come to light, and it is hard to envisage such problems arising.

I contend that, in the longer term, the EU should eliminate subsidies and, if necessary, impose import tariffs. The EU would then cease to be a sugar exporter, as it would not be competitive in the world market. The range of outcomes within the EU is bounded by two extremes. One is that tariffs rise high enough that production within the EU is profitable and imports are choked off; the other is that the size of the tariff required to maintain the profitability of home farmers is too high to be acceptable to consumers, so that sugar production in the EU ceases. In setting the tariff, the EU could seek a balance between the two extremes so that Europe was largely self-sufficient.

Sugar producers in the rest of the world may benefit from a strengthening world sugar market. If countries choose to defend their own markets and move to the principle of local consumption, then there may not be a bright future for any of them. For the traditional sugar-cane nations, the biggest potential might be to stop fighting battles of the past, exit the market for domestic sugar and instead ramp up the production of the biofuel, ethanol.

Beef

Cattle are herbivores grazing on grass pastures, so provided their fields are not contaminated, they should be a healthy source of food and nutrition. But there are problems with the beef business. These go deeper than concerns in the developed world about how much red meat is healthy, or the debate about the inefficiency of beef as a food source in terms of combating world hunger.

The fundamental economics of beef are that it is valuable for its weight and it is perishable once the animal has been slaughtered. This is a high-value market that needs special processes. In the developed world, there is a sophisticated system of production and supply, with supply chains reaching around the globe. This is a major commercial business run with industrial efficiency.

A consignment of frozen beef on the world market is sourced from a large producer who seeks to maximize profit, and is consumed by an unknown consumer who may be far away in another country. There are regulations to be enforced, of course. Everyone in the supply chain needs to comply. If the unbridled pursuit of profit is the aim, then there is temptation to dodge the regulations – if you can get away with it. There is no visibility of a particular person who might suffer as a result. It is in this impersonal market that the BSE crisis arose.

Bovine Spongiform Encephalopathy (BSE) appeared in the UK in 1985.[3] The exact origins are unclear. Some research has explored the theory that it originated in man and then crossed into cattle. One hypothesis is particularly gruesome and suggests that human remains of victims of Creutzfeldt-Jakob disease (CJD) ended up in cattle feed.[4] Another theory, which has more support but is no less appalling, is that the remains of sheep carcasses infected with scrapie (a closely related disease) were fed into the animal-feed production process. We know as fact that once BSE appeared in cattle, infected animals were themselves reprocessed into animal feed before regulations were tightened.

In the UK, the cost of measures to eradicate the disease at the height of the crisis was £1.5 billion in the single year 1996–7.[5] The follow-on effect on the UK beef industry has been much greater. The long-term cost of BSE within the EU has been estimated at close to 100 billion € by a panel of experts from the European Association for Animal Production (EAAP).[6]

The debate following the crisis focused on the effectiveness of the reprocessing of animal remains into cattle feed and factors such as the temperatures used. The prion that causes CJD is robust and hard to eliminate. But the lesson is much more fundamental than that. Cattle are not a commodity like sand or cement. The production of beef should not be seen as an industrial process in which anything goes as long as it increases short-term profits. Beef is food and we must be sure that it is safe to eat. Besides, long-term profitability in the beef business comes from maintaining the strength of the brand. To maximize the value of the market, it should be seen as a high-quality food with complete transparency in the process from the field to the table.

The industrial practices shown up by the BSE scandal are, in hindsight, blatantly wrong, but we continue to fail to learn the lesson. The procedures now in place to prevent CJD re-entering the food chain still do not address the underlying structural weakness. Industrial processes in beef production are still taking place, remote from the consumer, which will lead to another crisis like BSE. One such candidate is a bowel disorder called Crohn's disease.[7]

BSE was a huge threat to human health and very expensive for both the government and industry. It is interesting to contrast the developed world's methods with an example from rural Africa in which Africa comes out rather well in comparison.

A Lesson from Africa

Driving over a large flat plain in northern Cameroon, I noticed a lone tree (presumably a local landmark) and a group of people gathered around it. As I drew closer, I noticed that there were a multitude of bicycles around the edge, and a solitary cow in the centre looking bemused. As I observed from a discreet distance, I watched the cow killed and butchered. Once my initial horror had subsided, I thought about the process.

On one level it was humane. The poor cow had no prior knowledge of its fate, unlike in modern abattoirs where the stench and sounds of death are all-pervasive. It was also part of a highly efficient process. The cow was cut into pieces and transported by bicycle to markets in the surrounding villages. The meat would be sold and consumed in a relatively short space of time. In an underdeveloped part of the world with little reliable refrigeration this was an efficient and safe system.

There was also a close connection between the farmer who raised the animal and the consumer. In such a short supply chain it is easier to maintain quality control over the product. If an unfit-looking animal was offered into the process then no doubt it would be rejected. With the farmer and consumer living within the same community, there are strong natural safeguards even where there are no formal control mechanisms or inspectors.

In the developed world, we will not want to be quite so exposed to the realities of beef production but we should copy the strengths of this system to improve ours.

Building a Better Market

For our beef market, we should be uncompromising in outlawing industrial practices and reconnect the farmer and consumer. Governments, the public and those businesses striving for long-term profitability will realize that short, transparent supply chains work better.

From a consumer perspective, beef is a luxury; there are cheaper ways to get the nutrition to survive. The rich can be expected to pay a premium for a guarantee of quality. The less well off trust their governments to ensure that regulations are in place to ensure that their occasional luxury is safe. When the next crisis like BSE arises – which is inevitable with the current industry structure – then governments and the industry will be forced to change.

The first lever a government can apply is over the general cost of transportation, but for a product with a high value for its weight this may not have a great effect. A distance-to-market tax would be much more effective in forcing the move to shorter supply chains. Regulations over the movement of live animals may also play a part; as well as supporting animal welfare and preventing disease transmission.

In considering the second lever – that of tariffs – beef is not a vital industry in terms of needing to maintain a national capability. If another country can produce beef safely and more cheaply, taking into account transportation costs and taxes, then importation makes economic sense. So there does not seem to be a case for tariffs unless there are political reasons to support a beef industry.

The third lever – barriers on the grounds of national health – is more likely to be used. It would be entirely reasonable for a country to ban the import of beef from countries unless it could be certain of safety. I argue that it would be entirely reasonable for a country to ban all imports of beef without exception using the precautionary principle. The decision to do so may have a political dimension to protect the farming lobby, but this would not undermine the defendable logic of the decision.

The outcome would be a closing down of world markets for beef. Levers would be applied within countries to favour local producers. There would be premium products that sold to a wider market but these would be the exception. If this analysis is correct, then the industry will change. Those who set in train the changes in advance of the next crisis will reap the rewards.

The future beef market envisaged would consist of closed loops of local farmers using natural methods linked into smaller local abattoirs and short distribution chains. Compared with the current market, such a system would have a relatively high cost base, but this would not be some sort of grand farmers' market. As big companies see that this is the future, they will orchestrate the local networks, leveraging their knowledge, expertise and technology to ensure the processes are optimized.

Forestry

Timber is a highly versatile commodity that can be used in construction and manufacturing. Obvious examples are furniture and floors, but the possibilities are limitless. One traditional UK sports-car manufacturer still uses it in structural components of its cars.[8] Its manufacture is entirely natural; using water, a few nutrients and lots of sunlight. It has a highly advanced structural design, is biodegradable and, at the end of its working life, it can be burnt to provide energy. If we were to invent the perfect material for making all those things that have a limited lifespan, wood would be the result.

The timber market requires long-term thinking, with fast-growing trees providing softwood ready to be harvested after a couple of decades; valuable hardwood takes more than one person's working life to produce a return.

The world possesses a considerable current account of living wood in its trees and forests. It is tempting to spend it all now: cut down the trees and sell or use the timber. However, the deforestation that would result comes with a cost. Some areas would become fertile farmland, but many others would become barren, or even desert, without the forest's ecosystem to sustain the land. It is better, of course, to draw the interest on the capital, leaving the forest intact and only extracting mature timber using sustainable logging practices.

Virgin forests are the world's original heritage and a special case. They contain a considerable pool of biodiversity to which mankind has more than a sentimental attachment. They provide a bank of genetic material for new drugs and other purposes. The large tropical forests, such as the Amazon, are also regarded as the lungs of the planet, locking away carbon from the atmosphere in a process akin to that which, over geological time, produced coal, oil and gas.

Much of the developed world's virgin forests were cleared centuries ago. It is in mankind's interest to protect those that remain, which are mostly in the underdeveloped world. It is in our self-interest that they should be retained, but there is a limited amount of control that the developed countries can exert: these forests do not belong to us.

Protection for forests usually focuses on the prevention of logging. This must take into account the circumstances and needs of the country in which the forest lies. A poor and populous country may find it hard to implement effective controls. In an open world market for timber, enterprising (or desperate) people will get timber to market in any way they can (legally or illegally).

Controlling demand is where the developed countries can have the greatest influence. The governments of developed countries – in their efforts to protect world forests – could enforce sustainable timber controls and regulations. It was this demand-side approach that was effective in closing down the world trade in ivory. In this case, we do not want to close down the timber trade, but we do want to exert tight controls, where we have jurisdiction, in order to influence behaviour beyond our own borders.

This will require robust and hard-to-fake evidence of origin for all timber consumed. There are a number of technologies that can provide solutions to this challenge, and a business opportunity for the company that delivers a working system. We can assume that, in due course, a certified route from green trunk to table leg will be a requirement placed on manufacturers. Governments may also apply a distance-to-source tax in order to take further pressure off the remote forests of the world (relying on data from the evidence-of-origin system).

Further actions from governments will seek to ban timber imports from countries that allow their virgin forests to be cut down. To be effective, this will need concerted international agreement, but such a deal would be effective even if total coverage were not achieved. The outcome will be a sustainable world forestry industry, with a few non-compliant countries outside and excluded from the formal global market.

The opportunities in forestry look bright. Investing in forests (virgin and managed) will be a good double play. First, virgin and remote forest now has little income potential, so is currently cheap, but it will appreciate in value over the long term. Second, the sustainable timber industry will be a solid future-proof business. If a company builds a good reputation as a manager of sustainable commercial forests, it will be trusted to implement sensitive and limited exploitation of virgin forests. This will be better than attempting – and failing – to protect the forest completely; a less bad solution for the ecosystem and a profitable opportunity for business.

For a business that requires timber in its production processes, it will be cheaper in the short term to buy from the world market at the best price without looking too closely at the origins. Companies that take action to become sustainable at this early stage will incur increased costs, but may be able to recoup these through an enhanced reputation or green branding that justifies a premium retail price.

It may be hard to profit in the short term, but the sustainable approach will deliver robust profits in the future. This will require purchasing sufficient forest (worldwide) to satisfy the anticipated requirements for timber. Sustainable management of the forest should then be implemented, with the aim of being seen as a good employer and partner to the country concerned. Such an integrated supply chain will take effort to build and will need to be part of a long-term plan. The pay-off will come when controls along the lines outlined above start to bite. The company would then be well poised to exploit its position.

Countries that are destroying their virgin forests will find that timber exports are banned. Responsible multinational companies, operating with effective controls in a transparent manner, will have a strong case for circumventing the ban. A company that acts as the only conduit for timber to reach the legal timber market may help the country to reform its forestry policy – and will also be in a profitable position.

The Future for Agriculture

We can be confident that agriculture will grow in stature and importance as the Sustainable Revolution gathers pace. We all need food, but agriculture can also provide materials and energy in a totally sustainable manner. Sunshine and nutrients come together to make items we use for a while before releasing the energy as heat or power. The carbon returns to the atmosphere to start the cycle once more.

In the developed world, safer, more sustainable agriculture is entirely feasible. Consumers will have to pay more for non-local produce but this will affect mainly those who can afford to pay. Overall agricultural capacity may become the main issue, with increasing demand for non-food crops and a world population that continues to expand. Moving beyond the industrial era of agriculture fuelled by fossil fuels will therefore not be easy, but it is essential for the health of people, and of the planet, that we do.

16 Dealing with Waste

Current attempts at improving waste management are well intentioned but largely ineffectual. Regulations about allowable levels of pollution and efforts to recycle piles of mixed garbage are little more than playing with the symptoms. The system is inherently unsustainable. Each time a new threat to the environment emerges, regulations have to be discussed, agreed and implemented. We are forever chasing the problem. Effective waste management needs to become automatic and second nature.

Waste is not something we like to think about. For our own bodily waste, we go to the smallest room in the house and flush it away. For things we no longer need, we chuck them in the bin. We need a system that works despite our indifference.

For industry, there are rules to be complied with, such as the amount of industrial effluent that can be discharged into the sewage system, and there are contractors who have to be paid to take other waste away. Currently the thinking need go little further than getting waste safely off-site. This will have to change.

The issue of waste does not grab our attention until something goes wrong with the system. If our refuse collectors go on strike, or our toilet becomes blocked, then our waste becomes a highly visible problem. In the former, our streets start to fill with putrefying garbage. The latter is not something we discuss in polite company. We do not like being brought face-to-face with our waste.

When early mankind had made a mess of their local surroundings, they packed up and moved to a new site. There was plenty of land, and Mother Nature could be relied upon to clean up the mess so that the tribe could return there within a generation. This behaviour became so ingrained that it is an instinct that has remained with us until the present day.

A Global Market for Waste

When we mix our primordial instincts with globalization, we get a dangerous cocktail. In a world of open markets and free flows of goods and materials, there is always somewhere else our waste can be shunted off to. It can be dumped, but not in our own backyard. It can be shipped abroad, as long as there is something to place on file that says we have complied with regulations.

The global market in waste has a structural weakness. The most dangerous substances tend to migrate to where there is the minimum of regulation and monitoring. This is also likely to be where the expertise to deal with waste safely is lacking. Whatever guarantees might be sought, or paperwork produced, such trade will leak over time just as surely as steel drums 'lost' in the deep ocean will. The only mechanism capable of working is to close down such trade.

This will force us all to deal with our own waste and decommission our obsolete products and equipment within our own borders. This will be doubly effective in that it provides a strong incentive to progress quickly with eliminating dangerous substances from our societies.

We will have a real problem with all the waste that already exists, and all the processes that we currently use. The temptation to hide (or fail to identify) hazardous substances will be great.

The transition period will be dangerous for the environment. Tighter regulation will outlaw many substances and processes as we find alternatives. Getting rid of the legacy chemicals already in the system will take effort, as by definition these are substances that nature cannot handle. We will have to take specific action to deal with them. 'Losing' such substances will be the least expensive 'solution'.

The oceans are the most remote and least regulated part of our planet. This is where our chemical stockpiles will end up, unless we take care. It might seem better to abandon our unwanted products and substances in landfill. But these will, over time, corrode and leak and the ocean will still be the final destination, as hydrology washes the pollution into the seas. We must consider the expense of special measures to deal with legacy waste or accept that we will allow it all, over time, to end up in the oceans.

It is hard to identify hard-nosed economic imperatives or politically acceptable policies for dealing effectively with legacy waste. The best we can do in today's society is to keep our existing dangerous waste on land to await a future when there is the political will and economic spare capacity to deal with it. I have high hopes that future generations will do this, and more. I hope they will send high-tech submersible vehicles down into the deep ocean trenches to 'rescue' containers of toxic waste dumped there during the 20th century. We owe it to them to start keeping 21st-century waste in safe, secure storage on land to make their job much easier.

Globalization of waste is more than just an ability to export waste. Dirty activities can also be outsourced to another country. This does not need an explicit decision; companies in countries with weaker controls can use their cost advantage to win the business. This is a consensual relationship: the poor countries want the business and the richer nations are happy to let those parts of their industry depart. There is nothing criminal going on (or not necessarily) – it is a natural consequence of globalization.

Global regulations that apply to all countries are therefore vital, but tough limits on acceptable levels of pollutants are often resisted on the grounds that they discriminate against countries that cannot afford the advanced processes required. Also, where such regulations are agreed, under the mechanism of globalization there is a risk that these become targets to be met, rather than ceilings that should not be exceeded.

Better waste management is clearly needed. We have homes, gardens, farms, communities and nature reserves that we want to preserve. Our first response – driven by our selfish desire to have a clean local environment – is to stop others dumping their waste near us. We oppose landfill sites in our backyard and support the banning of importation of waste into our country. This is a precondition for developing the processes, policies and behaviours to deal with our waste in a safe and sustainable manner.

In the developed world, we can be confident that, when we focus on the challenge, we can build sustainable waste management into our societies. But our efforts will not be enough to protect the shared environment of the atmosphere and oceans. Other countries will also have to make similar efforts. We should, therefore, seek to agree worldwide standards for waste management and pollution control. We should want this so that our fellow human beings in places remote to us can also live healthy lives; but the more compelling reason will be to protect the systems we all share.

There remains a glaring gap. Many countries do not have the strong governance or resources to enforce the environmental regulations we need. These are often the poorer countries, and whilst it is clearly a local problem for them and their society, it is also a global problem. A weak country – in a world where waste has a price – becomes a magnet for waste from the countries with strong controls. It should concern those of us who live in the rather better-managed countries that in protecting our own environment, we are inadvertently and indirectly forcing an increase in the pace of pollution in other poorer countries. We have limited power to intervene in the internal affairs of such countries, but we do have the power to prevent our waste from leaving our borders and evading our tough controls.

The combination of protecting our own local environment and safeguarding the shared world systems of the atmosphere and oceans will shut down the world trade in waste. The focus for us all will then be to take responsibility for dealing with our own waste. This is intuitively the right solution.

Our Current System

Our current system regards rubbish as inevitable and being able to throw away things as a right. We see it as the responsibility of our government and local public administration to get rid of it.

Some useful material is extracted from our waste stream and recycled, but much of it is taken away to landfill sites. These are on poor quality land, or land that is populated by fewer people, or poorer people less capable of objecting to them.

Disused quarries are one of the least intrusive types of landfill sites. These can be backfilled with rubbish and then the topsoil replaced so that the land can be returned to other uses. However, the quantities of waste are so large that we are running out of suitable sites. Looking for more sites is, once again, tinkering with symptoms. We need to change the system. This is evident and widely acknowledged, but we do not accept any personal responsibility to make the change. We believe, as we always have, that rubbish is not important.

Our nuclear industry is producing waste that we really should be worried about. Even some respected environmentalists seem to have been misled by their primeval instincts into ignoring the significance of the problem.[1] This is not waste that nature can reprocess; this waste will still be dangerous 10,000 years from now. We must, therefore, take great care to plan for ultra-safe storage. The plans are impressive but the progress towards implementation is not.

The US Department of Energy (DOE) plans to build a highly secure facility at Yucca Mountain. But it has run into considerable opposition from the state of Nevada. The facility was originally due to open in 1998 but, on current plans, it will not open until 2017.[2] States do not want long-term storage of nuclear waste on their land. We like the power that nuclear reactors generate, but we also want them to be remote from population centres and we want the waste they produce to be stored in someone else's backyard.

We could be forced to accept responsibly for nuclear waste by linking the decisions over nuclear power and waste at a lower level. If the choice to include nuclear power in the energy mix at state level included an inseparable requirement to provide a long-term storage site, we might see more effort go into developing a policy that did not include a nuclear component. We could go further and link the decision at county or even city level. If, in order to get electric power from nuclear sources, a city had to accept the power station and long-term waste-storage facilities within its own city limits, then it is highly unlikely that it would accept nuclear power until we have solved the challenge of clean fusion reactors.

For now, we must deal with the problem of dangerous waste from our fission reactors. As safe long-term storage is so difficult, other options have been suggested, such as encasing the nuclear waste in a stable material and dropping it into the deep ocean. Fortunately, responsible people in the nuclear industry argue that such waste needs to be stored on land, deep underground in stable geology where it can be monitored. Unfortunately, however, as the resistance to such sites stiffens, and the ongoing cost of storage rises, the temptation to use the deep-ocean option will grow. We want nuclear power, but no one wants the waste.

Changing attitudes and behaviours is going to be tough, but we must do this if our waste management is going to become sustainable.

There are early signs that substantive change is starting to take place. The EU's Waste Electrical and Electronic Equipment (WEEE) Directive[3] is one example, with countries in far-east Asia and some US states also adopting similar measures. The WEEE Directive, along with the complementary directive on the restriction of the use of certain hazardous substances (RoHS),[4] came into force on 13 August 2005 and is aimed at reducing the quantity of WEEE going to landfill through measures such as collection schemes and recycling.

The WEEE Directive also provides an insight into the future direction of waste-handling with measures to support improved product design and a producer take-back scheme.[5] These early beginnings give a foretaste of the much more substantial change that will follow.

The Future for Waste

Throughout the preceding chapters a number of developments have been signalled which will change the way we view waste, including cradle-to-cradle production and generating energy from biowaste. If we bring these together, we can build a picture of future waste-handling.

When looking at manufacturing and production, we saw that maintaining a separation between technical and biomass is the key. I further proposed a residual-value system in order to implement full recycling of technical material. In this way, technical mass becomes a valuable material input to industry. 'Buy-it-and-chuck-it' will be designed out of our products. People who cannot be bothered to recycle will pass the value on to rubbish contractors or the informal army of rubbish scavengers who will do the job for them. For many years monstrous hybrids of materials will continue to enter the system; a legacy of all the things we have owned in the past. Authorities will monitor the recycling system and take action when they discover evidence that companies are continuing to sell non-compliant products.

All our technical mass will then be managed within the recycling system. The bioloop will contain all our other rubbish, for example food scraps and packaging. It will also contain all those items made from biomaterial that we no longer need. These could be any manner of item from carpets and furniture to clothes and toys. This biowaste has true value: first as a source of energy and second as fertilizer.[6]

In summary, a sustainable future for waste management requires that we:

- ban the international trade in waste;
- set up and enforce a residual-value system for all products sold to facilitate the technical-mass recycling loop (by implementing the proposals made in Chapter 13); and
- enforce tight regulations amounting to a complete ban on all chemicals and substances that are not biodegradable in order to protect the biomass recycling loop (and our hydrology – see Chapter 14).

Note that the actions listed do not include any garbage-handling processes. If we create the right framework, appropriate processes and behaviours will evolve which will make rubbish obsolete. Such a system is inherently sustainable and stable.

The future described is perfectly feasible. It is also an attractive future. We can see a shared vested interest in moving towards it. It requires a lot from government, in terms of framing regulation, and a lot from industry, in terms of implementation; but it requires little from the individual. People can continue not to worry much about waste, as the system will be naturally self-regulating. The system will behave like the dung beetles of Africa, which spirit away the faeces of other animals for the valuable nutrients they contain.

The Bio-Recycling Loop

The bio-recycling loop has to achieve multiple outcomes; getting rid of waste is only one of them. Just as important will be the generation of energy and the production of fertilizer to use in agriculture. Coordinating all three requires coherent policy, but, once implemented, the solution is much simpler than single-outcome processes.

Dry biowaste will be collected to be burned for energy. The residents of buildings could decide to collect their own (such as paper and cardboard) to power their own small combined heat and power plants. Alternatively it could be released into the community collection system to power municipal power plants.

There will be the same choice with wet biowaste: to use it at either building or municipal level. It will depend on how well our engineers do at designing reliable methane generators. If fuel prices are high, single-household systems will become popular, but municipal facilities can be more sophisticated and could deal with the waste without any extra effort from us.

Helsinki Metropolitan Area is an example of early progress in biowaste management. Separate collection of biowaste started in 1990, greatly reducing the amount of biowaste going into landfill. The Waste Management Department had tested composting mixed household waste in the late 1980s. It found that separating organic waste from mixed refuse before composting required less work and produced a better product that contained less heavy metal residues.[7]

Finnish waste management regulations require that residential properties comprising ten or more dwelling units, and other properties producing more than 50 kg of biowaste a week, are obliged to separate biowaste from other refuse. Most properties have collection points for waste paper, and from 2006 properties with more than 20 apartments have had to collect recyclable cardboard.[8] The acceptance rate amongst inhabitants is 85%.[9]

The current Helsinki system has two big drawbacks. First, the weekly dedicated collection vehicle is an overhead in cost and energy. Second, the system is missing the value of controlled closed composting with the intention of generating and capturing methane. The system is still 'waste-centric' rather than being a truly balanced bio-recycling loop.

In theory, a fully featured bio-recycling loop – together with cradle-to-cradle production and consumption – would negate the need for a general refuse system. All items sold will either be fully biodegradable (including the packaging) or will contain technical mass with a residual value that will be reclaimable when it has reached the end of its useful life. These principles will apply to everything from bicycles and phones to all our food products and even clothes. This is hard for many people to envisage, but entirely feasible. Policy makers should already have this outcome in mind as we enter what will be a long period of transition.

The Transition to Sustainable Waste Management

If we decide that the system outlined above is where we want to end up, then we have to pull the appropriate levers. The first of these is restrictions on the transport of waste through national borders, or even between districts. There will be exceptions when it is demonstrably better to shift the waste to another location, such as legacy waste that requires highly specialist processing. But these need to be recognized as special cases which are supported by sound logic to ensure that the 'anywhere-except-my-backyard' attitude does not resurface.

The second is to encourage or cajole other nations to improve their waste-handling (and protection of the shared environment) through import restrictions on goods from countries with weak controls. If current WTO rules hinder such action, then the WTO rules will have to be reformed.

The countries that lead the transition will find some short-term resistance as they clamp down on the trade in waste and restrict imports of goods from countries with low standards. The most vocal complainers will fall into two categories. The first is home businesses that are either exporting waste (or junk labelled as second-hand goods) or have outsourced the production of components made with dirty processes to overseas contractors. The second category will be consumers who will have the choice taken away from them to purchase goods made more cheaply using lax environmental standards.

Despite complaints from these groups, the government's action could be likened to restrictions on smoking – the government would be saving them from their own short-sighted weakness. A business relying on cost-cutting through exploiting lax environmental controls in other countries might be milking short-term profits but is sitting on a time-bomb that may destroy the business. Consumers buying products that are cheap, due to poor environmental standards during manufacture, are likely to be buying short-lived inferior products.

Once any initial resistance is faced down, countries will find that being in the vanguard of sustainable waste management is handing their own business communities a considerable advantage. As in other areas of sustainable policy, a strong home market provides the platform to sell skills and expertise into overseas markets. Some economists will point out that such behaviour risks undoing the work of free-trade and open markets, and lead to stagnation of GDP. To an extent they will be right, but in the context of the Sustainable Revolution their voices will carry less weight than they do now. The government would be behaving responsibly in its wider obligations to society and the environment. Not only that, but I believe that the leading countries will find that their GDP holds steady or rises, leaving the slump to take place in countries that are slow to see the need to change.

To get the transition moving, governments should signal their intention and announce forward plans. We can expect some political wheeling and dealing around the margins to make the policies palatable to voters and to protect the country's own industries. In Chapter 21, I will look at mechanisms such as capping emissions and then selling permits to pollute. These will prove helpful in facilitating the transition and have a good record of ensuring that investment flows to where it can be most effective.[10]

The timescale for our waste management reaching the mature sophisticated system described above is decades, but it may not be many years before the transition begins in earnest. Businesses that accept my analysis, and take a bet on the outcome, could be initiating a period of profitable growth that lasts for the next 20 to 30 years. By keeping alert to the next tightening of the policy ratchet, they can move ahead of regulation and their business opponents. The blind followers will be second-best for decades to come, perhaps without realizing why, as they rush from one compliance crisis to the next.

It is certain that we will eventually move beyond our throwaway society to a world in which true recycling is universal. It will be a very slow transition and whilst we develop the policies, processes, methods and behaviours required, the damage inflicted on the Earth could be considerable. It is in the direct interests of us all to push for collective action to force the pace of change.

Part Three

SURVIVE AND THRIVE: FORCING THE PACE OF CHANGE

17 The Leaders of the Revolution

Whether we merely survive the transition to a sustainable world, or thrive from the opportunities that arise, will depend on how well we anticipate the future and the extent to which we shape it.

Human society is on a collision course between its continual drive for greater consumption and the capacity of the Earth to provide. The changes required within our modern world are huge. It is not a job for reformists seeking slow and gradual change. What we need are revolutionary leaders who can move away from the behaviours that have become the norm.

At an individual level, it is doubtful that many of us would change to a low-impact sustainable lifestyle by choice. Individuals or small communities can, and have, developed sustainable lifestyles. The people behind these initiatives can sleep secure in the knowledge that they are not contributing to the world's problems. But, on reflection, it can seem futile to be occupying only that ecological footprint which is your equitable right, when much of the world is charging on regardless of the environmental impact. Why should I act before anyone else?

The leaders of the revolution have to overcome this inertia, and it will not be easy.

Political Leadership

In looking for leadership, the nearest we have to a world-level governing body is the UN. It is also the home of the world's conscience over issues that transcend national borders. However, we should not expect too much of the UN: it works through building consensus, so on each issue it tackles, it is only as strong as the strength of the agreement it can broker. It is unavoidable that the processes of the UN are slow and ponderous. We cannot, therefore, afford to wait for the UN to take action. Fortunately, there are sound selfish reasons why countries should act before a UN framework is complete, as I will show.

Eventually, we can expect the UN to put in place effective high-level agreements to support a sustainable world. The UN will then have the authority of the world community to bring pressure on rogue countries that are yet to conform. The UN will also be the secretariat – where we can reach agreement – for fair and equitable rules and regulations brought in worldwide and implemented simultaneously. This will provide the framework to take concerted action for the global good. Such action will inevitably be local in nature but the sum total will be the global protection required. Without such a UN framework, some individual countries might find it hard to take the necessary measures when the direct benefits are few, if implemented in isolation.

The UN is vital and its role is important, but the UN is not a revolutionary. Neither are national governments; they have elections to win and public support to be courted. We associate revolution with the overthrow of a legitimate government, so obviously a government in power has no interest in bringing forward its own demise by adopting extreme policies. Even if such policies are the 'right' policies, if they are likely to be resisted and to destabilize the bureaucratic system on which the government relies, then a government in power would be unwise to pursue them.

A revolutionary politician who captures the mood of the people can get elected, but, once in government, will have to contend with the inherited system. Bold new ideas can get ground down beneath the wheels of government machinery, but this is not just inertia from government officials. A population will vote in a new leader on a small number of high-profile issues or statements of intent. In facing the reality of execution, it will be found that there are negative impacts of the promised changes. In dealing with these, the revolutionary politician may lose popular support long before the government's official mandate expires. There may even be civil resistance to further implementation. The revolutionary leader, therefore, effectively has one term in office to show that the package of sustainability measures is better for the country and the majority of its people.

I hope that we can win over many of our politicians to the concept of sustainability. At this early stage, they should plan to influence and even manipulate public opinion, as their actions can go only as far as the consensus they can build. This will need bold leadership and a break with the common practice in modern politics of bending to the output of focus groups; putting poll ratings above steadfast beliefs.

This constraint on our politicians to adopt sustainable policies is about to be lifted, as focus groups report increasing concern for the environment. Younger politicians hoping for a long career will have to market themselves as pro-sustainability. Politicians who believe in a sustainable society, and are willing to risk short-term unpopularity by sticking steadfastly to their principles, will be the leaders of our world a decade from now.

Such courageous political leaders need some early success. We should not mind if they are selective in choosing the least difficult of the measures I outline in this book, if it helps to give them the mandate they need. It will be the public who finally decide when the new generation of politicians are handed control.

Collective Power of People

Although only a privileged few private individuals are either rich enough or sufficiently principled to adopt a sustainable lifestyle by choice, the general population does have considerable power. They may not often be the source of new ideas, or have the foresight to see where they are heading, but as a group they can shift direction in a surprisingly rapid and cohesive manner.

The fall-out from just one incident can turn against a government or a policy almost overnight. Support for nuclear power is a good example. The response to the Chernobyl accident in 1986 was an irrational anti-nuclear backlash. The merit of nuclear power is an important and complex debate (discussed in Chapter 8), but the true situation before and after Chernobyl did not change. It was public opinion that swung quickly and decisively anti-nuclear.

The pendulum swung back two decades later in the aftermath to Hurricane Katrina, when the world was reminded of its reliance on oil as production in the Gulf of Mexico was shut down. Nuclear power again became the technology of choice to keep the lights burning.

Public support for a new policy may not happen as quickly as the knee-jerk reaction to crisis, but it can be influenced. Governments can look for early wins that will receive positive press coverage in order to stifle dissent until the benefits become widely tangible.

We can expect the message from opposition parties to become louder, saying that the threats to our environment and society are real and frightening, and adding that it is possible to address them and that they are the party to do it. These will not be the green parties: although a strong voice to influence change, they are too far removed from people's everyday lives and the reality of our commercial and consumer society to be elected. It will be the mainstream parties trying to gain power, or resident governments seeking to retain power, who will shift their ground.

There will be individuals who accept the concept of sustainability, and consider taking action to change their own lifestyle. But there is little real incentive for people to change if this means accepting constraints that do not apply to others. As the negative effects on the environment grow, we can expect support to increase for measures that apply to all members of a particular society.

The policy of proximization is the way we can harness the parochial attitude of the individual. We should not expect to be able to persuade the majority of people to care about the health of planet Earth, but when decisions, actions and effects apply to their own local environment, they will take notice and expect corrective action. When they observe with envy the success of other communities and countries, they will want to emulate them. In the voting booth, faced with a choice between two competent parties, a package of policies to ensure a safe, stable and sustainable society will look increasingly attractive.

Eventually the collective power of the peoples of the world will vote in governments with a mandate to move towards a sustainable future. Not because people have become committed and considerate world citizens, but because they care about their own locality, their own future and the prospects for their children.

The Role for Business

When it comes to the challenge of implementation, business has the required behaviour to lead. Governments might drift, ordinary citizens might be lethargic, but businesses that behave in either of these ways do not survive for long. It is on business that we can rely to be the source of action.

This means that business will implement sustainability in a commercial and profitable way. This statement will not be palatable to some people and some organizations, but we must accept that the engagement of business is a prerequisite for success.

In turning to business to solve our problems, we should remember that business is not the fictional white knight in shining armour, but the real-world mercenary employed to get the job done. We will not always like the methods, but provided the outcome is the one we seek, we should be tolerant. Business is capable of confronting some of the tough choices that liberals try to avoid, such as closing a factory that is not capable of operating in a sustainable way, or forcing through changes that are unpopular but necessary.

Business will not be judged on how well it is implementing sustainability, but on its ability to deliver shareholder value, often measured by annual or quarterly financial results. Being a good world citizen in this context is a luxury. However, equity markets look to the future when considering price/earnings ratios. I argue that the Sustainable Revolution will reach a tipping point where the long-term value of adopting a sustainable business model will be understood by investors: not because they have become ethical investors (although perhaps that, too) but because they see their investments building long-term value.

In addition to enlightened investors, we need leaders across all sectors of society, in political and business circles, who can wake society up to the need to make real changes.

18 Mobilizing Business

As a society, we must decide whether we believe in a sustainable world or not. There will be some particularly selfish people who do not accept the need to consider further than their own immediate needs and desires. However, I believe that the majority of people within the developed world can be persuaded to accept the principle of sustainability, provided that it is explained and can be implemented fairly. We will then be in a position to give our politicians the mandate to set in train the necessary changes, which will then apply to us all. One of the first actions should be to give the business community the incentive and support to become the primary agent for change.

The Sustainable Revolution will then provide the circumstances for a dramatic mobilization in business activity. We are seeing the early stages, with investment capital flowing into the emerging carbon economy; but, up to now, progress has been slow and limited in scope.

Corporate Social Responsibility (CSR) is the term that has arisen to describe current efforts to make business more accountable to its wider role within society. This is now a highly topical subject in business schools. A search of the abstracts of published research papers for the term gives over 3,000 results for the five-year period up to 2007. This is over five times more than those published during the preceding five years. The issues discussed span a wide range, from corporate governance and the requirements of Sarbanes-Oxley,[1] to corporations behaving as good world citizens, working with communities and preserving the environment.

A lot of words have been written, but the concept of CSR has failed to deliver significantly more responsible behaviour by corporations or improved profits to their shareholders. It has been successful only in putting down a marker for the need to change.

To place CSR in a realistic perspective, we can contrast it with corporate financial responsibility. This we expect to be deeply entrenched in the company ethos and inseparable from any important business decision. Responsibility lies firmly with the general management, not the bookkeepers or even the finance director. CSR is not like this. In many companies, CSR is a bolt-on activity with the aim of deflecting problems of social or environmental impacts arising from the activities of the company. CSR has to become entrenched in general management thinking if it is to fulfil its potential.

The Progress So Far

The Secretary-General of the United Nations challenged business leaders to join an international initiative – the Global Compact – that aims to bring companies together with UN agencies, labour and civil society to support universal environmental and social principles.[2] The Global Compact was launched in 2000 and sets a world framework of ten principles (see box).

The Global Compact had over 3,700 businesses signed up by May 2007, but only 21% of the world's largest corporations had joined: 13 from the UK and only 10 from the United States.[3] Research carried out by McKinsey for the UN Global Compact found that 40% of the compact's participants said that the Global Compact had had a good effect on their corporate citizenship.[4] This is, therefore, a move in the right direction. But such figures – together with the low rates of

---

UN GLOBAL COMPACT

The Global Compact asks companies to embrace, support and enact, within their sphere of influence, a set of core values in the areas of human rights, labour standards, the environment, and anti-corruption.[5]

Human Rights

Principle 1: Businesses should support and respect the protection of internationally proclaimed human rights; and

Principle 2: make sure that they are not complicit in human rights abuses.

Labour Standards

Principle 3: Businesses should uphold the freedom of association and the effective recognition of the right to collective bargaining;

Principle 4: the elimination of all forms of forced and compulsory labour;

Principle 5: the effective abolition of child labour; and

Principle 6: the elimination of discrimination in respect of employment and occupation.

Environment

Principle 7: Businesses should support a precautionary approach to environmental challenges;

Principle 8: undertake initiatives to promote greater environmental responsibility; and

Principle 9: encourage the development and diffusion of environmentally friendly technologies.

Anti-Corruption

Principle 10: Businesses should work against all forms of corruption, including extortion and bribery.

participation – also indicate that the Global Compact is having limited value in driving change within the business community.

I carried out a crude piece of research in November 2006 to see what companies said they were doing about sustainability. I searched through the web sites of the world's top 20 corporations.[6] The two biggest companies, General Electric (GE) and Exxon Mobil, were trumpeting major strategic initiatives into sustainability. Regarding Exxon Mobil, a company based on the extraction and sale of fossil carbon, an element of cynicism is bound to intrude. As for GE, a close look at their 'Ecomagination' initiative indicates that the company really is betting the future of the business on the Sustainable Revolution. I believe that GE has made a very good strategic move and has probably secured a safe and profitable long-term future for its shareholders.

The other three oil companies in the top 20[7] also profess to be active players on CSR. They must know that their core business will become obsolete, and this is perhaps the start of the process of reinventing themselves; but they need to be careful that their actions are seen to be more than 'greenwash'.

Of the three companies who appear to say least about CSR, two draw their wealth from the fossil carbon economy and the third is focused on the tobacco industry. It may be that they have initiatives running that they have not yet published. However, the long-term future of their industries looks bleak. There would be a certain commercial logic in milking such businesses, leading up to their demise, without wasting resources on CSR.

Two companies stand out from the top 20 global corporations. Johnson & Johnson (ranked 14th) is interesting in that the company's 'Credo', adopted over 60 years ago in 1943, still reads today like the principles of a company adopting CSR. So CSR is not so new; perhaps the success of Johnson & Johnson shows that a principled approach can pay off over the long term.

Wal-Mart is, perhaps, the other surprise. Their website home page offers a sustainability tour around its supply chain, where it plans to use its buying clout to force changes. The CEO, Lee Scott, admitted that this started as a defensive PR measure,[8] but it seems to have grown into real action based upon a commercial judgement over changing customer expectations.

The insurance giant, American International Group (AIG) (ranked 16th), show a commitment to support research into climate change, with a clear business objective of ensuring that underwriting reflects the risks for clients and investors. This is enlightened self-interest and indicates a rather sharper edge piercing through the smokescreen of CSR.

The above research must be treated warily, as it is based on the aspirations and intentions that the companies have chosen to present publically. Rather more rigorous research in the UK has tackled the uncomfortable question of whether expending resources on CSR increases shareholder value. The study, published in 2006,[9] examined the relationship between corporate social performance and financial performance in UK companies. A collection of indicators was used for the environment, employment and community activities. Financial performance was gauged by the return on investment from the shareholder's perspective.

The researchers in this study failed to find a positive correlation between expending resources on CSR and delivering shareholder value. In fact, they found that a better investment strategy would be to invest in a portfolio of shares of companies who expended least effort on CSR. This piece of research bodes ill for the further adoption of CSR, in its current form. Championing CSR has the potential to improve company behaviour from society's perspective, but unless there is closer alignment with other business metrics, such as shareholder value, there is little real incentive for management to take it seriously. Government will have to do more to reward good social performance (Chapter 20) and bring in measures to protect the environment (Chapter 21) but I also explain how business can exploit the Sustainable Revolution (Chapter 23). My approach is clearly focused on increasing long-term shareholder value. I argue that these measures will be how we break the impasse.

Breaking the Impasse – The Business Perspective

Despite CSR's poor showing so far, there are many business leaders who profess to be taking an active interest in sustainability. At business forums the need for change is being acknowledged. I went to one some years back where the headline theme was 'Sustainable Business'.

The delegate sitting in the next seat complained to me quietly that he had expected to hear about financial issues such as long-term funding and consistent profit growth. He wondered why there was all this talk about the environment and social responsibility. Despite this inauspicious start, the discussion at the session was constructive.

The conclusions we reached were perhaps typical of how business views sustainability. Business leaders would like to behave more responsibly towards our social and environmental obligations, but to act alone would be commercial suicide. As a group, we agreed that what was needed was a level playing field. Changes needed to be planned and ample notice given to allow businesses time to make the required investments. This was a rational position to take, although rather dull and unambitious. On reflection, I felt that there were huge opportunities being ignored.

A notable intervention by UK business was when a group of business leaders from a number of large companies wrote to the British prime minister in 2005 to urge action over the issue of climate change and to offer support. Their words demonstrate the dilemma they found themselves in:

> At present, we believe that the private sector and government are caught in a 'Catch 22' situation . . . Governments tend to feel limited in their ability to introduce new policies . . . because they fear business resistance, while companies are unable to take their investments . . . to scale because of lack of long-term policies.[10]

There appears to be an impasse that has to be broken if the Sustainable Revolution is to succeed; business needs to know the regulatory framework within which it must work, and government has to get on with crafting it, without alienating business or popular support. It is as if no one is willing to make the first move.

A shift is required from the back-foot defence typified by the current CSR agenda to proactive leadership. Business will need to be nimble, quick and strong. This is no place for the weak competitors. It will not be about compliance with regulations, side-stepping litigation or avoiding bad press. It will be based on pursuing the opportunities and making healthy profits. For a leader of the Sustainable Revolution, there will be no compliance problems, negative press, nor the need to invest in greenwash or the bolt-on stance of CSR.

Moving Forward

The main issue for business is to understand how the business landscape will change as sustainable thinking gathers credence. Business will need to ensure it is engaged at local level. Global companies that are disconnected from government and society will find it increasingly difficult to do business. Global synergies will still provide opportunities, but the ability to act locally will be paramount.

When a sustainable future is rather clearer to see, then the business community will have the level playing field that many of its decision makers are demanding. Until then, most businesses will bide their time; but some will start to flex their muscles sooner than their competitors. As the best business leaders know, second-guessing the future – particularly if it is not obvious – is a winning strategy. First-mover advantage, access to the right technology and early entry into new markets can give significant competitive lead. This can be further enhanced through engaging with the debate to influence policy. There will be considerable potential to profit from leading the Sustainable Revolution, not just in terms of enhancing a business's reputation, but in hard financial results over the long term.

Whilst business is debating whether to wait or act, there lies a dangerous trap for corporations. For example, BP was a signatory to the letter to Tony Blair discussed above. A sharp-eyed journalist spotted that BP was at the same time lobbying against a carbon cap in a bill being considered by the US congress.[11] BP appeared to be seeking greenwash press coverage at the same time as campaigning to protect its bottom line by resisting measures to curb carbon emissions. To be fair to BP, the company said that the amendment they were supporting was 'an achievable step in creating good climate policy,' but to most people it did not seem that way.

It is clear to me that real action will derive from business. This will partly be forced on corporations by government policy backed up by legislation. But governments will also be wary, not wanting to put at risk the benefits that capitalism brings. Governments know that a vibrant business community balances the books and helps to keep them in power. Governments and business will tiptoe around each other's stated position, delaying taking substantive action. Finally, when business can see that governments have (or will soon get) the mandate to act, and governments have seen that their industry is poised to exploit the opportunities, real action will follow.

But can the equity markets support this new paradigm, or will they, too, need to be reformed?

19 Capital Markets and the Power of Ownership

The capital markets are an area for reform. They have developed to suit a narrow economic focus. We need to acknowledge that capital markets, as currently operated and regulated, do not make it easy for the Sustainable Revolution to take hold. The relentless drive to deliver short-term results is not conducive to building a sustainable future.

As we move to a sustainable world, the shortcomings of the capital markets will be exposed and we will have to respond. There will be surprise at the measures I propose, but I also expect support as we push for change. There will be losers, who will complain loudly. They might be right according to current mainstream economic thinking, but their motives should be looked at very closely.

Capital markets are at the heart of the world's financial system, pumping ever greater quantities of funds around the world. Without these markets, the world economy would grind to a halt. It is estimated that the sum total of the world's financial assets in 2003 was $118 trillion compared with $53 trillion a decade before. Extrapolation into the future indicates that the total could reach $200 trillion by 2010.[1] Where, just a few decades ago, financial markets were predominantly national, markets are now increasingly global.

The financial markets of the 21st century are not only large but also sophisticated. Technology has automated much of the system, making the transfer of funds (even huge amounts) little more than the passing of a number-string between computers over IT networks. Ever more exotic financial instruments are being conceived, and some of the world's brightest minds are employed working out algorithms to make profits from trading them.

These deep and liquid markets are just what free-market economics needs. Capital is free to flow to where it can be employed to best advantage. Investors are free to search for the maximum return, reducing risk through spreading their investments by country and region, as well as by sector. Conversely, governments and corporations can trawl widely to get the investment funds they need at the most competitive rates. Removing restrictions on the transfer of capital is – from an economic viewpoint – efficient. But restrictions also act as a natural brake on the system. A market without brakes can be a dangerous one. Capital can flow out as fast as it can flow in, precipitating financial crises.

There are numerous cases where the role of capital markets can be questioned, for example in the formation of financial bubbles like the dot.com boom of the late 20th century. Although it would be wrong to blame free and liquid capital markets, free flows of capital makes it much easier for irrational exuberance to take hold. Another example is easy access to debt. This is good in support of a robust business case; but there are poor countries saddled with debts so great that there is little prospect that they can ever pay them off. On an individual level, there are people borrowing amounts far greater than they can afford on the assumption that house prices will continue to climb. For the countries and the people involved, it is their own fault, but it would be sensible to restrict access to debt for the more vulnerable borrowers.

In the corporate world, there can be perverse outcomes as executives are urged to deliver shareholder value as measured by the markets. This leads to situations where manipulation of the share price takes preference over management of the business. Enron[2] in the United States and Parmalat[3] in Italy are examples. The executives of these companies used complex and opaque accounting to convince the equity markets of the value of their companies, right up until they imploded. In each of these cases, the market was not the problem, but the nature of 21st-century financial markets makes such awkward results more likely.

The economic theory is not at fault as we look at the downside of our existing capital markets. The problem is a narrow focus on economics that is disconnected from other factors. What is needed is a re-examination of capital markets in the context of sustainability. Perhaps an eminent economist should write a book as influential as Keynes' *The General Theory of Employment, Interest and Money*,[4] written in 1936 following the crisis of the Great Depression.

Ironically, the problem we have is a lack of crisis. It is not widely acknowledged that the world's financial system is in need of reform.

Loading all the world's problems onto the capital markets would be both unfair and unhelpful. This is what some campaigners seek to do, focusing on the narrow perspective of perceived inequality in the system. However, if we ignore the more emotional complaints, there is still a strong case for reviewing the way the markets operate and making changes where they are needed.

Let me start by putting down a marker that capital markets are a vital service to support commerce and society. The allocation of investment capital to support enterprise, and cash management to grease the wheels of the exchange of goods and services, are their true purpose.

If financial markets become the master rather than the servant, however, a problem is looming. When the markets become primarily a playing field for speculators and hedge funds, with the support of enterprise becoming simply an adjunct, then a rethink is required. The market needs to serve society, not to be put up on a pedestal to be worshipped.

Regulation is the way markets are controlled. This should ameliorate the negative effects whilst retaining the market's unbiased ability to root out inefficiency and waste. Markets that are well regulated can be good servants. Such a servant is loyal and honest, working under the ethos of serving the master of the house. You would not control a servant with a straightjacket – he or she needs to be fully capable and free to act. The same applies to the capital markets. Appropriate regulation is required to achieve the desired outcome, focusing the power of the market, not diffusing it.

In bringing the markets to heel, countries and regions will start to take action that will constrain capital flows and the operation of markets. Such measures may not conform to pure economic models but within the wider needs of society they will make eminent sense.

Review of the World's Capital Markets

The world's financial system is a cooperative arrangement amongst countries. The most powerful group is the G8[5] countries, which meet to discuss the world's finances and to propose and agree measures to adopt. The most powerful financial institution at world level is the International Monetary Fund (IMF). These world-level bodies seek to orchestrate the world's financial system but they have very little power of their own, as the following statement by the Managing Director of the IMF illustrates:

> *The international community needs to work together so that the necessary actions are both politically feasible and economically effective – and the IMF, with its constituency of 184 member countries, needs to help foster that cooperation.*[6]

The World Bank is another global financial institution but it has a limited remit to focus on the needs of the developing world. It describes itself as:

> *The World Bank is a vital source of financial and technical assistance to developing countries around the world. We are not a bank in the common sense.*[7]

The real power to control capital markets resides with individual countries, the most powerful of which is the United States. The United States provides the hub of global capital with the largest financial markets and the world's unofficial reserve currency, the US dollar. The euro is gaining a reputation as a strong and stable currency and may take on greater significance in the future of world finance, but the US dollar is still unrivalled. The United States is the dominant player and also the biggest debtor. Huge imbalances are building up in the global system with other countries, notably China, as massive creditors. Perhaps there is a crisis looming after all.

The flows of capital are increasing, with $1.5 trillion flowing through the currency markets daily, much of it speculative. Cross-border ownerships are increasing. Foreign ownership of US financial instruments in 2005 was: equities 12%, US corporate bonds 25% and US government bonds 44%.[8] Such global economic interdependence has not been seen before. Is this a strength or a weakness? Is the world financial system a robust self-regulating system or a house of cards waiting to collapse? The amorphous nature of the system makes it hard to judge. It is certainly looking like a system in which we all either stand or fall together. It may be that more connections bring greater resilience and reduce the chances of collapse, but if collapse does come, there will be no hiding from the consequences.

Country Perspective

Countries are at the mercy of the rather nebulous system of world finance. The more open and connected to the world markets that a country is, the greater the potential benefits, but this comes with a loss of control.

An example is the UK's decision to join the European Exchange Rate Mechanism (ERM) in 1990, only to be forced to leave just two years later, on what came to be known as 'Black Wednesday'.[9] Currency speculators, most notably George Soros (who earned over US $1 billion as a result), were behind the ignominious exit.

A devaluation and exit might have been required eventually, but if the UK government had controlled the process it would have saved the country over £3 billion. In 1997, the UK Treasury estimated the trading losses at £800 million, but the main loss to taxpayers arose because the devaluation could have made them a profit. *The Financial Times* reported[10] that if the government had maintained $24 billion foreign currency reserves and the pound had fallen by the same amount, the UK would have made a £2.4 billion profit on sterling's devaluation.

Smaller countries are most at risk from global speculation, illustrated by the pressure that Iceland and New Zealand came under when speculators seized upon on the krona and New Zealand dollar in 2006.[11] Support for reform of world financial markets is most likely to arise in such smaller countries as they rally together to seek change.

Each country has to make its own choices within the world financial system. If it gets it wrong, then it can turn to the IMF for assistance but it will have to cede some control of its economic affairs. The IMF stipulates requirements for the loans it makes: there is no point in lending funds to a country to keep it solvent only for it to default again in a few years' time. This is not negotiable; countries must conform in order to get funds from the IMF. However, the measures that the IMF has enforced have often been unpopular. This has run deeper that a simple dislike of unpleasant medicine. Each country has a different set of conditions and needs an appropriate solution; the IMF has not always appreciated that. What works well in one country with sound institutions and strong governance may not work in the same way in a different country with different systems and a different set of values.

The situation the IMF faces illustrates weak cross-connections with social and environmental policy at world level. As countries attempt to make policy to suit all aspects of their society, many of them are giving priority to taking back control of their economic affairs. Many Asian countries have built up huge reserves since the crisis of the late 1990s, partly to ensure they are free of IMF control. South American countries such as Argentina, Brazil and Venezuela have also adopted a policy of paying back IMF loans in order to gain the freedom to make their own economic decisions.

It is not that the IMF is deliberately undermining the countries to which it lends; its intention is quite the reverse. The issue is that the dogma of the IMF – heavily influenced by the United States – is not in tune with the way that many countries want to run their societies. As the concept of proximization gathers support, an increasing number of countries will want to be able to stand alone, or side-by-side with regional partners. The IMF, although quite correct to seek to protect the loans it makes, will need to be sensitive to a range of possible economic policies and adapt to the new reality, or risk becoming irrelevant.

The governments of the world should take back control of the world's financial markets and work out ways that they can serve society rather better. The challenge they face will be to tame and redirect the market mechanisms without neutering the positive contribution they can make.

Capital Flows

Within economies, capital should flow freely to where it is needed within a national policy framework. This is what free-market economics requires.

Moving up to world level, global capital flows have inherent dangers. The world capital market is little more than a loose coordination between separate economies. Encouraging the free movement of capital on the assumption that this is good for the global free market assumes a level of global economic stewardship which just does not exist. For example, the proportion of currency trades which are short term and speculative is far higher than the true need to move capital for investment or trade. The positive view is that traders are simply keeping the market liquid and therefore perform a valuable service. But it is not just market making, it is market manipulation.

James Tobin put forward a proposal in 1978 to introduce a tax on all currency trades to limit the role of the speculator.[12] In order to introduce such a 'Tobin tax', there are certain practical problems to overcome, not least of which is the need for a coordinated global agreement.

One problem is how to apply the tax receipts. Tobin suggests that they could be held centrally to help fund aspects of the work of the UN. A number of not-for-profit organizations have jumped on this as a good idea, distorting the focus of the proposal. The Tobin proposal is aimed at making currency markets work better; getting into a dispute over where the tax should go sidetracks the issue.

The Tobin proposal is an interesting idea which may yet be worth pursuing, but the effect would be limited. Instead, I will focus on an area with greater potential for improvement, looking at the power of ownership and the influence it has over corporate behaviour.

Ownership

Financial markets are all about facilitating alternative forms of ownership. At its simplest, instead of bartering, we use money as something notional that represents value. The modern financial system is a highly complicated web of financial instruments. It is easy to forget that the only true value any of these have is when they are converted back into something tangible. If finance is all about coupons in place of ownership, then ownership is a very important issue.

Ownership is at the centre of modern society. There is a balance between what we share and what we own. A Buddhist monk emphasizes the shared nature of existence by owning nothing. If we all adopted that approach, pride in ownership and the status derived from it would disappear. We would all occupy only the space we need and consume only what we require, but without ownership no one would be responsible. Unless the shared culture is strong (as in some communes), the inevitable result is a decline for everyone.

Ownership brings responsibility, so that it is in the owner's interest to look after an asset. Ownership can also have negative effects if it encourages people to be greedy, especially if status is defined by ownership, but this can be turned around. People who own more than they need can afford to behave in an altruistic manner, especially if this improves their standing in society.

Where the asset is a business, the owner decides how it is to be run. Culture and strategy is heavily influenced by the character and priorities of the owner. There is, therefore, considerable scope for business assets that are directly owned by private individuals to be operated in a range of ways. It could be run with a single-minded focus on profits. Alternatively, the owner could choose to run the company in a philanthropic manner. For a public listed company, the management do not have that choice available to them. Before looking more closely at the constraints we place on listed companies, I will consider other forms of ownership.

Public Ownership

Public (or state) ownership is for the common good. National parks are a prime example. The land is permanently removed from consideration by the financial system. It will never be sold or used as security for debt. It does not, therefore, have a financial value. The common infrastructure of society also falls into this category of being owned by the state for the common good.

If it is decided that state-held assets can be sold, then that decision conjures up new financial value that did not exist before. States can bolster their finances in this way but the windfall, although often substantial, is a one-off receipt.

Because assets held by the state have no book value there is no requirement to make them pay. Parks and other public facilities can be run on operating costs alone without consideration of the notional capital tied up in them. This approach facilitates using such assets for the good of society. Historically, this is how the public sector operated. This sort of ownership is naturally compatible with a sustainable world.

However, public assets also include organizations that run, for example, mass transportation and utilities. The danger here is that isolation from the financial markets includes insulation from the tough disciplines of commerce.

This is the background to the policy of privatization championed by Margaret Thatcher in Britain in the 1980s, which transferred the ownership of many government assets to the private sector. Included in this was the responsibility to provide the service required. This provided a one-off windfall to the government of the time but also, more importantly, brought greater efficiency and greater accountability to the public services. The responsibilities of the government were then passed to a regulator, with business doing what it does best, delivering a product as efficiently as possible. It cannot be disputed that this has brought huge improvements.

Privatization has worked in Britain because there is a stable system of sound governance. The process has been handled in a fair and open manner. There is now a positive tension between the government and the private sector with the regulator acting as umpire. It is clearly understood that the regulator answers to society through the government. However, this model is not universally applicable. The opportunities for corruption are immense if governance is weak. The initial sell-off is particularly vulnerable. States assets might end up in the ownership of cronies of the political elite, instead of being auctioned to get the best value for the country. We have seen this situation in some African countries (often acting under the guidance of the IMF) and in Russia following the collapse of the Soviet Union.

Public ownership is the best form of ownership – in theory – to support sustainability. In practice, privatization has been shown to work rather better in many respects for services when sound governance can be assured. So although sustainability encourages us to consider forms of collective ownership to ensure our assets are operated for the common good, governments should be very wary about taking assets back into public ownership. The business community is the engine of innovation and developer of best practice. Nationalizing business assets will, over time, risk destroying their value. Therefore, nationalization should be reserved for those things that are being permanently taken out of play in an economic sense – national parks, parks, playgrounds and shared public buildings such as schools, libraries and town halls.

Mutual Organizations

Mutual organizations are owned by their customers. Examples are cooperative societies running shops or pension companies investing savings for clients who are also owners. Combining the roles of owner and customer is a powerful mechanism for ensuring that the business is run for the good of society, or at least those members of society who are members. Such arrangements have high potential; it seems strange that they are a dying breed.

The ownership of mutual organizations is typically a diffuse group, with each owner owning a very small share. These owners are not generally business savvy and have little influence over the management. There is, therefore, a tendency for mutually owned organizations to become lazy and inefficient.

The other central attribute of mutual organizations is that, over time, they grow in value. Only part of the financial worth is passed back to the owners/ customers. Physical assets, in particular, grow in value. Unless the mutual organization releases the value, through taking out loans against assets to pay dividends, the value stays inside the organization.

At any given point in time, the members own a share in something that has value. This provides a great temptation for the current members to sell out and take a windfall profit. It might also be personally beneficial to the current executives to sell, provided they share in the windfall through share options or increased salaries. Demutualization takes place because it benefits the current members and management.

Despite the rush for the exit over recent years, mutual ownership is an excellent concept. Revitalizing mutual ownership has enormous potential, but defending the old model mutual organization is probably a lost cause.

There is potential for a new breed of organization to evolve to fill some of the gaps identified in this book. Such organizations will closely resemble commercial enterprise but the main difference will be a different ownership structure, leading to wider responsibilities than simply delivering shareholder value. They will have some of the attributes of our old mutual companies and could be described as 'altruistic commercial companies'. We can expect considerable discussion over how they might be constituted and controlled. The Community Development Corporations in the United States are examples from which we can draw inspiration.[13]

Such companies – with a broad role in supporting society – are currently few. The majority of our businesses are public listed companies, shares in which are traded on the equity markets.

Equity Markets

These markets serve society by allowing the transfer of ownership of business in small easily tradable chunks. Investors can purchase a stake and thereby share in the profits. Commercial enterprise can raise the capital it needs to invest in building the business. For modern equity markets, this simple description of their core purpose sounds almost quaint. Equity markets have become much more powerful and complex.

The requirements of the market have become the principle method of managing a listed business. Increasing shareholder value (the value determined by the equity markets) is the primary aim. Business strategy is formulated around building shareholder value. The chief executive is likely to be rewarded with share options tying his or her remuneration to the share price. Chief executives have other aims and responsibilities, of course, but the focus required by the market is clear and unforgiving.

Investors in shares also have a clear aim to maximize the value of their investment through selecting which shares to invest in. Investor capital therefore shifts around the market looking for short term uplift in value. From an investor viewpoint, the most profitable tactics are to buy a share whilst it is rising and sell once its price levels off.

The world equity markets, as currently regulated, favour a focus on short-term performance over long-term sustainable profits. This is undermining management's ability to carry out long-term business planning, which is so crucial to delivering sustainable outcomes. There is a clear case for improving the capability of equity markets, but it is not clear how to achieve it. To identify an improvement likely to deliver the greatest potential benefit, we must first examine the behaviour of public listed companies.

Public Listed Companies

Listing on the equity markets is the normal method of ownership for large businesses and corporations. Listing is the expected step for all businesses to take as they come of age. How this process works is fundamental to understanding how these companies behave.

Prior to listing, ownership is shared between the founder(s) and perhaps a venture capitalist (VC). The VC's aim is to grow the company until flotation, and then extract the investment in order to be able to repeat the process with another company. The VC wants to build a story that investors will buy into. This needs to be one of real progress to satisfy sceptical investors, although in the unusual circumstances of the dot.com boom, companies with little more than just the story succeeded in floating.

Following flotation, the founder is likely to remain a significant shareholder, not only because the prospectus will have included a lock-in clause, but also because entrepreneurs often have a close personal affinity with their company. They may retain an executive role (although if the general shareholders believe that the founder is not maximizing the return to shareholders then he or she will not remain an executive for long).

Founders are in a very interesting position. By virtue of what they have achieved, they have demonstrated drive and ability, and now possess considerable wealth. Their public listed company is no longer their personal fiefdom, and their influence has been neutered, but these are people who have the ability and the means to change the business landscape. I hope many of them will step outside the straightjacket of modern commerce and support the Sustainable Revolution.

As a listed company, the executive management team (if not already shareholders) are given a stake in the company through share options. The company is then owned by a diverse group of shareholders. Most will be passive shareholders with no closer involvement than choosing either to buy or sell, depending on their assessment of the prospects of the company.

There is also a breed of active shareholders on the look-out for sleepy companies that are not maximizing value for their shareholders. Such companies might be run by poor management who need shaking up. Alternatively, they might be run by very good management with a long-term view of a sustainable business. The corporate raiders will not differentiate. These active shareholders are free to buy a stake through the market and then push for changes in the way the company is run. Once the shake-up is complete and the share price has risen, they depart as quickly as they arrived.

This shows why listed companies can find it very hard to adopt sound long-term sustainable strategies. Good management running a company responsibly for a wide range of stakeholders, but failing to squeeze the maximum profit from the assets, is vulnerable to some sort of corporate raid.

We need to make it easier for our listed companies to support society more effectively. Society will be looking for changes to the way business is owned, and how shares are traded. I propose one small enhancement to start the process.

Reducing Volatility

A recurring theme in this analysis is the short-term and speculative nature of much of the capital sloshing around within the financial system. This is forcing the time horizon of management to be on the next year (or even the next few months) when it should be on the next decade and beyond.

The case for building a sustainable world is a strong one, which business can lead by selecting the effective and profitable ways forward, but it is also a long game that takes time and effort to line up all the pieces. Volatile markets are a hindrance and governments will realize this. Politicians will be asking for ways to spike the speculators.

It may be useful to provide some background to help explain the current volatility. As markets have become more global, the major corporations have been able to choose where to list. Equity markets have had to compete in the services they provide and the charges they levy. This applies to the investors as much as the companies; both are needed for an effective market.

Transaction costs have been falling; so have the taxes levied by governments not wanting to drive business from their markets. The United States does not tax share transactions, and in an open global market other countries have tended to follow suit. In the UK, tax on share transactions, Stamp Duty Reserve Tax (SDRT), was reduced from 2% to 1% in 1984 and further cut to 0.5% in 1986. Germany, Sweden and Finland abolished share transaction taxes in the early 1990s.

Reversing the trend and increasing the transaction taxes on share transfers will reduce volatility and encourage investing for the longer term. It is unlikely that one country will want to lead for fear of undermining their market and driving multinational companies to list elsewhere. If this proposal for a transaction tax on shares gathers support, a forum such as G8 could broker an international deal to agree a floor rate to apply to all the main equity markets.

Such a proposal is likely to be attractive to companies, giving more stability to their share price and more freedom to plan long term. Investors who actively trade shares will not like it at all, but if all markets have the same tax floor then they will not be able to escape the tax by shifting market. Their behaviour will change (for the better). They will look much more carefully at long-term prospects and switch ownership less often.

This leads to the really big losers, those running the markets. Reducing turnover reduces their income, impacting jobs in financial centres such as the City of London, New York and Frankfurt. Resistance will be considerable and the case against will be well argued and well presented. With respect to unilateral action they will be right, so governments should push hard for a concerted approach that covers all the main markets.

For the UK, a system is already in place; increasing the rate should be easy. The United States will be a major stumbling block. As well as having to make the ideological shift, the trading system would also need major redesign. However the idea of a transfer tax on share transactions has support. Robert Reich, Secretary for Labour under the Clinton Administration, also argues for such a tax in his book *Supercapitalism* published whilst this book was in production.[14]

I hope that chief executives, frustrated by the behaviour of some in the investor community, join with their governments in pushing for such transaction taxes, despite objections from a range of vested interests in the financial world. If they succeed, this will help to insulate business from the pressure for short-term results that is so destructive to long-term sustainable business planning. At the same time, governments might quietly welcome the prospect of increased tax revenue.

In brokering such a global transaction tax, a point of discussion will be the application of the tax revenues. At world level, talk may shift to a central fund to support one of the many pressing global challenges. This is exactly what happened with the Tobin proposal for a small levy on currency transactions. Tobin himself (perhaps unwisely) suggested this. If the debate focuses on allocating the taxes, it will be bogged down for decades. If politicians want to succeed they should not take this route. The prime purpose of the tax is as a mechanism to reduce volatility. International agreement should focus on setting a uniform floor rate. Individual countries should be left with the task of collecting and spending the tax.

Financial markets are about the efficient allocation of resources to run society. We need to encourage a move to longer-term performance measures, welcoming controls that make it harder for the speculators to play games with our economic tool box. The measure I propose is one way to start the process.

But we need to go further and also improve our social and environmental economics.

20 Social Economics

In the developed world, technical progress has accelerated so rapidly that it is possible to envisage, in the future, a fully automated society. We could run our whole economy with a combination of intelligent computers doing the thinking and planning and robots carrying out the tasks. In economic terms, people would then be an unnecessary appendage. This is not so, in terms of society, of course. The whole raison d'être of our economic system is the well being of the population. We forget this at our peril.

The developing world has been quicker to recognize the problem. Mahatma Gandhi, the father of modern India, recognized that employment was a social good and searched for ways to achieve it. Gandhi saw mechanization as a cause of job losses and therefore campaigned for low-technology, labour-intensive production. This might not be the solution those of us in the developed world would choose, but we will also have to find appropriate ways to maintain the social cohesion that work underwrites.

The developed world may have the highest levels of GDP, but we also have lawlessness, relative poverty (inequity) and unhappiness. One of the reasons is the relentless drive for automation and efficiency. We need fewer staff to do the same amount of activity. People without work are a drag on the economy (in terms of needing to fund payment of benefits) but they are also a drag on society, as people without work lose their sense of self-respect and pride.

Each time that levels of employment drop, we face a problem. We describe this either as unemployment or, in the jargon of economists, spare capacity in the labour market. In the latter depiction, the logical 'solution' is to increase consumption. This is what blinkered economic logic tells us. If we follow this logic to its conclusion – at the point where we have automated everything – then further increasing consumption simply means more robots and more materials sucked out of the planet. Ultimately, we cannot compensate for job losses arising from automation by increasing consumption; the Earth and environment cannot take the strain.

We benefit from wealthy societies with growing GDP, but we are coming up against the stops. The first signs of an energy crunch and a commodity squeeze are with us. We will no longer be able to consume our way out of our social economic challenges. Our predicament will boil down to finding economically effective ways to increase employment. In the not too distant future, governments in the developed world will face this challenge. The challenge already exists but we see it as a problem of insufficient growth. Risking the wrath of many economists, I redefine the looming problem as one of insufficient jobs.

Adopting Attitudes from the Developing World

Those of us who live in the developed world should be glad that many leaders of less developed countries are choosing not to pursue our levels of industrialization, despite some of the advice coming out of the World Bank and others. Kamal Nath, when Indian Minister of Environment and Forests, echoed the words of Gandhi when he said, 'God forbid that India should ever take to industrialization after the manner of the West . . . If an entire nation . . . took to similar economic exploitation, it would strip the world bare like locusts!'[1] He went on to say, as Minister of Commerce and Industry, when speaking on employment in 2006, 'Every country has its own demographics and own solutions.'[2] This sums up the world situation well. The challenges of social economics require local solutions, not global recipes.

For the developed world, we must learn to break the cycle of using rising consumption as the way to maintain employment in an increasingly automated world. Job creation in the mould of low-paid manual work might be anathema to us, but the future problems facing the West are similar to those faced by Gandhi.

Social Economics in the Developed World

We need to shift from driving GDP to driving social provision. GDP might still rise, but the change of focus is fundamental. In the old world order, GDP worked well as a proxy for progress; we now need to move on to more enlightened thinking.

Automated production facilities are already with us, but we have technologies that can automate many more activities, such as RFID[3] to replace shop checkouts. Even classic service industries, such as hotels, can be largely automated. The need for workers will evaporate. We will still need hairdressers (if only to provide the conversation that goes with the service) and presumably doctors and lawyers. But even the plumber of the future might be a robot (a worrying thought), and buses will be controlled by computers not human drivers. Perhaps we will all sink into a life of leisure, letting the machines scurry around doing our chores. On a superficial level this might seem attractive, but I foresee automation tending to polarize society.

We will still require leaders in political and commercial circles. These people will be well paid, powerful and content being in control of their own destinies. Another group who may well be happy in what they do is professionals doing people-facing tasks such as teachers, doctors and lawyers – assuming that we do not also pass these tasks to machines (a feasible but depressing thought).

There will also be at least two other classes. There will be well-paid managers controlling the automated world at the interfaces where machines cannot cope.

These people might be cash rich but time poor and feeling the pressure. Another easy-to-identify category is the unemployed, who are bored and feel disenfranchised.

Governments will have a problem. This scenario is already playing out but it is set to become much more extreme.

The scenario we would prefer is a society in which the whole population is engaged, happy, prosperous and safe. Such a society should be 'people-centric' with humans as an active and integral component. This means designing our society with interesting and fulfilling activity available for its members; this I call work. The challenge is to find a sound economic basis that can achieve this without descending into inefficiency and stagnation.

We must plan to stop using rising consumption to maintain employment. We should go further than this, and undo some of the excesses of the 20th century by reducing material consumption. One way, which economists like because it also raises GDP, is to concentrate on services. Consuming services – not goods – will require cultural change to focus on quality of life, not material ownership.

We will also find that our commitment to a sustainable world naturally leads us to improve our social economics. Throughout this book, we have come across numerous examples where building a sustainable society requires more effort and more hands-on work. Rather than acting as a brake on progress to our desired goal, this should spur us on, knowing the social economic value it will have.

Moving to cradle-to-cradle production and the residual-value system generates work (formal and informal) as well as reducing the quantity of virgin commodities sucked into the system. Using more stone in construction to replace concrete is much more skilful and labour-intensive than energy-intensive concrete. As the attitude of the rich shifts to unique design and highly personalized products as a sign of wealth (to replace conspicuous consumption), this will require more human effort, not less.

Lessons from Finland

In the Nordic countries, the welfare state has been built on the principle that everybody should have the right to fulfil his or her duty to work. Finland has grown its own version of Nordic social economics derived from its geography and history. Part of its success has been the rich choice of options to which it has been exposed. Finland navigated its way through the 20th century sandwiched between the capitalist system of the West and the socialism of the old Soviet Union.

It has also been a late developer from a poor rural economy, and is better for that. It has been able to observe the successes – and more importantly, perhaps, the failures – of the nearby countries that led the industrial age (particularly Germany, but also the UK and to an extent the United States). It has become a successful advanced economy by being selective in the policies it borrows.[4]

Finland is not perfect but it does show that explicit social economic policies can work. Finland has been careful to build its strength in social economics on a sound economic base, only making improvements when it could afford to do so. The deep recession of the early 1990s reinforced this lesson, for the government and the workforce. Success comes not from paying people for idleness but from building an inclusive society in which work is a necessity, a duty and a source of dignity.

Real New Jobs

Real new jobs can be hard to find in our increasingly automated economies. There is often a trade-off between employing people and capital expenditure on machines. People provide a personal service, are flexible and adaptable and a workforce acting as a social network can be very good for the business, increasing reputation and drawing in customers. Machines, on the other hand, are immune from HR problems, incur low operating costs and are easy to relocate or scrap.

The level of automation to apply is a matter of business judgement. Regulation such as the minimum wage puts a floor to the figures with regard to people costs and in marginal cases will favour automation.

I have worked with a lot of business plans to support IT implementations and there is a common argument that automation will reduce manpower and therefore costs. Quite so, but staff reductions have entered the business mindset as invariably a good thing, even if closer analysis might show otherwise.

We seldom, if ever, follow the converse thought process and examine whether we can employ more people in order to save on capital expenditure. This is contrary to our experience and contrary to what we see as the march of technology having to offer the business. New real jobs are, therefore, very hard to find without continuing the model of ever-increasing consumption and ever more stress on our planet's systems.

Public Sector Policy Options

Holding employment at sustainable levels requires a tricky balancing act of generating work for the populace without undermining core economics. The dichotomy society will face is how to draw more people into paid employment without undermining commercial competitiveness. Employing huge armies of people to do very little is clearly inefficient, but if our society is run by machines where is employment to be found?

One source of employment is the public sector; but if the number of jobs exceeds the requirement for efficient administration and cost-effective public services, then it is simply wasteful. However, we often have a choice between ways of delivering services. We can compare people-intensive methods with capital-intensive automation, weighting our decision to take account of the cost savings of taking people into employment.

Future civil servants might be given explicit targets to increase the number of people employed in the public sector. Crucially, though, budget caps and other performance measures will also need to be retained. This will require radically different thinking. This would not be about overstaffing or retaining lazy or non-effective staff in employment. This would be looking for ways to deliver the same outcome by using more people without costing the government more.

One workable measure, although narrow in scope, is conscription, in which young people are required to give a period of their working life to serve in the country's defence forces. The headline reason is for the protection of the country, but conscription also provides useful activity for a segment of the working age population and instils certain disciplines and values. Conscientious objectors can opt for community service, such as working in a hospital, but the benefits are much the same. In macro-financial terms, the government has taken x man/years out of the labour pool, spending the same (or less) than the liability to pay unemployment benefit.

Military service has been mandatory in Finland ever since its independence in 1917. Every man[5] is required to serve for a period of between 6 and 12 months (13 months for the public service alternative). The recruits are provided with food and accommodation but very low levels of pay (less than 10€ per day). In addition to their defence role, soldiers can often be seen helping with the arrangements for local or national events (including providing young officers as dancing partners for unaccompanied female guests at the President's Annual Ball).

It is fully accepted that a period of conscription is the normal post-school activity. Few take up the public service option because of family and social pressure to conform. It is directly good for the security of the nation, and indirectly helps to instil values of work ethic, national pride and kinship with fellow citizens also going through the same tough regime.

Finland shows that conscription can be much more than emergency legislation in times of war: it can be an integral part of the social economic system.

The Role of the Third Sector

The not-for-profit sector (also called the third sector) has the potential for greater social economic impact. There are all sorts of 'good' activities that governments cannot afford to fund. There is merit in the concept of allowing the same level of expenditure that would otherwise be paid as unemployment benefit going to charitable organizations to pay people to carry out these activities.

For the workers, these are real (but low paid) jobs and society is being provided with a service that it could not otherwise afford. If this is seen as forcing charities to employ the long-term unemployed, then there will be a stigma attached to this kind of employment. But, if handled carefully, it could be quite the reverse. For example, some people may opt to take early retirement in order to do low-paid but enjoyable and satisfying work in the third sector.

The key to success will be the attitude that society takes to such work; it should be regarded as normal and respectable to choose to take on low-paid work doing something that is useful for society.

Social Economics and Borders

The concept of needing to design useful activity for a population relies on the presumption that there is a prescribed population for which a government has responsibility. This needs a closer examination, because a problem is lurking.

Immigration is often seen as a good thing; it expands the workforce and expands the economy. Drawing in new workers who are willing to work for low pay, or do the unpleasant jobs that the existing population avoids, is beneficial for the economy.

As we think in a more sustainable way, beyond the pure economics, we notice the additional responsibility that immigration brings with it. The immigrants go on to have children with full rights of citizenship. They aspire to a good education and good jobs, and so they should. A caste system – like that in India – in which people are born into a stratum of society and are expected to remain there[6] does not fit with the Western concept of an equitable society.

A more acceptable model (if we insist that we need cheaper labour than our own society can provide) is where guest workers do not get a right of residence but simply a right to work for a set period. In this way, a steady stream of low-paid, low-expectation workers can be maintained (assuming there are relatively less well-off countries to act as the source).

Designing sustainable societies requires a clear definition of membership. I foresee that governments will exert tighter control over the definition of the right to live in a society in tandem with improving their social economic performance.

Response by Governments

Governments have a responsibility to society which transcends economic performance, but they also do not want to undermine their economies. Politicians will have to balance carefully the social and economic implications of their decisions. If handled well, this will stabilize society, improve social cohesion and develop a deep-rooted sense of nationhood amongst the population.

The starting assumption is that the government has a responsibility to all its residents, which can be expressed as a financial liability for each person of working age (equivalent to the costs incurred if that person is out of work and reliant on the state).[7] The government could then restructure its internal finances in a cost-neutral manner to reflect this liability. The existing budget for any part of the provision of state services could be split into two components. The first would be the financial liability avoided through employment. The second would be the delivery of the service.

Where savings can be made through reducing the workforce, budget holders would also lose that component of their budget equating to the number of people put back into the labour pool. Conversely, departments could attract a higher budget by designing service delivery that required a larger workforce. The amounts involved are only the equivalent to the level of unemployment pay (presumably less than staff salaries), so the general principle of only employing the staff needed is not undermined. But this will give the employment greater weight in decisions, particularly in comparison with capital expenditure.

In an economy where there is a shortage of workers, this measure would be ridiculous. It only works when unemployment is endemic. Government departments are then forced to take full account of the social economic effects of their decisions. The costs or benefits from the expansion or contraction of the number of people employed in the public sector would become true figures from the perspective of a total national budget.

Governments will also look to reward or encourage industry to structure their operations to be more people-intensive and less automated. A simplistic measure would be to pay companies to hire the unemployed. This requires a lot of control. In reality, whatever the red tape, it would end up with companies attempting to milk the system in order to get money from the government to employ staff to do work that needs to be done in any case. Some limited short-term arrangements, to give work experience to the young or re-engage the long-term unemployed with the world of work, will continue to have a place. But the simple model of paying companies to hire people is inherently wasteful and unworkable.

A soft approach that governments could take is to promote people-intensive activity that does not require expending material resources, such as personal services and entertainment. There are also hard economic levers that could be used, but which, in the light of current economic thinking, may seem peculiar. The discussion of these below is deliberately kept very simple in order to portray the principle. Of course, complexities would arise if these ideas were adopted, as the cat-and-mouse mechanism of companies finding loopholes, and government closing them, takes place.

The first assumption I make for the basis of this discussion is that actions will be tax neutral, with the overall level of tax paid by business remaining the same.

The simplest mechanism a government could consider is offsetting a fixed figure per employee against corporation tax. This might be at a similar rate to the residual liability to the state of the workforce if they were out of work. This would link the issues of a potential responsibility to pay unemployment benefit with corporation tax. The headline rate for corporation tax would then need to be adjusted up to be tax neutral to the government.

A more complex, and more interesting, idea is to set corporation tax on a sliding scale relating to the ratio of employees to profit. Such a mechanism (according to a carefully worked-out equation that tax experts could argue over) would provide a tax incentive for profitable companies to draw more people into their workforce.

This tax incentive to retain or expand the workforce has no effect on a company making losses. In this case, cuts in the workforce are one potential area to stem the losses, so there would be no change in behaviour there. If the company continues to struggle and profits are low, then, again, the incentive has little effect. Such companies are in survival mode and cannot afford to improve their social economic contribution.

The incentive kicks in when profitability is high. There is then a strong commercial incentive to adopt a strategy that employs a larger workforce in order to minimize the tax bill. When profits are growing strongly, a company's tax advisors will be urging the company to find ways of increasing the headcount.

The overall effect is that such a tax regime would reward profitable companies that make an explicit effort to employ people. The government's need to increase employment and businesses' drive to maximize profitability would then be aligned. Tax experts could, no doubt, tune the formula used to generate the outcome required.

The Business Context

Governments will make efforts to counter the tendency to eliminate jobs, as discussed above. For business to benefit, there are a range of approaches that can be adopted, for example, building a community of employees for whom quality of life is an explicit aim. This already pays off, as many companies know through the retention of good staff and the ability to pay lower salaries (for the same level of skill and experience). Such communities, characterized by commitment towards its employees by the company and loyalty to the company by the workforce, also reduce the risk of damaging strikes.

The recent business focus on cost savings from outsourcing will need to be reconsidered, and is already under scrutiny as the following example illustrates. British Airways (BA) outsourced its in-flight catering business to Gate Gourmet in1997.[8] At the time, it seemed a sensible commercial restructuring of the business, following in the steps of many other companies across industry. This part of the business operations could then go out to competitive tender at regular intervals, driving down the costs to BA.

This reduced the headcount of BA, and headline costs, but BA was also undermining its wider community of workers. Many staff, now employed by the contractor, had been employed by BA and still had relations and friends on the BA payroll. By 2005, the contractor was in financial difficulties, and Gate Gourmet was forced into job cuts and reductions in benefits.

This impacted on the wider BA social community. Gate Gourmet owned the problem and, in a commercial sense, BA was not at fault. This was no insulation from the sympathy strike that followed in August 2005 by BA's ground staff. The strike cost BA £40–60 million[9] in direct losses and more in terms of loss of reputation.

In hindsight, BA can reflect on whether the financial saving of outsourcing improved profitability over the longer term. Perhaps catering should have been kept in-house to reduce risk and maintain a strong support community, even if this would have meant passing over a potential short-term saving.

If government bring in legislation to provide incentives for employment, such as those outlined above, it could lead to much less outsourcing and other changes in corporate behaviour. The figure 'number of employees' would become a business metric to reduce the tax bill.

Large corporations would seek to retain people-intensive business units or subsidiary companies in order to reduce the profit-per-employee figure. Targeting groups of low-cost employees, such as older employees approaching retirement or young people entering the job market, would make commercial sense. It would also make sense to build a workforce that is larger but less well paid, using non-monetary incentives to attract and retain good staff. Employing relatively low-level support staff to take on routine administrative tasks will become fashionable again, reversing the trend of recent years of putting everything on the intranet and expecting managers to run their own administration. This will also reduce some of the pressure on highly skilled essential staff, improving their quality of life as well as performance and retention.

An Opportunity: Larger Workforce and Lower Costs

In this example, I use a factory that makes a product or carries out a process (assuming, of course, that this factory requires workers and has not been completely automated). Normal working is five-day operations by a full-time workforce. Surge production moves into the weekend when overtime is paid.

This facility could move to a different model of working by doubling its workforce and changing to a six-day working week. Each employee would work a three-day week with pay levels proportional to the old five-day week, so this would be close to cost-neutral for the company. The attraction for workers would be improved quality of life. The attraction for the company would be potential tax breaks (if the government targets increased employment) and regular utilization of the production facilities over six rather five days.

Families who want to maintain a high-income lifestyle could choose to have both husband and wife working three (different) days. Others might welcome having more time to work in the community as a second job or as a volunteer. Some might simply enjoy having more time for their family and leisure pursuits without feeling any guilt.

Such a model fits with both the social economics and the business profitability of a sustainable world. This could become a very normal way of building a happy and contented work force.

Quality of Life

From automation springs the prospect of a life where we work less and have more time for leisure and family. This is not how it has worked out. Instead, the benefits of increased productivity and efficiency have been taken as higher real incomes and more consumption. The time has come to use machines to improve the quality of life rather than expand the quantity of material possessions. I suggest that we do not crave a hedonistic lifestyle; success on a human level is not about wealth derived from little work. Lottery winners and those born into great fortune attest to that. People need constructive engagement with society and the best demonstration of that is through work.

Those of us who live in the developed world are at a very fortunate point in history. We have the capability of designing fulfilling lives for ourselves and our fellow citizens whilst being insulated from the pressure of finding the next meal. We have ample resources available to us, and machinery to take on the drudgery of many tasks, but we have a choice to make. We can conserve our natural resources and be content with living safe and fulfilling lives as part of a cooperative community; or waste our resources on a fight for who can earn the largest salary, consume the most material goods or live in the largest house in the neighbourhood.

If we get it right, we will see the boundaries between work and leisure becoming blurred. In the developed world, it is our fixation on the size of the pay cheque that has confused us.

As a teenager, I used to spend my summers on my uncle's farm in Scotland. The activity was seven days a week but it did not seem like work; it was a way of life. When I left to return home to the city of Oxford, my uncle would give me some money, saying that I had earned it. I had loved every minute of my stay and there was no need for payment, but I enjoyed the monetary bonus.

As a young man, my first few years of paid employment were as an officer with Britain's Parachute Forces. The challenges were immense and exciting. It still seems surprising to me that I got paid for such a way of life. There must be wealthy city traders who would pay a lot to purchase the level of raw adrenalin that came with my relatively low-paid employment.

When job-hunting, we tend not to focus on enjoyable and fulfilling activities, which include spending time with our families (instead we tend to focus on considerations such as paying the mortgage). As employers, we tend not to focus on providing security, community and a sense of worth. In both cases, these are qualities we should be focusing on.

The developed world has an attitude problem. We aspire to improve our status and lives through material advancement. This destructive mindset must be broken, but it will take a crisis to dent our material expectations and remind us of the value of security, personal relations, community and all the true indicators of quality of life. A major global recession with very high levels of unemployment may be the medicine required. This may be just what is on offer:

Our actions over the coming few decades could create risks of major disruption to economic and social activity, later in this century . . . on a scale similar to those associated with the great wars and the economic depression of the first half of the 20th century.

Stern Review report on The Economics of Climate Change[10]

21 Environmental Economics

The environment is an awkward inconvenience that does not fit easily into economic theory. Economists categorize it as an 'externality', meaning simply that it lies outside the economic model. It would be more useful if we could extend our economic models to bring conservation of the environment inside the system.

Much of the terminology has become familiar (such as carbon taxes, carbon trading and pollution credits) but the field is still not well understood. No doubt there will be much progress in the years ahead, as economists work out how to transform our desire to retain our natural world into real-world mechanisms. In this chapter, I will review two mechanisms for which robust theory exists: environmental taxes and cap-and-trade markets. A third rather more speculative idea is also introduced with regard to placing economic value on natural land.

Environmental Taxes

The principle of environmental taxes is to discourage bad activities (tax) and encourage good behaviour (incentives). As the tax-raising measure succeeds in its aim of stamping out the bad behaviour, tax receipts drop to zero. Governments should not, therefore, plan to base their core budget on environmental taxes; or there is a danger that a perverse incentive arises to retain environmental degradation in order to maintain revenue.

Environmental taxes can be very effective as a stick to wield during the transition to a sustainable society. Being short-term, the taxes are not required to underpin general finances, so they can be used to buy off the potential losers, making the changes required politically acceptable.

For example, in the discussion over energy in Chapter 7 we identified an appropriate policy for governments to adopt, consisting of driving up taxes on domestic fuel in order to facilitate appropriate adaptation in the housing sector. Politicians can diffuse resistance by using the tax collected to buy off the poor, the old, the disadvantaged and groups with political power. Crucially, we must not fall into the trap of using tax receipts to subsidize continued bad behaviour. In the case of energy, we must not subsidize the price of fuel. Although politically expedient, it would defeat the whole purpose of the tax. The inducement has to be in terms of support for investment in better fuel efficiency (such as low-energy appliances and good insulation) to peg the cost through reduced fuel usage.

A related example is escalating taxes on transport fuels. Again the tax receipts can be used to muffle dissent, but not through fuel subsidy for some people or subsidies relating to the costs of car ownership. The enticement in this case could be investment targeted towards reducing the need to travel (or transport freight), including investment in improved mass-transit systems.

Environmental taxes can thus be excellent tools to force adaptation. Another useful tool during the transition period is 'cap-and-trade' applied to harmful emissions.

Cap-and-Trade for Harmful Emissions

The principle is to set a cap on emissions and then reduce the cap over time. Ideally, the final target is zero harmful emissions. A market is then established of tradable permits (or credits). Market players can choose to buy permits to continue to pollute, or invest in reducing emissions, in which case they are in a position to sell credits in the market.

A key aspect is the initial allocation of permits. One way of doing this is to identify who the polluters are (and the quantities), and then allocate permits accordingly, accepting this as the starting baseline.[1] This process hands value to the biggest polluters, which may seem unfair, but it will reduce their opposition to establishing the market.

Bizarrely, if a particular type of pollution seems likely to become subject to a cap, then it would make commercial sense to ensure that emissions are maximized leading up to the initiation of the market (if it is based on a free allocation of permits). The other method of allocating permits is to auction them, which is more effective and fairer. Governments would also welcome the extra income. It is in the self-interest of industry to lobby for a free allocation of initial permits, but industry should expect governments to conduct auctions for most future allocations.

The cap-and-trade mechanism is very good in theory as a catalyst to mobilize investment and channel it to where it can have most effect; but it will work only if the system of governance within which the market operates is robust and well-controlled.

If the market is allowed to extend into countries with lax controls and weak governance, this undermines the value of the tradable permits. Companies buying credits from a dubious source might well be complying with the letter of market regulation (in their own tightly controlled market), but it would be galling to see good investment siphoned off and wasted. Such purchases could end up in the pockets of corrupt officials or businesses in some remote location without delivering watertight guarantees of emission reduction.

Individual companies will have to choose how to approach cap-and-trade. It will depend on which emission/pollutant is being targeted, the expense of adopting processes to reduce it, and the price of permits in the market. The calculation may show that it is cheaper to carry on as before and purchase permits.

Even so, I view this as investing in improving the performance of other players, which seems an odd way to behave.

As the cap is screwed down, permits can be expected to become more and more expensive. I suggest that buying permits will, in most cases, be a 'mug's game', simply delaying investment that will have to take place eventually. Buying permits will make it possible to trumpet loudly that the company is meeting its targets – when in fact it has done nothing – but damaging accusations of greenwash may then follow.

I suggest that the better tactic is to invest a company's own cash in delivering emission reductions, even if this is more expensive than the current price of credits. In this way, the company can be assured that the emission reductions are real, that any publicity will be good and it will act as a hedge against the future price of permits.

If reductions can be made that exceed the targets set, and put the company in the position of selling credits, then so much the better. In effect, other emitters will be paying for the company's investment.

Despite some of the drawbacks, cap-and-trade is a useful mechanism within tightly controlled markets to control the flow of investment. This is particularly useful where the costs of making reductions are markedly different between industries. In such cases, trading emissions permits will work well to ensure the most cost-effective reductions are taken first.

Extending cap-and-trade to global markets has been suggested. In my opinion, there is little chance of agreeing and implementing the watertight procedures needed. The danger is that global cap-and-trade becomes a smoke-screen for inaction. Cap-and-trade should be kept for where it can have most effect, at national or perhaps regional level.

The Market for Carbon

The most high profile role of cap-and-trade is in regard to carbon, in order to drive the transition to a world beyond fossil fuels.

The foundation of the system is a regulatory cap on allowable emissions. The market participants are then allocated carbon allowances. If the allowance is more than is needed, the excess can be sold on the market. Other players, who want to emit more carbon than their allowance, then buy credits, with the market setting the price.

Once in place, the cap can be tightened to reduce carbon release to the desired levels. Investment moves efficiently to where it has the most effect in reducing emissions. A price is set for CO_2 emissions, giving a figure against which to make well-informed commercial decisions, focusing decision makers on the cost-benefit analysis of moving to a low carbon economy.

For the cap to work, the following preconditions are required: the cap must apply across all market participants; there must be effective penalties for non-compliance; and initial allowances of carbon emissions must be allocated fairly and the allowances accepted by all the market participants.

Such carbon trading is seen as important to implementing the Kyoto Protocol, but the protocol does not provide the necessary preconditions for an effective market: major carbon emitters are not included; there are no penalties agreed; and the initial allowances are being disputed (particularly by the United States who, at the time of writing in 2007, had not joined the Protocol).

The EU Emission Trading Scheme (ETS) is potentially much stronger. It is aimed at delivering the EU's commitment under the Kyoto Protocol to achieve 8% reduction (compared to 1990 levels) in emissions of greenhouse gases by 2012. It covers all the main players within the EU.[2] If robust mechanisms can be agreed to allocate and enforce quotas, then this could develop into an effective market. Other carbon markets include the Chicago Climate Futures Exchange (established in 2003 by 14 of the largest greenhouse-gas emitters in the United States) and the Montréal Climate Exchange for the Canadian carbon market.

NGOs are also involved in setting up tradable emission reduction credits. The most credible of these is the Voluntary Carbon Standard (VCS) – the result of collaboration between The Climate Group (TCG), the International Emissions Trading Association (IETA) and the World Economic Forum (WEF) Global Greenhouse Register. Many of the projects funded by the sale of such credits can make a valuable contribution to reducing the growth in carbon emissions in developing countries. Other popular schemes involve planting or preserving forests – valuable work, but one that requires robust controls to keep the forest intact long into the future. Organizations that buy such credits are making useful charitable donations, and the VCS gives confidence that the money will be spent wisely. However, to use such purchases to justify avoiding taking action to reduce emissions and then claiming to be 'carbon neutral' is hypocrisy.

An interesting, but probably unworkable, initiative has been championed in the UK by Colin Challen, MP. He brought a Private Members Bill to the UK parliament to introduce a domestic trading scheme for carbon emissions. The concept is for an equitable system in which each person receives a tradable carbon allowance that they can use or sell, and, if necessary, they can purchase more.

There will be many more attempts to set up carbon markets, and expand those that exist, providing a wealth of opportunities to profit from the disruptive transition to a world beyond fossil fuels.

Whether this is a genuinely useful mechanism – in terms of protecting the environment – depends on how committed we are to curing our addiction to fossil fuels. Markets can only be as good as the regulations with which we bind them. As a society, we need to be clear about our aim. If we want to prevent further climate change, then our target must be to stop releasing fossil carbon into the atmosphere. If we simply want to delay the energy crunch, controlling consumption through carbon trading will extend the useful life of fossil fuels and support the development of marginal deposits. But by providing a stable market and delaying the switch from fossil fuels, we may be ensuring an even greater release of fossil carbon over the long term.

Carbon trading is a useful mechanism but we must not fudge the purpose. In my mind, the choice is clear: it must be a mechanism for eliminating the use of fossil fuel. Anything less will be counterproductive. The plan must be to screw the cap ever tighter at a pace based on the recommendations of climate scientists. This will make establishing carbon markets harder, but if we do not agree such robust controls then the system will have little more value than a lottery.

Putting a Value to Natural Assets

An externality that we must bring inside our economic framework is that natural land has no economic value in the current system. Unless we solve this, economic pressure will always attempt to pull it into the economy to make it productive, and so destroy its natural state.

Land in its natural state has little or no value because there is no yield. Sites with buildings have tenants who pay rent; farmland produces cash crops. Natural land is just there, as a highly important part of the world's ecosystem, but also worthless.

Currently, natural land can have value in our economic system as a source of speculation, where the buyer believes they will be able to change the status quo and bring it into the economy by development or clearance for farming. But if it is a natural habitat, subject to robust and secure arrangements to remain as such, then it has no value. This is the situation with national parks and nature reserves that have been permanently taken out of the economic system.

One way that governments can improve the stock of protected natural capital is to look for opportunities to acquire land and take it out of the economic system, so increasing the extent of national parks.

In the 1950s, Finland's state electricity company had plans to extend hydroelectric power by harnessing the power of the rivers Oulankajoki and Kitkajoki. The company bought all the land that would be needed through an aggressive purchase scheme. I spoke with a resident of the area who recalled that where there were competing claims to the title of a particular piece of forest, then the company simply paid for the land twice, such was the commercial focus on completing the purchase as quickly as possible. However, when the project came to the Finnish parliament for approval, it ran into opposition due to the natural landscape that would be lost. After a lot of wrangling, the final outcome was that the land was converted instead into the Oulanka National Park, one of the most remote and beautiful wilderness areas in northern Europe.

Well-run countries with spare resources can act like this. Governments that have an economy in crisis – or are simply corrupt – are tempted by the reverse approach and bring such 'protected' land back into the economic system, selling it for development and pocketing the cash windfall.

Our economic system operates around our protected natural areas, seeing them as an indulgence and a waste of potentially productive land. We rely on legislation to keep these pressures at bay. There is an open loop always available to suck in more natural land, but a weak return loop where little land is ever returned to its natural state. This must change or, bit by bit, we will lose it all.

Good examples of natural land outside the ownership of the state will become increasingly rare. Nevertheless, as attitudes change, driven by the Sustainable Revolution, affluent people will want to own their piece of natural land. This is a recipe for increasing value. It may be that the ownership of land kept in its natural state will be the new status symbol, more satisfying than a luxury yacht and much more exclusive, for example, an island with marvellous natural habitats and a luxurious lodge built using state-of-the-art green technology with virtually zero environmental impact. This will be how the mega rich show off as we go into the 22nd century, driving up the value of the best natural habitats still in private ownership.

Less spectacular sites, which are not places of great beauty, may not rise in value and will remain subject to pressures to bring them back into the economic system. Such sites, which are scattered amongst our farmland, or exist within the built infrastructure, provide refuge for wildlife and have a vital role in interconnecting natural ecology with man's world. We need a way to place a robust economic value on these sites, too.

A more comprehensive economic system would put a value to natural land so we have an economic basis for its protection. My proposal is to tax developed land in order to provide income to the owners of natural land. This would establish an economic reason to protect it, but it would also bring a major dislocation to the concept of wealth, which the potential losers would resist strongly.

There would be a number of ways of implementing the proposal. To illustrate the principle, I will flesh out one option for a national scheme, which assumes that the overall result will be cost-neutral to the government.

A National Scheme to Support Natural Land

I propose a flat-rate tax on all urban sites based on the land area occupied. The funds raised are then used to support a payment system for all natural land. National parks would be outside the system, assuming that they are subject to watertight legal protection that keeps them forever outside the economy. This urban tax would be separate from and additional to other property taxes, although for administrative convenience it could piggyback on the same collection system. (Land used for agricultural production would incur neither tax nor benefit under this scheme.)

Owners of natural land would find that they could draw a yield by keeping the land in its natural state. The size of the payment would dictate the strength of the incentive and some sort of inspection or certification regime would be required, of course. Amongst the beneficiaries, farmers might find that the income from letting their land revert to natural habitats was comparable with the income from farming, but with less effort. In operating the system, we would need to be vigilant that this does not go too far.

For valuable urban sites in the centre of cities or densely populated communities, the flat-rate tax would be a relatively small additional overhead, so it would have little or no impact on the taxpayers.

For low-density urban sites, the flat-rate charge would be a significant overhead, so the biggest effect would be on urban sprawl. Such a tax would compound the other negative factors of living in these areas, such as the escalating cost of commuting by car. As the attraction of living in these areas diminished, property values would fall and could precipitate a crash. This would be the price of unwinding the 20th-century model of urban expansion, but the regeneration that would follow would greatly improve the quality of community life.

I foresee developers spotting the opportunities and acting to regenerate such areas. The relatively large detached houses with wide drives and large gardens, particularly those of mediocre quality and poor energy efficiency, will be replaced. In their place, high-density, high-quality houses will be built around tight communities with excellent shared spaces. There are many reasons why such developments will dominate 21st-century construction (discussed in Chapter 11); this tax will play a small part in forcing the pace of change.

A further refinement to the proposed system could be to allow the income from any natural land to be offset against charges for urban land, so that a balanced portfolio of ownership would become one part of sensible tax planning. Another effect would be on the layout of our urban spaces. For example, a developer rebuilding one of the old suburbs could reinstate a balance of natural land within the plan. An appropriate ownership structure could be used to balance the urban-use tax with the payments claimed on the natural land, so each new resident would pay little tax as well as having access to a shared area of natural land where children could play with neighbours.

It is relatively easy to envisage such a tax influencing behaviour within the jurisdiction of one country. There would be much detail to work out, but the principle is straightforward. Applying the principle internationally would be much more difficult, but, in theory, it would be possible.

International Action to Protect Natural Habitats

Initiatives to put a value on natural land in a country's accounts – or 'Natural Resource Accounting'[3] – have been discussed at international level. To make this a reality would be a long negotiation brokered, presumably, by the UN. Let us assume that a system along the same lines as the national scheme proposed above could be implemented at international level, and explore the likely outcomes.

Each country would incur a charge on the area of its land taken up by urban development and a credit for natural land, with agricultural land exempt.

Highly developed countries, like many in Europe including Britain, would be net contributors. Countries rich in natural assets, such as Brazil with the Amazon rainforest, would be major beneficiaries. The new wealth would come from owning and preserving these natural habitats.

Rich developed countries would have to accept this as the price of keeping the Earth's ecosystem intact. Without a system that places a value on natural habitats, the world economic system would forever press to bring such land into play. In our present system, growing soya beans produces income; leaving the rainforest in its virgin state does not. Western governments now urge restraint on the destruction of natural habitats in the undeveloped world by relying on a country's willingness to be good world citizens. This will remain a weak argument unless backed up by a hard-nosed economic mechanism.

Countries with lots of natural capital could underpin their finances by drawing income from the rest of the world, provided they protect their natural assets. Many in the developed world will baulk at paying such a price.

But we have been paying many governments of the Middle East a handsome income as the price of pumping out and burning their oil. We have been paying them to help destroy the health of the Earth; how much better it would be to divert the income flow to countries that protect it.

Unfortunately, from the Western perspective, this looks like a double whammy. Not only must we wean ourselves off fossil fuels, but we must also pay to preserve natural habitats. This will risk undermining the balance of the current world economic system. I feel confident that Western society would survive, and businesses would continue to thrive, but the macro-economic toolbox would be different. Countries with extensive natural habitats would rise up the wealth league but, crucially, only stay there by careful stewardship and conservation of their natural assets.

There will be apparent anomalies or countries that cause concern within such a system, for example Bangladesh. This densely populated country, which has preserved very little of its natural habitats, would be a major contributor. This would be logically correct. Bangladesh's problem is population growth running out of control. If every country allowed its population to expand unhindered the world would be stripped bare.

We should want to continue to help Bangladesh, of course, not least because rising sea levels (through no fault of Bangladesh) will hit the country hard. Even so, Bangladesh should not be exempt, because that would undermine the principle. Instead, the country would require a large slice of its aid to pay its contribution to the preservation of the world's natural habitats. This would clarify the economics, even if we then chose to increase aid to Bangladesh to compensate, whilst supporting the country in moving towards a sustainable future.

Those who would be net payers into such an urban-use tax scheme will resist it and will be reluctant to accept the principle. As damage to the Earth becomes real, impacting on us all, attitudes should change. A major realignment in world economic power will follow. The economic power of oil has been a major influence on the economic system. Putting an economic value to natural land will be a new influence, but one that should be more enduring than the relatively short-term windfall income from oil.

The Evolution of Environmental Economics

Over the next few decades, environmental economics will have an important role to play in the transition to a sustainable world. Environmental taxes will force early adaptation. Cap-and-trade will channel investment to where it will have most effect.

After the transition period, we will no longer tolerate negative impacts on the environment, and environmental taxes will no longer generate substantial tax receipts. Complete bans on damaging emissions will take their place. A few environmental taxes and cap-and-trade markets will live on to regulate emissions that we are happy to allow but wish to hold to a sustainable level.

Environmental economics will have a continuing long-term role in maintaining, preserving and reinstating natural habitats. The detailed method that evolves will no doubt be different to the one I propose, but putting an economic value to natural land is unquestionably the way to preserve it. Without such a mechanism, our economic system will attempt to draw every piece of land into 'productive' use and thereby destroy the diversity of Earth's natural ecology.

Having considered some of the mechanisms of a sustainable world, from improved capital markets to social and environmental economics, I will turn to how to facilitate the transition using business as the primary agent for change. But, first, I will outline the concept of using 'adaptation laboratories' as an easy way to jump forward to potential solutions.

22 Adaptation Laboratories

The Sustainable Revolution will require some dramatic changes and novel solutions. We do not need to start from scratch. We can look closely at our world for ideas that we can transpose from one place to another or from a past age to the present day. I call this concept 'adaptation laboratories'.

In scanning the world for possible solutions to the challenges we face, we should look for extreme situations in terms of climate or society. Such situations lead to unusual or unconventional methods and could be just what we need. For example, societies in very hot or very cold environments have evolved coping strategies to stay comfortable within the available (or affordable) energy supply. We will find some answers to the coming energy crunch within these societies. To address the challenge of water conservation, we will find ideas in societies in very arid areas.

Social extremes can also be a source of inspiration. If we find a very happy or very healthy society, we want to know how it has achieved this, and will look closely at it to see what policies we can borrow. The converse, a highly stressed and unhappy society, indicates what we should avoid.

Rather than research and development within a scientific laboratory setting, the concept I seek to describe here is that of adaptation laboratories embedded within living society. Here the methods or behaviours are already established, so we can expect that any problems will have been ironed out. These then need to be extracted from the societies where they have been found in order to attempt to solve the adaptation challenges we face. The fit will not be perfect: changes will be required and anomalies will be exposed. But even if the borrowed idea is ultimately rejected, the innovation can spark a new line of investigation.

Another source of potentially useful ideas derives from social history. For example, in the past, people had to cope before we had such extensive access to fossil fuels. Our ancestors must have had methods that we could apply today. If we give the old method a complete makeover in terms of using modern design and technology, the result can be a winning system or product.

One adaptation laboratory used extensively in this book is Finland. It is a beautiful country on the northern edge of Europe which regularly appears at the top of world rankings for environmental stewardship[1] and world competitiveness.[2] From 2001 to 2006 it did not drop below third place in either index. How it achieves this double win is worth examining.

Finland as an Adaptation Laboratory

Finland has been successful in breaking the fatal link between economic growth and the environmental load. Thus, we have responded to one of the main tasks of sustainable development.

Minister for the Environment, Finland[3]

Finland is the northernmost country in the EU with some of the best protected wilderness areas in the world. It also has a dynamic economy from which, for example, the Finnish company Nokia has grown to become a major multinational corporation. It is hard for an outsider to identify the secret of the country's success; it is not any one thing. It is partly the way everything interconnects so well, and it partly stems from a national state of mind, an attitude which in turn has come about due to the harsh climate.

The first snows can be expected in October and it may not melt in many places until the beginning of May. The main national radio station reports in its morning weather forecast when the sun rises and sets. In the winter, it also reports which towns have entered the period of continuous night, starting with the small town of Utsjoki, where the sun sets towards the end of November and does not reappear until mid January. As Christmas approaches, towns further and further south are included. This is not a country where living comes easy.

In the past, in the area that is now modern Finland, if you were not prepared for the winter you would not survive. If you relied on someone else to provide a service in a climate where the temperature stays below −25°C for weeks at a time, it could be your life that hinged on its successful delivery. The sense of community that this strong interdependence generates is palpable and flows through the society.

Finland has not built its sustainability credentials on denying the benefits of technology and global trade. Finland has a dynamic economy that embraces modern technology and methods, but it also manages to be more sustainable than most other societies in the developed world. The Finnish historian, Pauli Kettunen, writes about the Nordic modernization process that it is characterized by the 'intertwining of three different ideological elements ... the idealized heritage of the free independent peasant, the spirit of capitalism and the utopia of socialism'.[4] Finland's secret is achieving a fusion of the best aspects of a range of ideologies.

Even though Finland is not perfect and the Finnish way is not universally applicable, if we could all adapt to our piece of the globe as well as the Finns have to theirs, that would be a great step towards a sustainable world.

Concepts for Energy-Neutral Buildings

The best way to illustrate the concept of adaptation laboratories is to follow through an extended example. The challenge I will address is that of energy-neutral buildings, which were briefly discussed in Chapter 7. This is one of the elements in securing a sustainable future, yet in the contemporary developed world it seems impossibly ambitious, so it will be a tough test of the concept.

First we need to frame the context. We are not looking for an energy-neutral building that we can place anywhere in the world. That would be using the old-style thinking that has led us into the trap we now find ourselves in, with similar building designs migrating to all corners of the globe.

I will look at the challenge of designing energy-neutral buildings for Britain before moving to other contexts. I will pick up lessons from northern Europe, the Middle East, Africa and India. My first stop is Finland.

Our family house in Finland is a standard design with highly efficient insulation and triple-glazing. The heating system does not seem to contribute much until the outside temperature falls below zero. If this house were transplanted to Britain, heating might not be needed at all except for the handful of days each year when British temperatures drop below zero. There would be issues to solve in terms of copying the house design and applying it to the British context. A one-off design would be expensive, requiring importation of materials and appropriately skilled tradesmen, but, once the fittings and methods became standard, the price premium would drop.

It would be possible for brave developers in Britain not to fit a central heating system at all, shifting capital expenditure from heating to vastly improved insulation. As fuel prices climb, ultra-low fuel bills will become an increasingly powerful sales pitch. The reluctance to buy a house without conventional heating might not be overcome until there is a track record of successful energy neutral buildings. Residents will also have to learn to adapt their behaviour, for example, learning to open two windows where in the past there was just one, as this is the standard way that triple glazing is implemented in the Nordic countries.

From Finland, Britain can learn how to eliminate virtually all need to use energy for heating; but it would still need energy to keep cool in hot summer weather. Here we can look to the Middle East. Three simple measures are used: thick walls that act as heat sinks; providing shade from the sun; and carefully designed natural ventilation. Applying this to Britain takes a little thought and perhaps some advanced automated engineering. In Britain, we want to use solar gain for most of the year, so south-facing areas should be enclosed by glass to capture the heat. This makes cooling more difficult. Even so, computer-controlled ventilation and fold-out sunscreens together with careful positioning of thick walls should be able to negate the need to use energy for cooling.

Having resolved heating and cooling using lessons from the edge of the Arctic and the desert, there is still a need for energy to run the activities inside the building. For this we can turn to Africa. Rural Africa is a long way behind the West in terms of development. In most places, there is no power grid, telephone network or piped gas. Even so, they are finding ways to join in with the developed world, and teaching the more advanced countries a lesson in the process.

Systems are being developed in Africa to deliver energy for the key requirements of modern life: refrigeration, light (for the evenings), a mobile phone charger and power to run a computer. The solution is low-cost photovoltaic (PV) panels with a modicum of battery power to last through the night. For these demands (without heating, cooking or air conditioning), solar PV power can suffice.

These self-sufficient power systems from Africa require living within the PV power available. Britain has a range of renewable power sources including solar, wind and biowaste. We will need to learn to live within this energy budget. The use of high-efficiency lighting systems and natural light will be one component; controlling computers' demand for power will be another. As in rural Africa, we should think carefully how to prioritize our energy needs to match the sources available.

The final lesson I want to draw on for our energy-neutral building comes from India. Here there is a problem with cooking over open fires. It is bad for people's health, it is a major source of air pollution and carbon emissions, and it is a cause of deforestation. A simple system has been developed to generate methane gas from organic waste.[5] This allows people to cook in a much cleaner and more sustainable way. Although there is a natural aversion to using gas derived from human faeces for cooking, this is being overcome because the improvement in health is so noticeable in those who adopt it.

In the developed world, there is no reason why we, too, should not cook in the same way. The design makeover in taking the system out of India should concentrate on overcoming Western sensitivities to the source. The other refinement needed is safe long-term storage capacity so the methane can also be used for general energy needs to cover low points such as exceptionally cold weather or overcast or windless days.

So we have pulled out of our scan of the world a number of elements to meld together in response to the challenge of an energy-neutral house in the UK. Such an amalgam works, as Professor Susan Roaf's Ecohouse in North Oxford demonstrates.[6] We can build such houses in the mild climate of Britain using intelligent design if, as customers, we define being energy-neutral as our requirement.

The challenge of energy-neutral buildings in Finland is much more difficult. Here, surprisingly, we can turn to Mediterranean countries for inspiration. In southern Spain, many places have winters so mild that their houses do not have central-heating systems. A cold spell of weather leads to low room temperatures, but these are not the sub-zero temperatures of Finland. Dressing more warmly and putting a thicker duvet on the bed is all that is required.

Spaniards do not find this adjustment in behaviour difficult. The lesson I draw is that the Finns should accept a lower indoor temperature in the winter to reduce the temperature differential and energy needs of their buildings. Paradoxically, for a cold country, Finns are not used to having lower indoor temperatures in the winter. Their houses are kept at a constant 22–25°C throughout the year. Due to good insulation, the fuel bill is affordable. When Finns visit countries where indoor temperatures drop below 20°C they can be observed shivering and complaining. Warm buildings are so ingrained in modern Finnish culture that moving to cool buildings in the winter (and dressing accordingly) would require a major psychological adjustment, but Spaniards show it can be done.

Another place to look for ideas is Finland's own history. A traditional old Finnish farmhouse would have a large communal room called a 'tupa'. Winter living was concentrated here. It was kept warm with a stone stove of massive proportions to act as a heat sink. The building had other accommodation with little or no heating, and which was used for migrant summer workers or for the children to have their own space in the summer months. We can use this concept of a kernel of warm space in our modern buildings, with other rooms being kept cooler or not heated at all when not in use.

To attempt to make buildings energy-neutral in Finland, we have identified two adaptations: lower internal temperatures in winter and differentiating between areas that must be warm and others that are heated only as required. But the winters are so cold that this will not eliminate the need for additional energy. Fortunately, Finland is a sparsely populated country with a large forestry industry. Biowaste from this industry already provides a significant energy contribution. The lessons we have learned above will allow reductions in demand to match this renewable energy source. It is unlikely that Finnish buildings can be energy-neutral, but it is feasible to close off the wider sustainable loop within Finland, negating the need to import fuel for domestic heating.

For a final consideration of the challenge of energy-neutral buildings, I turn to the high temperatures of the Middle East. It is hard to see where to eradicate the energy needs for cooling. Certainly, glass-box buildings mimicking Western design in the cities of the Middle East are poor examples, requiring massive energy-hungry air-conditioning systems. It is better to look back into the region's own past, to the mosques with thick walls and small windows and the Bedouin's use of ventilation in their tents. Mixing these lessons with modern design and technology should provide the basis for a solution.

The Middle East has plenty of cheap fossil fuel so there is little incentive to bother to solve the energy-neutral building challenge. But oil also provides considerable revenue in the short term which could be invested in constructing buildings for the future beyond oil. It might also be welcome – in a political sense – that the urban landscape of the Middle East moves away from Western-inspired design to something that is more in keeping with their heritage.

For the Middle East, if the extreme heat beats our efforts to be energy-neutral, then there is a wider sustainable loop we can use. The Middle East has acres of space and ample sunshine. Taking additional space (more than a building's own roof area) to capture the additional energy necessary to power cooling systems would make sense.

In addressing the challenge of energy-neutral buildings, we have found that such buildings seem to be feasible in the mild climate of the UK. We have also found that to meet the challenge on the edge of the Arctic or in the deserts of the Middle East is a much tougher task, but we have identified ideas to apply. The candidate solutions we have come up with are highly specific to the context, drawing on ideas from adaptation laboratories around the globe.

Concepts for Water Conservation

Water conservation is a different challenge, which I will consider briefly to give a broader perspective on the concept of adaptation laboratories. In this example, a city is coming under a number of pressures leading to an imbalance between supply and demand. The city is growing; climate change has led to lower rainfall; and the city has realized that continuing to pump from aquifers is not sustainable.

The place to look, of course, is at societies that have to cope with a shortage of water. First stop is Ascension Island, a tiny speck in the middle of the Atlantic Ocean. This arid island has one mountain of note, aptly named Green Mountain. The moist sea air passing by is forced higher and leads to precipitation. The small area at the top of the mountain is lush and green. A large concrete catchment area has been built amongst the greenery to harvest the rainfall, store it and then pipe it to the residents. The lesson we should take from Ascension Island is rainfall harvesting.

Our next stop is Lanzarote in the Canary Islands off the northwest coast of Africa. Harvesting rainwater from roofs is common practice; also domestic water (grey water) is reused to water garden areas. This is done at night when the water has most effect, and the morning sun soon dries off the odour of unclean water before most tourists are up and about. Our second lesson is to reuse water, cascading down from the highest level needs for clean water, such as cooking and drinking, to the lowest level needs, such as flushing away waste. Interestingly, Lanzarote also has a highly specialist agricultural technique that uses a layer of jet black volcanic ash on top of the soil to capture moisture during the night (but this is highly specific to volcanic islands and so less useful elsewhere).

Using these lessons, we see that there is enormous scope for cities to reduce demand on their external water supplies. The two main methods identified are rainfall harvesting from the roofs of buildings, and using grey water for secondary purposes such as flushing lavatories or watering parks and garden areas. All it takes is the effort (and investment) to design these capabilities into our buildings.

We do not have to start from scratch; we have examples to copy, adapt and apply. Chapter 14 outlined the market mechanism for sustainable water supply; we can find the technical solutions from adaptation laboratories.

I suggest that the adaptation laboratory approach can be applied to any of the challenges we face. The transplanting of ideas from one setting to another, or rethinking old ideas with the benefit of modern technical expertise, leads to innovative and unusual ideas.

Another example of a difficult challenge that we need to solve is true, complete recycling of our products. I will not follow this example through but will indicate one place to look. Cuba has been largely isolated from the world economic community for nearly half a century, and has had to find ways to keep its society running without importing a mass of new products. I do not expect Cuba to be an economic model that we would want to copy, but there may well be some useful methods or behaviours hiding away in Havana which have evolved in this isolated community.

Adaptation Laboratories as a Source of Advantage

Countries or regions that push policy towards becoming adaptation laboratories, forcing the transition to sustainable living, will reap the rewards. Costs for local consumers may be pushed up in the short term as the local businesses grapple with finding and applying the most cost-effective solutions. But they will also become world leaders, strengthening their own economies and benefiting the world.

Denmark has used its natural asset as a good site for wind power to build a world-leading wind turbine industry. Australia could use the huge potential of the solar radiation that shines on its vast empty interior to lead in developing the processes to deliver a transportable fuel from the desert. The United States is currently a pariah nation in the sustainability stakes; but it has the agility and business processes to adapt very fast, and a huge internal market in which to test and grow ideas. It, too, could take advantage of the opportunity to become an adaptation laboratory. Another colossal potential player is China, which is already showing signs of pushing for sustainable technologies to underpin continued development.

Corporations will also find that searching the world for ideas to borrow and adapt will be a lucrative activity. Those that start prospecting before the demands of the Sustainable Revolution are widely understood will gain a head start on their rivals.

23 Profiting from the Transition

If the Sustainable Revolution is to succeed, it needs the support of business; but no one should expect business to become quasi-charitable. Business will only take on the challenge if it is commercially viable. Fortunately, there are healthy profits to be made, so provided the regulatory framework is carefully crafted, there is every incentive for business not only to support the revolution, but also to lead it.

The leaders are already positioning themselves, ready to cherry-pick the easiest opportunities as they ripen. Other businesses, which choose to ignore the shift to sustainability, will have to work hard to survive the changes when they arrive.

The complex interaction between environmental and social issues means that the route to a sustainable future is uncertain. Business needs to be poised to take advantage of whichever way the revolution heads. Some of the paths that business will open up will not be profitable and will need redefining or abandoning; others will provide an unassailable commercial advantage that lasts for many years.

There are some things we can be sure of; these can be factored into plans. For others a contingency is needed in order to be able to react quickly. One fact we can rely on is that mankind will get it right in the end. If we continue to ignore the issue of sustainability, then we will find ourselves down a dead end that is becoming increasingly unpleasant. There can be no doubt that, at some point, mankind will pull back from further 'progress' along this route and turn back to look for another path towards a more pleasant future. The longer it takes, the harder it will be to backtrack, but there can be little doubt that it will happen. Only the timing is uncertain.

Setting business strategy requires a view of the future. If that future is a smooth progression then it will surprise no one. All the players will vie for advantage on terms they understand, and competitive forces will constrain profits for all. Alternatively, if the possible future is a step change, not obvious and not taken seriously by all players, then the potential is huge. For businesses that are open to new ideas and which are comfortable embracing innovation and new business models, the potential to power ahead into uncontested territory is enormous.

The Sustainable Revolution provides the opportunity. Businesses with ambition should be planning to exploit it.

Loosening the Straitjacket of Corporate Strategy

The central theme of corporate strategy is a drive for competitive advantage: performing better than rivals across a wide range of measures, such as efficiency, productivity, features, value for money, services and support. As globalization has taken hold, the comparisons are not just with domestic rivals or regional players, but the whole global industry.

The unrelenting drive to eliminate costs and drive up profits has included shifting production to the lowest-cost countries. Within Europe, the new entrants to the EU have become the low-cost-base countries. Worldwide, emerging economies such as China and India are the favoured destinations for much manufacturing, and remote services such as call centres and writing software code.

Outsourcing is being used extensively, even for activities once seen as core to the business. Any service or manufacturing process that can be put at arm's length through a tendering process can be outsourced.

This search for improvement in profitability has eroded the concept of a company as a community. Many companies have been honed down to eliminate all but the essential activities that directly contribute to the delivery of a product or service at least cost. The ultimate expression of this is the virtual corporation, in which the only management activity consists of orchestrating a network of suppliers and contractors.

Some of the longer-term negative effects of this focus on cost reduction have started to show through. Where manufacturing is taking place halfway around the world, lead times are longer, flexibility is reduced and quality control is challenging. Where call centres have been moved abroad, direct costs have reduced but the quality of the interaction and rapport with the customers has suffered.

Outsourcing can lead to considerable staff resentment and unforeseen problems, coupled with savings that have often been illusory. There has been much to remind management that competitive advantage is just one aspect of strategy.

One of the biggest dangers is that large companies adapt too well to their environment. Perfect adaptation leads to maximum efficiency, a position of unassailable leadership and high profitability. When the environment changes, especially if it is a step change, they run the risk of being caught in the trap of their own success. The dinosaurs were perfectly adapted and unassailable, but also doomed.

The last decade has favoured straight-line thinking with a fairly stable macroeconomic environment. After the Sustainable Revolution has run its course, such focused strategic thinking might again have its place, but to survive the coming revolution a different approach will be needed. What is needed is not perfect adaptation, but a perfect ability to adapt.

Riding on the Back of the Sustainable Revolution

Business should not be afraid to profit from the Sustainable Revolution. There may be some resistance from green activists to the proposals I outline, but when they see the outcomes that business can deliver, their complaints will be muted. I envisage people of all persuasions supporting businesses that engage in sustainability: investing in them (to make money); buying their products (to get a better deal) and seeking to work for them (to be able to apply their talents to saving the world).

The process of strategy development described here starts with a strategic appraisal of where the business is now. This then guides strategy towards deciding which lines of business should be retained and reinforced, which should be divested and new areas where seed investments should be made. This can be carried out at a product or business level. The latter is where I will focus.

The intention is to build a portfolio of businesses and capabilities with sufficient variety not only to survive but also to take advantage of major dislocations in society. We can make use of a matrix that plots future profitability against environmental/social impact as shown in Figure 23.1.

All the businesses within a corporation can be plotted onto the matrix. Those in the top-right quadrant have a positive impact on the world and projected high profitability. These I term the 'Leading Lights'. We can be confident that these will ride the crest of the wave as the revolution starts rolling in. Current profitability might be low or non-existent, but this is where the profits of the future are to be found.

For businesses in the lower-right quadrant, their impact is again positive but profits are expected to remain flat. These I term the 'Salt-of-the-Earth': solid, safe performers. Typically, these businesses will be providing a necessary but unglamorous product or service. These are not attractive as sources of profit, but valuable to society, and to the corporation in a number of ways. For example, they have a strong customer base to which other products and services can be sold, leveraging the loyalty from providing a basic service in an environmentally sound manner.

The top-left quadrant contains the 'Sinners'. These are businesses that will continue to be profitable as the Sustainable Revolution gains support, but their negative impact will attract increasingly bad publicity and opposition from green activists and other concerned groups.

The final quadrant is the 'Pariahs'. These are businesses that have a substantial negative social or environmental impact. They may be profitable now, but are not projected to remain profitable following the Sustainable Revolution.

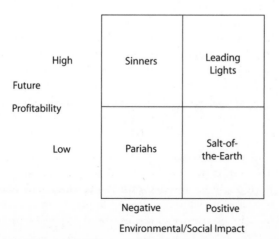

Figure 23.1 **The Sustainability Matrix**

Pariahs

Pariahs are potential liabilities for which divesting or exiting is the best option. There will be an opportunity before the revolution to spin out such businesses, generating a value derived from their current profit figures. However, the window available to get best value will stay open only as long as there are still buyers. There could be large capital assets within the operations which have a value now but will be nearly worthless after the revolution. The general principle is to cut losses on pariahs, and to do it quickly.

Over time, society will expect pariahs to be closed down. Those who sell out now will be doing a service in hastening the pariah's demise, as well as saving the value of their investment. The potential losses can be handed on to other corporations who wait until society forces them to act.

In terms of managing pariahs, a short-term view would be to continue to book the profits and do nothing except starve it of further investment, milking the business for as long as possible. However, ignoring its looming pariah status is incubating problems for the future. The potential liability could become large enough to sink the company. Doing nothing might be tempting for executives who plan not to be around for the future, but it would not serve the company well.

A better approach is to work out the cost/benefit of exiting or divesting. As well as considering whether there are likely to be any willing buyers, consideration must also be given to whether liability can be divested, too. A quick sale, even at a good price, if liability is retained, will be a time bomb ticking away in the ex-parent company's future. Once the business is outside the corporation's control, the new owners will have no compunction in pushing any problems that have been exposed back to the original owners. It is, therefore, worth putting effort into defining exactly what the long-term liabilities are.

The process of identifying the potential liabilities will generate reports. These will record and document the date when a particular CEO or management board knew of their responsibilities. This might worry some executives who have an inkling that there might be problems but would rather not be told explicitly what they are. Some shareholders might also be unhappy if a company goes further than the current legal requirement in digging up information that, if it became public, would depress the share price. Such concerns may count against initiating such an analysis. But choosing 'not to know' would be a weak defence if it came to trial (which, for pariah companies, is quite likely as society looks for the reasons behind the environmental damage we will face in the decades ahead).

Having worked out what the liabilities are, the company should put a cost against the remedial action. If this cost is more than the value of the business, then the only choice left might be to retain ownership, as we shall discuss below. Assuming that the cost of remediation is affordable, the recommended actions should be initiated and the business sold off. Even if the action is not complete, the deal can be concluded with the capital for the remediation work ring-fenced accordingly. Such an approach should minimize the long-term liability in that the company has, in good faith, dealt with the problems according to current best practice. It should also increase the sale value of the business, offsetting some of the costs or even exceeding them.

Other businesses classified as pariahs will not find a buyer, where the potential liabilities are greater than the residual value. If the liabilities are contaminated sites or facilities, these can be put to an alternative use within the corporation. Provided any external impact, such as ground water contamination, is contained, and the health and safety of the workforce is not compromised, then a new factory or facility can replace the old. It may not be possible to sell the site, or to use it as collateral for borrowing, but there will not be any external parties digging into its history (physically or metaphorically).

Where the liability is in potential claims against the company, then the company will have to invest in managing those claims. This could involve investigating potential solutions through sponsoring research. The company will need to behave in a demonstrably responsible manner whilst also seeking to minimize costs, perhaps working in conjunction with insurers. In this way, legal costs can be avoided and the impact of bad press coverage reduced, even if the final payouts made are the same, or more, than might result from a more combative approach.

Finally, there will be some pariah companies that cannot survive in any form. These companies will have liabilities so great, and processes so environmentally unsound, that they cannot adapt. It will be impossible for them to compete against new entrants who come without baggage. Once this becomes clear to the market, the shares will be worthless. Death might come quickly with a rapid transition from an apparently profitable company to bankruptcy. There will then follow extended legal wrangling over the unfunded liabilities that the company has. Questions will be asked. Is there a previous owner still in business who can be held liable? Did the current and previous management do all in their power to limit the impact on the environment?

Shareholders of companies that look like they might be classified as incurable pariahs should jump ship now. Management might do likewise, but there is still a salary to be drawn and a job to be done. Executives should be careful to act with probity and transparency in managing the ship safely into a breakers yard, or risk being taken down with the business as it keels over and slips beneath waves of recriminations.

Sinners

Businesses classified as sinners are a normal component of our existing unsustainable society. Currently, there is no stigma in being in this category, but this will change. Most, if not all, car manufacturers are sinners with their current model range, particularly sports utility vehicles (SUVs). Leaving aside the cases where there is a real need for rugged off road transportation, these vehicles are a menace to the environment and other road users, but it is not clear where society's disapproval should focus: the companies that make them or the people who buy them.

Sinner businesses need to be looked at very carefully. These businesses are legal and there is a demand for their products and services, but they are also bad for the environment or society. On one hand, they are profitable businesses. On the other, as attitudes change, bad press will reflect badly on the corporation as a whole. It could be that putting distance between the sinner business and the rest of the corporation is sufficient as a short-term fix. Utilizing a different brand may allow the corporation to continue to milk profits for some time.

But being a sinner business is a problem waiting to be exposed and it should ideally be reformed. If the business case is hard to make, then one tactic is to offer the current product or service twinned with a premium environmentally sound alternative. This pushes the responsibility firmly to the customer. The aim would be to sunset the old product but retain the customer base.

During the transition, the new product would grow in value in people's minds. As the business finds they can drop the price of the premium replacement, people will feel they are getting more for their money. Those customers who are incorrigible lowest-cost purchasers can assuage any guilt they feel by indirectly helping to develop better alternatives from the same company – whilst continuing to purchase the current product until it is obsolete.

Such action has to be part of a real transition, and not just greenwash, or the future backlash and accusations of duplicity are likely to be worse than keeping a low profile and taking no action.

For sinners to reform, it will require investment and the timing will be critical. Some investments will deliver profits at an early stage. Others may not be profitable until the Sustainable Revolution shakes up the external environment. Act too early and the business will take an unnecessary hit to its profits; too late and the business will miss the wave. The secret will be preparation and defining early the investment that will be needed, tackling the long issues head on; such as developing the technology, working out how processes need to change and developing appropriate business models.

This will be tough for management, because such thinking is a distraction from the day-to-day challenges of running the current business. The first action should be to shut off investment that is not compatible with the future. Equipment that will become obsolete should not be upgraded. Lateral thinking might come up with less obvious savings, such as pulling marketing campaigns that are incompatible with the future direction.

The majority of current businesses could be categorized as sinners in one way or another. The intention should be to migrate to the right of the sustainability matrix, timing investment carefully to maximize the return. Initial costs can be small but the management engagement time required will be high.

Society will not change overnight; many unsustainable processes and activities will continue for some time. As viable alternative methods and technologies become available, sinner companies that adopt them early will be able to continue operating with impunity. The action of making the transition will be enough to give the current business legitimacy. The business may then end up in the salt-of-the-earth category, with a product that has better environmental credentials but lower profit margins.

Current business thinking would view this as a strange result, which management, with short-term profit targets, would seek to prevent. But as a component of building long-term sustainable value within the corporation, it would be the correct outcome.

Salt-of-the-Earth Businesses

Many of the businesses required to run a sustainable world may not be particularly profitable or appear commercially attractive, but they will be necessary. Water companies might be in this category. They are likely to be heavily regulated and margins will be tight as politicians seek to keep charges down concurrently with building a sustainable supply infrastructure.

There are a number of ways that salt-of-the-earth businesses can provide value to a corporation. I shall consider three.

First, a soft benefit, with elusive value, is improved reputation. Being recognized as an organization underpinning the drive for sustainability could be a powerful brand enhancer. The strength of this effect will depend on the strength of society's commitment to a sustainable future, which in turn will depend on just how bad the negative impacts (such as climate change) have become. Positive reinforcement of reputation might be useful glue to cement the corporate strategy, but it will be hard to quantify.

Second, although the steady-state situation may not be attractive, the transition period may be. The changes required are large, which will throw up a number of challenges in delivering products or services in a sustainable way. The businesses that develop the processes and technology required could then supply key components to all the main players. Provided they can protect their developments through patent, they will have a monopoly on some components for some time beyond the transition. Salt-of-the-earth companies may find they can spin out highly profitable businesses in this way, using the expertise gained from running their rather dull central operations in a sustainable manner.

Third, salt-of-the-earth companies will find opportunities to benefit from consolidation within the industry. Where there are a number of competitors, some will find it hard to comply with the increasingly high regulatory hurdles.

These players will be forced out of the industry and perhaps out of business. Successful salt-of-the-earth companies could pick up these companies, or their assets, on the cheap and use their expertise to decommission or retro-fit and so incorporate them into their business.

Salt-of-the-earth enterprises are likely to be solid foundations for corporations. They can underpin reputation and be a launch pad for profitable spin-out activities. They are, therefore, a valuable part of the corporate portfolio although not necessarily a major contributor to bottom-line results.

The Leading Lights

Leading light businesses, such as technology for renewable power or ultra-lightweight efficient cars, have very low environmental impact and deliver a valuable product or service. Mature businesses that are already in this category can expect to maintain sustainable profitability into the long-term future. Many more will be at a very early stage with high potential, but which do not suit the current environment.

For example, the product or service may be too expensive until a threshold is exceeded where economies of scale drive costs lower. The regulatory framework may still be too loose to give the new process or method a significant advantage. The barrier could be simply that the fashion has not yet shifted. Some businesses will be high risk, with success dependant on how effective the business is at developing the technology or processes. Others will be certain to deliver the defined capabilities, but will only succeed if the revolution builds the market expected.

The best environment in which to grow the leading lights is one of freedom, in which they can innovate, think laterally and experiment. This will suit forward-looking entrepreneurs. It can be expected that increasing amounts of venture capital will flow into companies in this area.

At first, this will be a small proportion of funds, but as the revolution gathers pace it may become a flood, with more money than there are good business plans. At its peak, the Sustainable Revolution may exhibit some of the characteristics of the dot.com boom. We will see some businesses that ride the wave of funding only to plunge when reality re-enters the markets.

Forward-looking corporations can also be the incubator for leading light companies, provided their special characteristics are recognized and managed accordingly. Existing corporations have a strong advantage in access to capital and an existing customer base to sell to. But the culture of budgets, long-term plans and preset objectives will not suit the behaviours required.

Corporations should set up business units with considerable autonomy, access to seed capital and encourage their most innovative staff to join them. To achieve sufficient separation, these activities may have to be completely separate businesses that are free to try different business models and which are unconstrained by current processes or culture.

Some business leaders will view investment in potential leading lights as an overhead on current operations and a drag on short-term profits. The contrary view is that such investment is building the capabilities for the future and is vital to long-term profitability. Making seed investments in such companies is also an insurance policy: as particular aspects of the business suffer from the negative effects of society's growing demands for sustainability, the business as a whole will thrive.

A portfolio of businesses with nothing but leading lights would have high potential but may not have the cash or profits in the short term to survive, unless backed by investors with very deep pockets. (Conversely, a corporation with no leading lights may be maximizing short-term profitability but will be highly vulnerable as the Sustainable Revolution gathers pace.) Start-up companies are likely to dominate this quadrant but there is no reason why existing corporations should not lead the revolution – as some are already attempting to do.[1] Investing resources in leading lights is the way to obtain the agility needed to adapt.

Formulating Strategy

It has been shown that the sustainability matrix provides a way of viewing and categorizing a corporation's business. Because the characteristics and key management issues that relate to each quadrant are different, the matrix is also useful for crafting corporate strategy.

The leading light businesses are where the future of the corporation is entrusted. These do not represent just research and development in technology and methods, but also complete new business models. High-level management will be very interested in progress, but the open culture required to encourage and support innovation is not one that will welcome intrusive supervision, detailed plans or tight controls. Members of staff are likely to respond to flexibility and autonomy. There will be scope here for green, almost missionary, zeal in looking for widely applicable technology and methods, the best of which are capable of being grown into new lines of business and new companies.

One aspect of leading light businesses where tight control should apply is in the protection of intellectual property. The other constraint is that leading light businesses will need seed capital. It may be possible to draw investment in from other parts of the corporation or link up with venture-capital providers. In the latter case, the corporation would lose some ownership but there could be advantages. This would bring in not only the capital needed but also an additional commercial edge in deciding which opportunities to invest in.

Sinner businesses are likely to be the main source of current profitability and the basis of success in the short term. They should be managed with a prime focus on delivering the bottom-line results, milking them for their ability to generate cash. Investment should be avoided unless it is compatible with a sustainable future, even if it means some operational disadvantages versus competitors in the short term.

It is quite likely that the management of sinner businesses will spot ways to become a salt-of-the earth business, that is, trade off profitability for sustainability. This will be contrary to the focus suggested above, and will need to be passed to higher management for consideration. The decision will have to balance short-term profitability with long-term potential. Corporations that rely on short-term profit targets as a primary management tool will find this very hard. They should seek to alter their culture to a longer-term horizon and understand the contribution that salt-of-the-earth businesses make to the corporation as a whole.

Salt-of-the-earth businesses will be the foundation of the corporation. The focus should be on efficiency and economies of scale in order to deliver sustainable products or services at a comparable cost to other suppliers. The sales pitch should be a green one. The tactics should be to try to match industry pricing levels, not undercut them. The corporation will expect them to move into profit in due course, but must understand that delivering the sustainability agenda will hold back profits in the short-term.

Salt-of-the-earth businesses will be the ideal testing ground for prototypes coming out of the leading light businesses and a source of ideas. These could be new methods or simply the identification of areas where sustainability can be improved. The innovative culture of the leading lights can then focus on the problem. Where the people who think up such ideas come from within the salt-of-the-earth business, they could remain located with the business but their formal line management and costs should be moved to the leading light's organization to give them freedom to experiment.

The fourth category of business is the pariahs. Here the management role is likely to focus on selling or divesting the business to release maximum value and manage the risks going forward. The business and its risks must be securely ring-fenced so that liabilities do not emerge in the future. For the highest risks, it will be preferable to retain control so as to understand and ameliorate the risks and lock down the problems so they cannot resurface. The corporation will try to put as much distance as it can between the corporation and its pariahs but there may be exceptions. Expertise in decommissioning or tackling pollution may be the basis of a new line of business.

When it comes to placing a business in the matrix, it may not be clear which quadrant it belongs to. It might lie somewhere in the middle, sharing characteristics of all four. This simply reflects the complexity of the modern business world. The management approach that suits each quadrant is different and distinct. For a business that is stuck in the middle, there will be a lack of clear strategic focus. To make practical use of the insights that flow from the sustainability matrix, the business needs to be broken down with sufficiently fine granularity that the pieces separate out into different quadrants of the matrix.

In theory, these elements could then be reassembled like with like into a corporation of four divisions. However, such a conceptual structure may not be feasible and may hinder exploiting synergy between the four quadrants.

Synergy

Although the focus of this discussion has been on the corporate level, we should remember that the sustainability matrix can also be used to look at processes, products or services, depending on the analysis required. In doing this, we find that the linkages between quadrants turn out to be a valuable source of advantage. I shall consider three of the possible synergies.

The first is based on the concept of dual products, linking a sinner with a leading light. We could then have two products or services that deliver much the same customer value, but one does so in a wholly sustainable way. The idea is that the two businesses (or business units) come under a single point of executive control (crossing division boundaries if necessary). With the objective of migrating the customer base from the old to the new product or service in a way that maximizes the cash generated for the corporation over the medium to long term.

Management would be able to utilize the positive cash flow from milking the old product or service to fund investment in its replacement. The new sustainable product would at first be a premium product. If economies of scale are foreseen which will reduce costs to below (or will match) the old product, then the decision can be taken to move faster. If it looks as though customers will not shift and costs remain stubbornly high, then the switch might be very slow or even stalled.

The detailed implementation can have many more synergies. For example, although the two business units will be competing against each other for customers, it will be to a coordinated marketing plan. Coordination could be extended to human resources. When employees are forced out as the sinner business contracts, the leading light will be needing staff. A twinned sinner/ leading light approach might exhibit a very positive tension in which staff see a win-win for them and the corporation.

The second synergy comes from twinning a salt-of-the-earth business with a leading light. This might be based on a novel or new production process. It might be something very different, which could be sold to the same customer base or use similar technology in its manufacture. The objective is to maximize the value of the leading light to the corporation, leveraging the skills and commercial capabilities of the salt-of-the-earth business as a test bed and source of practical advice.

The third synergy comes from twinning a pariah with a salt-of-the-earth business. This may seem odd when the aim is to put distance between the corporation and its legacy past, but some pariahs will cause less trouble if they and their problems are retained.

As management seek to extract value from the pariah business, the proceeds could be invested in the salt-of-the-earth business. Where attempts are made to claim punitive damages from the pariah, the attacks might be less voracious if they are also seen to damage the new salt-of-the-earth business that is rising out of the ashes of the old. This would not be a guarantee of immunity, but it might diffuse some of the more emotional attacks on the pariah's legacy business.

The discussion above shows the use of the sustainability matrix as a tool to craft strategy. The initial result can be a list of activities, processes, products or services grouped by the four categories. By using this, together with any synergies that are judged worth making, a corporate strategy and structure can be put together.

Implementation

In making the strategy work, the key to success will be in managing the leading lights. This is where the future of the company lies and where long-term profitability will be built. They may not be big businesses yet, but they have big ambitions. Together, they comprise the capability pool from which adaptation to the changing environment can take place.

Only some leading lights can be expected to succeed. Some will not fulfil their apparent potential because the ideas do not work, or the technology fails to deliver its promise, or development is too slow and another company gets there first. Others will find that the anticipated demand guiding the early-stage growth does not materialize.

In order to implement the strategy, there needs to be a mechanism for trawling through the corporation for ideas and concepts – including identifying problems that need a solution, as these could be the spark from which to grow a leading light. There also needs to be the organizational means to manage the process (which is outside the normal bureaucracy), so that the required culture can develop.

When ideas arise from any source, the people behind them should have the opportunity to transfer to the new organizational structure to develop their ideas further. If the idea works, they should be able to remain within the new business as it grows, sharing in its success. If it does not, they should have the security of a job back in the mainstream business.

The role for senior management, after putting the strategy in place, would be to keep the portfolio of nascent businesses under review, identifying which have the greatest potential value to the future business.

When the timing is judged to be right, the corporation can put its full might behind the new businesses that best fit the evolving market and have the most defendable lead. This is where the big corporations can beat the new entrant start-up company. Access to capital, customer bases and infrastructure such as distribution networks can be a winning launch pad. In choosing which to back, there are parallels with gambling. If it is a sure bet, then someone else will have placed money on it and the returns will be less. The best returns will come from non-obvious, unusual or unique business ideas that – if proven to be correct – will leave competitors struggling to catch up.

A final element to implementing the strategy, and cementing sustainability at the core of future profitability, is management behaviour. Senior management has to be comfortable and confident in dealing with innovation and dynamic change. Those managers who aspire to reach the highest levels of the organization will need to be groomed for the role. The expected career profile should include leading and growing one of the leading-light opportunities. This will shift the corporate mindset towards an entrepreneurial green attitude, which is just what is needed to profit from the Sustainable Revolution.

Self-Adapting Corporations for a Sustainable World

This chapter has provided a framework for business to handle the complex uncertainties of the Sustainable Revolution. The key will be the ability to scan the changing landscape, spot the issues as they surface and react quickly. A corporation that adopts strategy generated in this way will be largely self-adapting to the changing environment.

Business leaders can concentrate on selecting the best of the emerging businesses and timing investment in them, balancing the risk profile with the anticipated long-term returns. The ability to ride the Sustainable Revolution will be hard-wired into the organization. Chief executives can then choose to take the time to campaign in support of environment and society, bringing forward the revolution, knowing that their businesses are well placed to take advantage of the disruption. This will be easier and more satisfying than defending the business models of the past.

Middle management may find it hard to cope with the demands of such a fluid entrepreneurial culture, but the best of them will rise to the challenge and may become enthusiastic converts. As public opinion swings behind the Sustainable Revolution, we can expect staff (and their families) at all levels to take pride in working for a corporation that is committed to a sustainable world.

24 Shared Destiny

Our future is a shared destiny between civilization and the natural world.

The concept of a sustainable society that respects our natural heritage is starting to migrate from pressure groups on the fringe to mainstream politics. But we are trapped. Those of us who live in countries with strong economies do not want to give up any of the benefits. Those who live in poorer countries want to follow our example. When we try to reconcile our economic aspirations with our desire to improve our care for the environment, we find that the mechanisms of current modern society cannot cope.

The current glacial pace of change is insufficient to diffuse the tension building up. The changes required are dramatic. The blockage that arises from our ingrained mindset will be hard to shift. When mankind does wake up, the flood of change that follows will be nothing short of a revolution, reconfiguring society and the economy.

We can see that, collectively, we are destroying our world, but there is a limit to what each of us individually can do about it. We live our lives within the parameters that society maps out for us. No one of us is responsible for the destruction we are causing, and no individual person can be the solution. But we also jealously want to guard a future for our families and close associates. The Sustainable Revolution will be based upon the selfish determination of people to build sustainable communities that are capable of delivering a better life.

The effects of our lack of respect for natural systems are becoming clear. Climate change is the most visible, measurable and immediately worrying consequence. We will now have to live with the changes that have already been initiated by our behaviour in the past. Global temperatures will continue to climb and sea levels will rise, but we now understand the cause. We also know that catastrophic change is feasible; it would be sheer folly to continue with a lifestyle that increases the chance of such an outcome.

Other consequences are the loss of natural habitats and biodiversity. Continuing on our present course would lead to a world dominated by urban areas and commercial agriculture. The only animals found outside our zoos will be those we plan to eat or process into products. There will still be national parks, but as isolated islands slowly being strangled as the climate alters. Less noticeably, the threat to our oceans is one of the biggest risks we are taking. They are out of sight and out of mind. The full extent of the damage we are causing to the oceans will not impact heavily on anyone alive today, so we do not feel a driving need to take corrective action.

However, mankind is very good at taking action in response to crisis. For example, fighting a war brings communities closer together and people will make enormous sacrifices for the common good. We can be astonishingly successful at recovering from such man-made crises, for example, our ability to rebuild following World War II. A new Europe rose out of the ashes, and a vibrant Japan emerged from the terrible destruction of Hiroshima and Nagasaki.

We now face destruction on a global scale that mankind cannot repair alone. The coral reefs submerged by rising sea levels will be able to grow back over time (provided we have not pushed the poisoning of our oceans too far). But it is hard to see how we could reinstate the rainforests once they are gone. The problem is that we do not yet see the impending changes as a crisis, so do not engage mankind's enormous adaptive ability. The sooner society is hit hard by the symptoms – such as climate change – the better it will be for the world. Mankind will then be forced to respond.

Our modern world is impressive: our technology is the best the world has ever seen; standards of living have never been higher; but it is a sham. By continually raising GDP through the use of cheap fossil fuel, encouraging a throwaway consumer society and developing more and more land, we are stripping the world bare and polluting it with substances that are alien to nature. It does not have to be this way.

We can rescue ourselves by adopting sustainability and building in a balanced manner on the three legs of the economy, society and the environment. At the heart of our analysis we have found another trio: land, agriculture and energy. These are inseparable and interdependent. The land we have is finite, our agricultural capacity is limited and the demand for renewable energy from biofuels is set to soar. A sustainable solution is not easy. We have the choice of taking tough decisions now, in order to be in control of our future, or waiting until crisis point. If we wait, we may find that it is too late as we run out of capacity to power our society and feed the world's people.

In the long future, our continued expansion might be on other planets. Our children's grandchildren might look out through the observation window of a colony on the moon to see the blue planet shining out of a clear dark sky. To them, swimming in the open sea or wandering in the forest will be nothing more than experiences recorded in virtual reality systems. Whether those back on Earth will still be able to enjoy those pleasures first-hand depends on what we do over the coming decades.

For now, we have just one world and we need to live within its constraints. When resources can no longer support the population, civilization will start to disintegrate. We will suffer not only passive destruction such as starvation, but also war and mass exterminations as people seek survival for their own close family and community.

The changes required will benefit everyone and demand individual action from everyone. But there is little incentive to act when good behaviour is undermined by our neighbour who does nothing. If we are to accept constraints, then they must apply to us all.

The problem of compliance is particularly acute at world level, where some countries are clearly less sustainable than others. Some of these countries are poor and are to be pitied, but we envy the richer ones, coveting their lifestyles. This emotion needs to be converted into contempt for their profligate ways. We must reverse the situation so that the unsustainable rich countries come to envy the sustainable societies we can create elsewhere.

Leadership is needed to break the vicious cycle of decline in the quality of our world and to create a new, virtuous cycle that will rebuild it. But we need to know that we are not alone. We need to find ways of penalizing bad behaviours and rewarding good ones. Whatever action we decide to take to change our own lives, the best action we can all take is to support proposals for collective action.

We can succeed, even at world level, as the elimination of CFCs has shown. Further global agreements in other areas will be vital, but progress will inevitably be slow as building consensus takes time. Much faster action will come from the governments of individual countries, where the real world power lies.

When the majority of people are persuaded, we will vote in governments with a mandate to force through sustainable policies. At this early stage, people can record their concern by voting for green parties, but real action will come when the main political parties change their policies.

Because the changes required are so radical, there are huge political opportunities for opposition parties to make a bold move. They should make an uncompromising push for sustainability – beyond the point of current public acceptance – and accept the risk of remaining in opposition a little longer. However, as groundswell opinion shifts, it will move to match the party's position. The early principled stance will build reputation, an understanding of the required policies and a rock-solid support base of concerned people from across the political spectrum.

The developed world is set to move beyond our industrial heritage to renewable energy supplies and cradle-to-cradle production in a society designed for people rather than cars. We can hope that the old developed world leads the adaptation, but countries that have been slower to industrialize – such as China – could change direction and overtake us. Countries without a significant industrial legacy could leapfrog over the excesses of the Western model by adopting sustainable policies and developing the required technologies.

The biggest potential player remains the United States. It is currently one of the most unsustainable societies on the planet. It has been the biggest consumer of fossil fuels for many years and is regarded with dismay around the world for appearing unwilling to engage with the world's efforts to make reductions. However, the eagle is capable of changing its feathers to utilize its powerhouse of innovation and entrepreneurship in sustainable ways. If a US president were to declare that the United States was going to become a sustainable society, the country could rise to the challenge.[1] A key to success would be spotting a political opportunity that made sustainability a popular vision to champion. The prospect of severing the United States from its reliance on oil from the Middle East might be just such an opportunity.

I live in Europe, where we feel we give the environment a high priority – and I hope we will continue to lead – but Europeans would have only admiration for a United States that chose to beat us at our own game.

I believe that a sustainable world is achievable. If we delay, our Earth will be damaged, perhaps irreparably. If we act now, we can make the transition. One person changing their lifestyle would be praiseworthy; many more individuals following suit would be inspiring; politicians willing to stick their neck out to campaign for substantive change should be voted into office. But the general public and politicians are a fickle lot. I believe that the best chance of early action is for business to seize the initiative.

Business should not be coy about profiting from building a sustainable world. Hard-edged business can act as the mercenary that the world needs to get the job done. The losers will be businesses that fail to understand the new parameters, resist the inevitable changes and continue to focus on the short term. Corporations that force the pace of change to drive home business advantage in a context of sustainability will be cheered on by politicians and customers, as well as investors.

Governments have an important role to play in setting the framework within which business operates. This must include, of course, regulation to kick business into acting; but it should also support good business by removing the shackles that hold it back. For example, governments should seek to reform equity markets that reward short-term profit-taking and WTO rules that undermine the growth of national sustainable businesses.

The public can also support business by purchasing green products or services, or, if the premium is unacceptably high, buying conventional products from companies that offer a green alternative, in order to support their further progress. We should also be keen to offer our services as employees to the companies that are leading the transformation, thereby aligning our careers with a sustainable future.

In my analysis, I do not hide my enthusiasm for and commitment to building a sustainable world. I have also made the assumption that many people want the same, but here I may be wrong. There is another elusive barrier to overcome, that of fashion. It may not be until the lifestyle gurus and role-model celebrities decide that sustainable is 'cool' that this barrier will also be overcome.

Driving an SUV will be a good barometer of where we have reached. Having one is a proud aspiration of many drivers now, but when fashion changes they will not enjoy the ridicule that will be heaped upon them. This will not be a clear-cut transition, as, even if we push the costs prohibitively high, there could be a small hard core who take pleasure in demonstrating their ability to pay. It will only be when they are shunned socially for their choice of vehicle, and the latest Hummer is no longer the thing to be seen driving, that the SUV will finally leave our city streets.

Concern for security is an issue that is not central to the argument, but which could be the final shove that tips the world towards sustainability. A world of open borders and huge flows of trade is a dangerous world if there are terrorists who seek to exploit it. A sustainable world involves less physical movement of commodities, goods and people. Such a world would directly contribute to improved security. For example, it would be harder to smuggle the components of a nuclear device into one of the world's cities if there were tighter controls and many less containers being shifted. Think for a moment of the costs of a terrorist detonating such a bomb in one of our major cities. The human cost would be terrible, of course, but so would the economic impact. The avoidance of such a huge bill would underwrite some of the perceived costs of restricting trade.

Building a sustainable world has other long-term security implications that are largely positive. Globalization fuels resentment (unfairly) against the West and the United States in particular. On the other hand, a sustainable world recognizes that each country should take pride in its unique culture and identity, and have control over its own destiny – not in isolation from the rest of the world, but as a member of the world community. The approach championed in this book is aimed at achieving a sustainable world, but this is also likely to lead to a more peaceful world through diffusing many of the reasons behind international terrorism.

On a personal level, as a young engineering undergraduate I used to walk through Durham Cathedral under the huge ribbed vaults of one of the greatest buildings in Europe. I marvelled at the scale of the construction, started in 1093 and completed less than four decades later. With all my modern engineering knowledge, I doubted that I could have designed or built a better building. It is also amazing that the local economy could have built such a cathedral so quickly. Although the local economy was more sustainable than it is now, it certainly was not poor. I expect that the cathedral will still be standing there a thousand years from now. It is my hope that, by then, man's world surrounding this great building will have re-evolved to a sustainable, and prosperous, way of life.

Building a better world requires innovation and drive, which man has in abundance. We need to engage these abilities in a more complex, and ultimately better, sustainable society. This need not be a kill-joy process of denial but an inspiring expansion in the quality of our lives. In our focus to get the economics right, we have not given the social context and our environment the atten-tion they deserve. If we change our policies and behaviours soon, we could still achieve a smooth transition. If we continue to deny that real change is needed, we can be sure that the Sustainable Revolution will be a traumatic and unpleasant transition. It is our choice.

Notes

1 ADAPT OR DIE

1 S. Solomon, D. Qin, M. Manning, Z. Chen, et al. (eds.), 'Summary for Policymakers' in *Climate Change 2007: The Physical Science Basis*. Contribution of Working Group 1 to the Fourth Assessment Report of the Intergovernmental Panel on Climate Change (Cambridge University Press, 2007).

2 The first derogatory use of the medical term 'autistic' with respect to economics was made in 2000 by a group of disaffected French economics students to describe the narrow perspective of mainstream economics. This has led to a movement called Post-Autistic Economics which encourages open-minded debate on how to make economics more relevant to humanity.

2 STRIVING FOR A SUSTAINABLE WORLD

1 Report of the World Commission on Environment and Development (WCED), *Our Common Future*, United Nations General Assembly document A/42/427 (Aug. 1987), often referred to by the name of its chairman as the Bruntland Report.

2 The Rio Declaration is the report of The United Nations Conference on Environment and Development (often referred to as the Earth Summit), Rio de Janeiro, 3–14 June 1992, United Nations General Assembly document A-CONF_151-26, Vol. I, (Aug. 1992).

3 The World Summit on Sustainable Development (WSSD) was held in Johannesburg, South Africa, 26 Aug.–4 Sept. 2002.

4 E. F. Schumacher, *Small Is Beautiful: A Study of Economics as if People Mattered* (Blond and Briggs, 1973).

5 The Rio declaration was a long time in gestation; it was drafted for the United Nations Conference on the Human Environment, Stockholm, June 1972.

6 Paul Hawken, Amory Lovins and L. Hunter Lovins, *Natural Capitalism: The Next Industrial Revolution* (Earthscan, 1999).

7 E. von Weizsäcker, A. B. Lovins and L. H. Lovins, *Factor Four: Doubling Wealth – Halving Resource Use* (Earthscan, 1997).

8 J. Elkington, *Cannibals with Forks: The Triple Bottom Line of 21st Century Business* (Capstone, 1997).

9 K. J. Hargroves and M. H. Smith (eds.), *The Natural Advantage of Nations: Business Opportunities, Innovation and Governance in the 21st Century* (Earthscan, 2005).

10 S. Solomon, D. Qin, M. Manning, Z. Chen, et al. (eds.), 'Summary for Policymakers' in *Climate Change 2007: The Physical Science Basis.* Contribution of Working Group 1 to the Fourth Assessment Report of the Intergovernmental Panel on Climate Change (Cambridge University Press, 2007).

11 US Environmental Protection Agency, 'Mercury Human Exposure' website, accessed 19 Aug. 2007 (www.epa.gov/mercury/exposure.htm).

12 Al Gore, *Earth in the Balance: Ecology and the Human Spirit* (Houghton and Mifflin, 2000).

13 Al Gore, *An Inconvenient Truth: The Planetary Emergency of Global Warming and What We Can Do About It* (Bloomsbury, 2006).

14 Speaking in New York, 21 Sept. 2006, Richard Branson pledged to commit all profits from his transportation businesses over 10 years – estimated to be $3 billion – to combat global warming. Reported on www.msnbc.msn.com.

15 There is some discussion around deliberate large-scale geo-engineering to modify the Earth's environment to suit our purposes, including correcting the damage we are now causing. Although these ideas cannot be discounted entirely, they are at an early stage. I believe that the direct re-engineering of planet Earth is too immature a concept to consider seriously at this stage, and is, in any case, too risky unless we have already caused massive irreversible damage and have no alternative to keep the Earth habitable at some time in the future.

3 OUR GLOBALIZED WORLD

1 John Negroponte, the US Deputy Secretary of State, speaking (when he was Director of National Intelligence) to the US Senate 2 Feb. 2006; reported in an article by Edward Alden, 'The Americas: Oil price rises strengthen our enemies, Negroponte warns', *Financial Times*, 3 Feb. 2006.

2 Adam Smith, *The Wealth of Nations*, Book IV, Ch. II (Edinburgh, 1776).

3 Adam Smith, *The Theory of the Moral Sentiments*, 6th edn., Part VI, Ch. III (A. Millar, 1790, first published 1759).

4 The opening of the border between West and East Germany on 9 Nov. 1989 and symbolic of the end of the Cold War.

5 Speech delivered 17 July 1990 by Michael Forsyth, MP, to the Adam Smith Institute dinner to commemorate the bicentenary of the death of Adam Smith.

6 See, for example, Martin Wolf, *Why Globalization Works*, pp. 211–12 (Yale University Press, 2005).

7 In 1991 Mexico lodged a complaint under the GATT dispute mechanism procedure that the United States was imposing its rules on dolphin protection on tuna imported into the country from Mexico (and other countries). The complaint was upheld.

8 In 2005, China had $711 billion worth of reserves. Source: 'The Frugal Giant', *The Economist*, 22 Sept. 2005.

9 US Energy Information Administration, *International Energy Outlook 2006*, Ch. 5, (www.eia.doe.gov).

10 Tony Blair, British Prime Minister (1997–2007), 'Europe Is Falling Behind', *Newsweek*, 28 Nov. 2005.

11 Arthur Scargill was leader of the National Union of Mineworkers during the strike 1984–5.

12 'Ten years of NAFTA – Free trade on trial', *The Economist*, 30 Dec. 2003.

13 'The art of the impossible – A survey of France', *The Economist*, 28 Oct. 2006.

14 Street protests in spring 2006 forced the French Prime Minister, Dominique de Villepin, to withdraw a modest labour-market reform designed to increase employment of young people.

4 THE SUSTAINABLE REVOLUTION

1 S. L. Hart, *Capitalism at the Crossroads: The Unlimited Business Opportunities in Solving the World's Most Difficult Problems* (Wharton School Publishing, 2005).

2 J. Porrit, *Capitalism as if the World Mattered* (Earthscan, 2005).

3 The World Commission on Environment and Development, *Our Common Future* (Oxford University Press, 1987).

4 G. Hardin, 'The Tragedy of the Commons', *Science*, Vol. 162, Issue 3859, Dec. 1968, pp. 1243–8.

5 This was originally a Catholic social principle that states that societies should not interfere in areas where families can decide on their own.

6 C. Hines, *Localization: A Global Manifesto* (Earthscan, 2000).

7 The UN defines living on less than $1 a day as poverty; less than $2 a day as very poor.

5 THE WORLD'S NATURAL SYSTEMS AND SOCIETY

1 James Lovelock, *Gaia: A New Look at Life on Earth* (Oxford University Press, first published 1979, reissued 2000).

2 Global Footprint Network, *Ecological Footprint and Biocapacity*, *(2006 Edition)*, (www.footprintnetwork.org).

3 J. Kitzes, A. Peller, S. Goldfinger and M. Wackernagel, 'Current Methods for Calculating National Ecological Footprint Accounts', *Science for Environment & Sustainable Society*, Vol. 4, No.1, 2007.

4 Proximization is selfish determination to build sustainable societies, aimed at social provision and driven by economic policy, whilst minimizing adverse impacts on the environment (see Ch. 4 for further explanation).

5 This policy is often described as contraction and convergence. The overall world average, to which we converge, must be within the ecological capacity of the Earth. The world ecological capacity of 11.2 billion ha divided by a population of 6.3 billion gives an allowance of 1.8 ha per person.

6 CLIMATE CHANGE

1 S. Solomon, D. Qin, M. Manning, Z. Chen, et al (eds.), 'Summary for Policymakers' in *Climate Change 2007: The Physical Science Basis*. Contribution of Working Group 1 to the Fourth Assessment Report of the Intergovernmental Panel on Climate Change, (Cambridge University Press, 2007).

2 Professor C. G. Rapley, Director of the British Antarctic Survey (BAS) (1998–2007) speaking at the 'Avoiding Dangerous Climate Change' conference held at the UK Meteorological Office, 1 Feb. 2005.

3 The Kyoto Protocol to the United Nations Framework Convention on Climate Change (UNFCCC) is an agreement to reduce emissions of CO_2 (and five other greenhouse gases). The objective is the 'stabilization of greenhouse gas concentrations in the atmosphere at a level that would prevent dangerous anthropogenic interference with the climate system.' The protocol came into force on 16 Feb. 2005. The main provision is that industrialized countries agree to reduce their collective emissions of greenhouse gases by 5.2% compared to the year 1990.

4 The Energy Information Administration, *World Carbon Dioxide Emissions from the Consumption and Flaring of Fossil Fuels 1980–2004* (www.eia.doe.gov).

5 Worldwatch Institute, 'Carbon Dioxide: The Lengthening Shadow of Coal and Oil', *State of the World 2006*, (Worldwatch Institute, 2006), Box 1-1, p. 9.

6 H. H. Lamb, *Climate, History and the Modern World,* 2nd edn. (Routledge, 1995).

7 The hundred-year trend updated for the period 1906–2005 shows the Earth warmed by 0.74°C according to the IPCC.

8 S. Solomon, D. Qin, M. Manning, Z. Chen, et al (eds.), 'Summary for Policymakers' in *Climate Change 2007: The Physical Science Basis*. Contribution of Working Group 1 to the Fourth Assessment Report of the Intergovernmental Panel on Climate Change, (Cambridge University Press, 2007).

9 'Lessons from Ancient Greenhouse Emissions', notes from a Symposium held at the annual American Association for the advancement of Science in St. Louis, Missouri, 16–20 Feb. 2006 (www.aaas.org).

10 Woods Hole Oceanographic Institution, *Abrupt Climate Change: What's After the Day After Tomorrow?*, a science perspective on the science-fiction movie (web article June 2004, updated July 2007, www.whoi.edu).

11 *The Montreal Protocol on Substances that Deplete the Ozone Layer,* (UNEP, 2000).

12 Ozone Secretariat, *Our Story* (UNEP, 2005).

13 The European Project for Ice Coring in Antarctica (EPICA), 'Eight glacial cycles from an Antarctic ice core', *Nature*, Vol. 429, 10, 2004, pp. 623–8.

14 *The Stern Review Report on the Economics of Climate Change,* commissioned by the UK government and launched Oct. 2006 (Cambridge University Press, 2006).

15 The Alliance of Small Island States (AOSIS), Small Island Developing States Network (www.sidsnet.org/aosis).

16 T. Flannery, *The Weather Makers: Our Changing Climate and What it Means for Life on Earth* (Penguin, 2007).

17 G. Monbiot, *Heat: How to Stop the Planet Burning* (Allen Lane, 2006).

18 The calculation used is: baseline fossil-carbon release = 20 years x 100% = 25 years x 80% = 40 years x 50%, where % relates to actual emissions achieved compared with the baseline. The extent to which the Earth's systems can slowly reabsorb some of this fossil carbon is uncertain and has been ignored.

19 The UN Security Council held its first-ever debate on the impact of climate change, 17 April 2007.

7 BALANCING ENERGY SOURCES AND NEEDS

1 British thermal unit.

2 *World Energy Output 2006* (OECD/International Energy Agency (IEA), 2006).

3 *Energy Policy in the European Union* (European Commission, Mar. 2005).

4 *A European Strategy for Sustainable, Competitive and Secure Energy*, EU Green Paper, COM (2006)105 final, Brussels, 8 Mar. 2006.

5 Energy Information Administration, *International Energy Outlook 2007* (US Department of Energy, 2007).

6 Department of Energy, Alberta, *Oil Sands Fact Sheet* (June 2006, www.energy.gov.ab.ca).

7 *Estonia's Fourth National Communication*, for the UN Framework Convention on Climate Change (Estonian Ministry of the Environment, 2005).

8 Proximization is selfish determination to build sustainable societies, aimed at social provision and driven by economic policy, whilst minimizing adverse impacts on the environment (see Ch. 4 for further explanation).

9 'Zero Carbon Cities', seminar held at the British Embassy, Helsinki, 13 Oct. 2003.

10 *Stern Review Report on the Economics of Climate Change*, commissioned by the UK government and launched Oct. 2006 (Cambridge University Press, 2006).

11 Source: Prometheus Institute for Sustainable Development (www.prometheus.org).

12 Copper Indium Gallium Selenide (CIGS) is an alternate PV production material. Although less efficient in converting sunlight to electricity, CIGS panels should be much cheaper.

13 North-facing in the southern hemisphere.

14 Espoo City biowaste is currently composted and the residue used as a soil substitute. It is successful in reducing the amount of biowaste going into landfill, but the system has not yet been extended to closed-system composting that would generate methane.

15 Developed by the Peabody Trust in partnership with Bill Dunster Architects and BioRegional Development Group, built on reclaimed land owned by the London Borough of Sutton.

16 Source: IEA Heat Pump Centre, (www.heatpumpcentre.org).

17 Statistics Finland, *Energy Statistics 2003* (www.stat.fi).

18 *Bio Fuels for Transport: An International Perspective* (OECD/International Energy Agency (IEA), 2004).

19 *Bio Fuels for Transportation: Global Potential and Implications for Sustainable Agriculture and Energy in the 21st Century* (Worldwatch Institute, 2006).

20 *Global Deserts Outlook* (UNEP, 2006).

8 THE ENERGY CRUNCH

1 Cases recorded 1992–2002.

2 *Chernobyl's Legacy: Health, Environmental and Socio-Economic Impacts*, report by the Chernobyl Forum, 2003–5 (International Atomic Energy Association (IAEA), 2006).

3 Torus-shaped magnetic chamber.

4 The International Thermonuclear Experimental Reactor, a collaboration between the EU, the United States, Russia, China, Japan and South Korea.

5 The European Safety and Environmental Assessment of Fusion Power (SEAFP) team was set up in 1992 to assess the safety of fusion power. The work embraced the conceptual design of fusion power stations and the safety and environmental assessments of those designs. The major conclusions reached by the SEAFP team in 1995 were that fusion has very good inherent safety qualities (www.ec. europa.eu).

6 J. Pamela, *Cleaner Energy for the Future* (European Union Fusion Development Agreement (EFDA), 2003).

7 Approximate figures extracted from *World Energy, Technology and Climate Policies Outlook 2030 – WETO,* (European Commission, 2003).

9 THE INSATIABLE APPETITE OF TRANSPORTATION

1 There were estimated to be 603 million passenger cars and 223 million commercial vehicles on the world's roads in 2004. Source: The Worldwatch Institute, *World Vital Signs 2006–2007* (Norton & Co, 2006).

2 Whether electric cars contribute positively to a sustainable transportation system depends, crucially, on the source of the electricity.

3 World population currently 6 billion; number of cars currently 600 million. To match the US figure of 7 cars per 10 people would lead to a world car population of 4.2 billion; 7 times more than now.

4 *International Trade Statistics 2006* (World Trade Organization, 2006).

5 'United Kingdom Fuel Duty Escalator, Domestic Best Practices Addressing Climate Change', survey carried out autumn 1999 by the Environment Agency of Japan for the G8 Environmental Futures Forum in Feb. 2000. Source: www.env.go.jp/ earth/g8_2000/forum/g8bp/report.html.

6 Alana Herro, *Historic Atlantic Crossing Powered by Sun*, reported in 'e2 – Eye on Earth', a collaboration between the Worldwatch Institute and Blue Moon Fund (May 2007).

10 ICARUS AIR

1 J. T. Bowen and C. Laroe, 'Airline networks and the international diffusion of severe acute respiratory syndrome (SARS)', *The Geographic Journal*, Vol. 172, Part 2, June 2006.

2 We should note that the Airbus A800 has good fuel-per-passenger-mile figures compared with other models in the current aircraft fleet so may have a future for some time on premium high capacity routes.

11 HEALTHY, COHESIVE URBAN COMMUNITIES

1 World Urbanization Prospects, 2005 Revision Population Database, Department of Economic and Social Affairs, UN, New York.

2 The UN defines megacities as urban agglomerations of 10 million persons or more. Tokyo is the largest with 35.2 million people, then Mexico City 19.4 million, New York-Newark 18.7 million, São Paulo 18.3 million and Mumbai 18.2 million (2005 figures).

3 I visited the small community of Sanday, one of the Orkney Islands off the north coast of Scotland. People know each other and notice what is going on. The island does not have a single policeman. People do not lock their doors or their cars; there is no need. The community is self-policing.

4 Charges are levied through parking fees and schemes like London's congestion charge. But these charges are limited in scope and currently small compared with the full cost of providing the road infrastructure.

5 The process of nuclear fusion will be clean and safe but the development of commercially viable reactors is at least 40 years away (see Ch. 8).

12 PUTTING KING CAR IN ITS PLACE

1 The McLaren F1 held the world production car speed record until 2005. Only 100 were made and production ceased in May 1998.

2 This is not a universal solution. For example, in northern Finland solar panels would produce no power at all during the depths of winter. Other renewable power sources would be required, such as a biofuel.

13 GLOBAL MANUFACTURING RENAISSANCE

1 The terms 'biological mass' and 'technical mass' (or 'industrial mass') are used by McDonough and Braungart in *Cradle-to-Cradle: Remaking the Way We Make Things* (North Point Press, 2002).

2 W. McDonough and M. Braungart, *Cradle-to-Cradle: Remaking the Way We Make Things* (North Point Press, 2002).

3 Source: www.valtra.com.

14 OUR THIRST FOR WATER

1 Samuel Taylor Coleridge, *Lyrical Ballads* (1798). The form of words used here comes from E. H. Coleridge's 1927 edn. of Samuel Taylor Coleridge's poems.

2 One organization dedicated to saving the world's oceans is Oceana, founded in 2001, which has offices around the world (www.oceana.org).

3 S. Moore, M. Moore, M. Leecaster and S. Weisberg 'A comparison of plastic and plankton in the North Pacific central Gyre', *Marine Pollution Bulletin* (Dec. 2001).

4 'Salmon and herring caught in the Baltic Sea, particularly in the Gulf of Bothnia and the Gulf of Finland, may subject consumers to higher than normal levels of dioxins and PCB compounds which are harmful to health.' Advice from the Finnish Food Safety Authority, 2006 (www.evira.fi).

5 A report for the UK Food Standards Agency (FSA) advises that shark, swordfish and marlin were found to exceed acceptable levels of mercury and should not be eaten. It also found high levels in tuna (but within EU guidelines) and advised that pregnant women and children should not eat it. 'Statement on a Survey of Mercury in Fish and Shellfish' from the Committee on Toxicity of Chemicals in Food, Consumer Products and the Environment (Dec. 2002).

6 'The oceans are very adaptable but through our endless exploitation of the oceans we've pushed their limits. In parts of the world it is not safe to swim in the seas and the possibility of enjoying swimming, surfing, windsurfing or fishing is ever decreasing.' Global Forum for Sports and Environment, March 2007 (www.g-forse.com).

7 Figures are for 2004. Source: E. Arnold and J. Larsen, 'Bottled Water: Pouring Resources Down the Drain' (Earth Policy Institute, 2006).

8 Reported in 'Helsingin Hanavesi Peittosi Pulloveden', *Helsingin Sanomat*, 26 April 2006.

9 'Finns' New Export – Water', *The Aquifer*, Vol. 19, No. 2, 2004.

10 Where the atmosphere is polluted, the rain might be acidic and cause problems to soils and vegetation.

11 Source: 'Are you being served?' *The Economist*, 21 April 2005.

12 'Groundwater Levels in the Chalk-Basal Sands Aquifer of the London Basin', report by the UK Environment Agency, June 2006.

13 'Coca-Cola: In Hot Water', *The Economist*, Oct. 6, 2005.

15 SAFE, SUSTAINABLE AGRICULTURE

1 Bovine spongiform encephalopathy, commonly known as 'mad cow' disease.

2 European Commission Directorate-General for Agriculture, *The Common Agricultural Policy Explained* (Oct. 2004).

3 A brain sample taken in 1985 from a cow in Sussex was confirmed during a review of the archives in 1987 as the first recorded case. Source: *The BSE Inquiry: The Report* (House of Commons, 2000).

4 A. Colchester and N. Colchester, 'The Origin of Bovine Spongiform Encephalopathy: the Human Prion Disease Hypothesis', *The Lancet*, 3 Sept. 2005.

5 Source: www.defra.gov.uk/animalh/bse/general/qa.

6 E. P. Cunningham (ed.), 'After BSE – A Future for the European Livestock Sector', European Association for Animal Production, Publication No. 108, 2003.

7 Mycobacterium avium paratuberculosis (MAP) is common among big herds in the United States. It causes Johne's, which is an incurable disease in cattle, and is linked with Crohn's disease (a human inflammatory bowel disease). Source: 'Follow the Map', *The Economist*, 8 Oct. 2005.

8 'The Morgan sports car is built around an ash frame . . . this gives the car unique strength, flexibility and, surprisingly, research showed that the frame made the car safer on impact tests'. Publicity material, Morgan Car Company Ltd, 2006.

16 DEALING WITH WASTE

1 James Lovelock argues that we need nuclear power to prevent climate change and save the planet in *The Revenge of Gaia: Why the Earth Is Fighting Back – And How We Can Still Save Humanity* (Allen Lane, 2006).

2 Source: www.YuccaMountain.org.

3 EU Directive 2002/96/EC.

4 EU Directive 2002/95/EC.

5 'Implementation of the Waste Electrical and Electronic Equipment Directive in the EU', report to the European Commission by the Institute for Prospective Technological Studies, EU Joint Research Centre, 2006.

6 This assumes that we have succeeded in implementing the elimination of non-biodegradable chemicals and substances from society.

7 Biowaste is collected weekly and transported by dedicated vehicles to the composting site near the landfill. It takes about one year for the waste to decompose into soil. Depending on the quality of the final product, it can be used for either soil improvement or landscaping projects.

8 Source: Helsinki Metropolitan Area (YTV), www.ytv.fi/ENG/waste, 2007.

9 'Helsinki: Closing the Nutrient Circle – The Collection of Bio Waste', case study in the SURBAN database on sustainable urban development in Europe, European Academy of the Urban Environment, updated 2001 (www.eaue.de).

10 The US cap-and-trade programme for sulphur dioxide (SO_2) emissions was established as a result of implementing the 1990 Clean Air Act. It has been a huge success. It is reported that this has been much more cost-effective than command-and-control mandates. Source: A. D. Ellerman, *Ex Post Evaluation of Tradable Permits: The US SO2 Cap-and-Trade Program* (Massachusetts Institute of Technology, 2003).

18 MOBILIZING BUSINESS

1 The Public Company Accounting Reform and Investor Protection Act of 30 July, 2002, is a US federal law known as the Sarbanes-Oxley Act (named after sponsors Senators Paul Sarbanes and Michael G. Oxley), passed in response to a number of major corporate and accounting scandals.

2 UN Secretary-General Kofi Annan addressed the World Economic Forum on 31 Jan. 1999; the Global Compact was launched at the UN Headquarters in New York on 26 July 2000.

3 Of the FT Global 500 companies, 108 had joined the Global Compact by May 2007. The 10 from the United States were: Cisco, eBay, Gap, Hewlett-Packard, Microsoft Corporation, Nike, Pfizer, Starbucks, Sun Microsystems and Coca-Cola. The 13 from the UK were: Anglo American, AVIVA, BP, BT Group, Cadbury Schweppes, Diageo, HSBC, Reed Elsevier, Rio Tinto, Royal Bank of Scotland, Shell, Standard Chartered and Unilever.

4 M. Blair, A. Bugg-Levine and T. Rippin, 'The UN's Role in Corporate Responsibility', *McKinsey Quarterly* 4/2004.

5 Source: www.unglobalcompact.org.

6 The top 20 global corporations taken from the FT Global 500, 2006.

7 BP, Royal Dutch Shell and the French company Total.

8 Marc Gunther, 'The Green Machine', *Fortune*, Vol. 154, No. 3, 7 Aug. 2006.

9 S. Brammer, C. Brooks and S. Pavelin, 'Corporate Social Performance and Stock Returns: UK Evidence from Disaggregate Measures', *Financial Management*, Vol. 35, Issue 3, autumn 2006, pp. 97–116.

10 Letter to British Prime Minister Tony Blair, dated 27 May 2005 and signed by 13 business leaders. It was written under the auspices of The HRH Prince of Wales's Business and the Environment Programme, managed by the University of Cambridge Programme for Industry.

11 Katherine Griffiths, 'BP shows two faces as it fights US bill to cut CO_2 emissions', *The Independent on Sunday*, 12 June 2005.

19 CAPITAL MARKETS AND THE POWER OF OWNERSHIP

1 Diana Farrell, Aneta Marcheva Key and Tim Shavers, 'Mapping the Global Capital Markets', *The McKinsey Quarterly*, 2005 Special Edn., pp. 38–47.

2 The US energy corporation, Enron, filed for bankruptcy in Dec. 2001.

3 The Italian dairy products corporation, Parmalat, went bankrupt in 2003.

4 John Maynard Keynes, *The General Theory of Employment, Interest and Money*, (Macmillan and Co., London, 1936).

5 The G8 members are France, the United States, the UK, Germany, Japan, Italy, Canada and Russia. The G20 is a wider group that is also consulted, consisting of the G8 plus Argentina, Australia, Brazil, China, the EU, India, Indonesia, Mexico, Saudi Arabia, South Africa, South Korea and Turkey.

6 'What the IMF Can Do', a commentary by Rodrigo de Rato, Managing Director, International Monetary Fund, *International Herald Tribune*, 19 April 2006.

7 Statement by the World Bank, 'About Us', www.worldbank.org, as at June 2007.

8 Diana Farrell, Aneta Marcheva Key and Tim Shavers, 'Mapping the Global Capital Markets', *The McKinsey Quarterly*, 2005, p. 38.

9   16 Sept. 1992.

10 *Financial Times*, 10 Feb. 2005.

11 Ivar Simensen and Sundeep Tucker, 'Iceland acts to head off currency crisis', *Financial Times*, 31 Mar. 2006.

12 James Tobin, 'A Proposal for International Monetary Reform', *Eastern Economic Journal*, Vol. 4, July, Oct 1978, pp.153–9.

13 Community Development Corporations first arose in the 1960s from President Kennedy's concern at the plight of people in poor urban areas. They have, in many cases, been successful in regenerating communities.

14 Robert Reich, *Supercapitalism: The Transformation of Business, Democracy, and Everyday Life*, (Alfred Knopf, 2007).

20 SOCIAL ECONOMICS

1   This quotation is attributed to Kamal Nath in Michael Tobias' book *World War III: Population and the Biosphere at the End of the Millennium* (Second Edition, Continuum, New York, 1998). p. 264.

2   Kamal Nath, Indian Minister of Commerce and Industry, speaking in a BBC World Debate, Davos, Jan. 2006.

3   Radio Frequency Identification Devices (RFID) are simple, small and their cost is tumbling. In due course, all products could be fitted with one. It would then be possible for a whole trolley of shopping to be automatically registered and charged without human intervention.

4   Pauli Kettunen, 'The Tension between the Social and the Economic – A Historical Perspective on a Welfare State' in Jari Ojala, Jari Eloranta and Jukka Jalava (eds.), *The Road to Prosperity – An Economic History of Finland*, (Suomalaisen Kirjallisuuden Seura, Helsinki, 2006) pp. 285–313.

5   Women can also choose to join the Finnish armed forces but for them it is not compulsory.

6   For example, the Untouchables (or Dalit) are the lowest caste in Indian society and have traditionally done society's dirty work. There are a number of mechanisms that hinder social mobility between castes in India.

7   This is a financial construct rather than reality.

8   Paul McDougall, 'Hiring Spin-Off Company to Handle Catering Services: A Case of Outsourcing Gone Awry', *InformationWeek*, 18 Aug. 2005.

9   'Catering for Suppliers' Strikes – The Dangers of Outsourcing', *The Economist*, 18 Aug. 2005.

10 The Executive Summary of the Stern Review report on *The Economics of Climate Change*, commissioned by the UK government and launched Oct. 2006 (Cambridge University Press, 2006) p. ii.

21 ENVIRONMENTAL ECONOMICS

1 The EU carbon-trading scheme commenced with a free allocation to the big emitters based on their current emissions. For those able to make reductions easily, these free permits brought a substantial cash windfall.

2 EU Directive 2003/87/EC dated 13 Oct. 2003 and which came into force on 1 Jan. 2005.

3 Natural Resource Accounting is defined in the Glossary of Terms provided by the European Environment Agency as 'A system of monitoring based on methodically organized accounts, representing the size of economically valuable and limited reserves of natural resources'.

22 ADAPTATION LABORATORIES

1 The Environmental Performance Index (EPI), issued by the World Economic Forum.

2 The Global Competitiveness Report, issued by the World Economic Forum.

3 'Finland placed first in environmental comparison: economic growth and a good environment go hand in hand', Jan-Erik Enestam, Minister of the Environment of Finland (2003–7), reported in *Energy and Enviro Finland,* Internet journal, Feb. 2005 (www.energy-enviro.fi).

4 Pauli Kettunen, 'The Tension between the Social and the Economic – A Historical Perspective on a Welfare State' in Jari Ojala, Jari Eloranta and Jukka Jalava (eds.), *The Road to Prosperity – An Economic History of Finland,* (Suomalaisen Kirjallisuuden Seura, Helsinki, 2006) p. 307.

5 'We're cooking with biogas', article 4 Nov. 2006, on www.off-grid.net.

6 Susan Roaf, Manuel Fuentes and Stephanie Thomas, *Ecohouse 2: A Design Guide* (Butterworth Heinemann, 2003).

23 PROFITING FROM THE TRANSITION

1 For example, General Electric (GE) with its 'Ecomagination' initiative.

24 SHARED DESTINY

1 'I believe that this nation should commit itself to achieving the goal, before this decade is out, of landing a man on the moon and returning him safely to the Earth', President John F. Kennedy, 25 May 1961. Neil Armstrong was the first man to set foot on the moon just eight years later, on 20 July 1969.

Index

Figures are indexed in bold, e.g. 213**f**.